THE WONDERS OF LIFE ON EARTH

THE WONDERS OF LIFE ON EARTH

BY THE EDITORS OF

AND LINCOLN BARNETT

TIME INCORPORATED · NEW YORK · 1960

LIFE BOOK DEPARTMENT

The Wonders of Life on Earth
was produced by the following editorial staff:

Editor
NORMAN P. ROSS

Art Director
CHARLES TUDOR

Assistant Editor
PATRICIA HUNT

Writer
LINCOLN BARNETT

Copy Editor
JERRY KORN
JAY BRENNAN, RICHARD MERYMAN, *assistants*

Chief of Research
BEATRICE T. DOBIE

Text and Picture Research by
PEGGY BUSHONG, SHEILA OSMUNDSEN, JANE T. HOWARD,
SHEILA MANDEL, MARY H. MELVILLE; MARGARET K. GOLDSMITH

Art Production by
ROBERT L. YOUNG, ALBERT J. DUNN, ARTHUR J. DUNN, *associates*
ALBERT KETCHUM, JAMES D. SMITH, *assistants*

Illustrations by
RUDOLF FREUND, RICHARD HARKER, WALTER LINSENMAIER, ROGER TORY PETERSON,
ANTONIO PETRUCCELLI, JOSEPH SIBAL, GUY TUDOR, RUDOLPH F. ZALLINGER

Photographs by
LOOMIS DEAN, JOHN DOMINIS, ALFRED EISENSTAEDT,
J. R. EYERMAN, ALBERT FENN, FRITZ GORO,
MARK KAUFFMAN, DMITRI KESSEL, YALE JOEL

Editorial Assistants
LINDA WOLFE, REBECCA D. CHAITIN,
ANNE HUMPHERYS, CAROLYN MILLER

JEROME S. HARDY, *Director*
ROBERT E. FOY, WALTER C. ROHRER, *Production Staff*
PHILIP E. JOHNSON, *Circulation Manager*

•

LIFE MAGAZINE

EDWARD K. THOMPSON, *Managing Editor*
PHILIP H. WOOTTON JR., GEORGE P. HUNT, *Assistant Managing Editors*
KENNETH MacLEISH, *Senior Editor*
JOSEPH KASTNER, *Copy Editor*
MARIAN A. MacPHAIL, *Chief of Research*

Publisher
C. D. JACKSON

This book is drawn from the Nature articles which appeared in LIFE from 1957 to 1959
and were produced under the direction of Nature Editor Patricia Hunt. Much new
material has been added, and many of the illustrations and photographs are here published for the first time. The following individuals and departments of LIFE Magazine
were instrumental in the production of the book: Ray Mackland, Picture Editor;
George Caturani, Foreign News Bureau Chief; Thomas N. Carmichael, Domestic
News Bureau Chief; Doris O'Neil, Picture Library Chief, and Reporter Diane Sawyer.

OTHER BOOKS
BY THE EDITORS OF LIFE

———————

LIFE'S PICTURE HISTORY OF WORLD WAR II

LIFE'S PICTURE HISTORY OF WESTERN MAN

THE WORLD WE LIVE IN
with LINCOLN BARNETT

THE WORLD'S GREAT RELIGIONS

AMERICA'S ARTS AND SKILLS

PICTURE COOK BOOK

THE SECOND WORLD WAR
with WINSTON S. CHURCHILL

THE LIFE WORLD LIBRARY

FOREWORD

THIS book is a companion volume to *The World We Live In*, which recounts the physical history of the planet Earth and the relationships between its varied domains and inhabitants through all the millenniums of time. *The Wonders of Life on Earth* tells the grand story of life itself: what it is, what has shaped it, and how—through ceaseless change and proliferation—it has unfolded the infinitely diverse panorama of flora and fauna that blanket the globe today.

In these pages you will see some of earth's most marvelous creatures, all manifestations of universal laws of nature that lay shrouded in mystery until they were uncovered little more than a century ago by the genius of Charles Darwin. Today the world seldom appreciates that Darwin's epic vision grew out of an extraordinary scientific adventure, a field trip on a voyage that took him completely around the world. But in this book—in photographs and paintings especially commissioned by LIFE—you will see many of the same sights that Darwin saw and noted. In his own words, you will share the insights and speculations inspired in him by the pageant of life on earth. In addition, you will observe the work of today's naturalists, some following in Darwin's footsteps, but all guided by the intellectual heritage of Darwinism, which has revolutionized the very basis of our understanding of life around us and of what we ourselves may be.

In the introduction to this book, the career of Charles Darwin is evaluated by Sir Julian Huxley, one of Britain's most distinguished scientists and the grandson of the famous biologist Thomas Henry Huxley, who was Darwin's greatest contemporary champion. The text of the chapters that follow, describing the wonders of life on earth in the light of Darwin's perceptions, is by Lincoln Barnett, who also wrote *The World We Live In*.

Chapter One takes you to the Galápagos Islands where, more than halfway through his voyage, Darwin found the first clues that inspired his epic theory of life. Thereafter, in chapters which retrace and generally follow the sequence of his round-the-world expedition, you will be guided through the living theaters of natural history on your own voyage of discovery.   —THE EDITORS OF LIFE

TABLE OF CONTENTS

INTRODUCTION

WITH brooding eyes, the statue of Charles Darwin gazes across the great entrance hall of London's Museum of Natural History. Unveiled June 9, 1885 by Darwin's friend, Thomas Huxley, the statue was received in behalf of the museum by Edward VII, then Prince of Wales. In the ensuing controversy over evolution, antagonists sought unavailingly to remove the statue. Today it stands secure as a memorial to the great naturalist whose genius helped mankind understand the wonders of life on earth.

DARWIN'S LEGACY

MORE than a century ago the theory of evolution was born in the dignified assembly room of the Linnean Society of London. Few if any of those who attended the scientific meeting realized the full implications of what was communicated to it. The idea whose force was to shake the world had been nourished in the mind of Charles Robert Darwin for 20 years and more, ever since his famous voyage around the globe in H.M.S. *Beagle.* The reading of the papers excited little attention at the time. "The only published notice of them which I can remember," wrote Darwin long afterward, "was by Professor Haughton of Dublin, whose verdict was that all that was new in them was false, and what was true was old."

"This shows how necessary it is," added the chief protagonist of natural selection, "that any new view should be explained at considerable length in order to arouse public attention." He was right. In the next year, 1859, his greatest work, *The Origin of Species,* was published—it was a long book, condensed from an uncompleted treatise which would have been five times longer —and not until then did the world begin to quiver and stir under the shock.

The idea of evolution, the hypothesis that living things might share a common descent, had been held by some before Charles Darwin was born in 1809. Darwin's own grandfather, Erasmus Darwin, had even groped toward the idea of selection, only to let it slip. The meticulous and obsessive mind of Charles Darwin discovered in a flash of genius evolution's agent: natural selection. As British Ornithologist James Fisher has written: "No subsequent synthesis of thought —not even the theory of relativity—has so humbled man, so purged his self-consciousness, so tempered his purpose, and so blessed his wisdom."

ORIGINAL MANUSCRIPT of *The Origin of Species* is shown at the Linnean Society in London where Darwin's theories were first put forth at a quiet meeting on July 1, 1858. It was not until a year later that the public storm on evolution broke.

from Dr. Butler for conducting chemical experiments in the tool house of the Darwins' home garden with his older brother Erasmus.

In 1825, when Charles was only 16, his father sent him and Erasmus to Edinburgh to study medicine. Charles dozed through most of the purely medical lectures. But he sat enthralled at the great American bird-artist Audubon's lectures to the Wernerian Society. When scarcely 17 he read to a student society his first scientific paper, on two small but interesting discoveries in marine biology.

Robert Darwin was a strict father. When it was clear that his son was not cut out for medicine, the elder Darwin decided that the young man should go into the ministry. Charles accepted with no overt struggle, conquered his scruples about belief in all the dogmas of the Church of England, and in 1828 entered Christ's College, Cambridge with the intention of taking a degree and becoming ordained. Years later he wrote, "I liked the thought of being a country clergyman," but he added (in a passage suppressed by his family from his posthumous *Autobiography* and published only in recent years), "It never struck me how illogical it was to say that I believed in what I could not understand and what is in fact unintelligible."

At Cambridge young Darwin continued to "waste" his time on the things that interested him, concentrating upon what he was supposed to do only to a sufficient extent to take him through his examinations, which he managed easily enough. It was not part of his prescribed course to attend the lectures of Professor J. S. Henslow on botany, or to accompany him on field excursions, or to hunt, play cards and drink with a sporting set, or to buy pictures, listen to music, invent new methods of collecting beetles, read works by the naturalist-explorer, Von

Who was this naturalist who so stirred the thinking world? What was the evolution of Darwin? It is worth dwelling on his formative years, for they teach us something of the flowering of genius.

WHEN he was a schoolboy Darwin read *The Natural History of Selborne* by Gilbert White, the curate who became the father of field natural history, and wondered "why every gentleman did not become an ornithologist." Beetle-hunting, mineral-collecting, bird-watching and shooting were the passions of Darwin's youth. His father, Dr. Robert Darwin, a successful, commonsensical and domineering physician in Shrewsbury, sent him to Shrewsbury school as a boarder under the famous Dr. Butler. There he stole apples, went fishing, forgot the lines of Virgil and Homer, enjoyed geometry—and earned the nickname of "Gas," as well as a public rebuke

Humboldt, and the philosopher-scientist, Herschel, or finally, having received his degree, to spend a vacation with Professor Adam Sedgwick, pursuing the complex geology of the ancient rocks of North Wales. It was at the end of this trip with Sedgwick in 1831 that Darwin's whole life reached its point of balance, and he waited with anticipation while others decided for him.

Returning to The Mount, the family home, he found two sensational letters awaiting him. One was from George Peacock, a Cambridge mathematician and astronomer, in whose hands lay the sole nomination of naturalists to the surveying ships of the Royal Navy. H.M.S. *Beagle,* a 242-ton brig, was due to voyage around the world. Would Darwin consider taking the job of naturalist? With Peacock's letter came one from Charles's Cambridge teacher, Professor Henslow, who had himself been offered the job and had regretfully turned

by SIR JULIAN HUXLEY

TO MODERN MAN

it down. "I have stated," Henslow told Darwin, "that I consider you to be the best qualified person I know of who is likely to undertake such a situation." Next day Charles talked things over with his father. Robert Darwin found the idea wild and disreputable to the character of a future clergyman. He felt that Charles would never settle down to a steady life on his return, having once more changed his profession, that his accommodation on the vessel would be most uncomfortable and that the undertaking would be useless. But Dr. Darwin added an all-important rider: "If you can find any man of common sense who advises you to go, I will give my consent."

Charles felt defeated. He wrote to Peacock refusing the post. But his uncle, Josiah Wedgwood II, who thought the *Beagle* trip an excellent idea, drove over to Shrewsbury to talk to Charles's father. Apparently Uncle Josiah was considered a man of common sense, for Dr. Darwin gave his permission.

YOUNG Darwin was 22 when he sailed on the *Beagle* from Plymouth on Dec. 27, 1831. He returned to England on Oct. 2, 1836, five years older, incalculably wiser, his notebooks full of facts, his head full of ideas and his boxes full of specimens from the long journey. The many fossil skeletons of mammals he had found in South America had shaken his belief in the unchangeability of species. These creatures were of the same peculiar family types as existing South American animals, but of quite distinct species. Darwin got his first glimpse of the fact that the arrangement of forms of life in the strata of the rocks showed a pattern of rise, success, fall and extinction that reflected the struggle for existence and showed that it was as old as the rocks themselves.

Darwin's good fortune in beholding the system of geology in the great South American continent was crowned by another decisive circumstance. The pattern of life he had seen around him and in the rocks forced him to think along broad lines in terms of continuity and gradual change. When the *Beagle* reached the Galápagos Islands, the conviction first dawned on Darwin that gradual change—in other words, evolution—must actually have occurred in living things and that new species must have been formed from others already existing. It is certain that among the ground finches (now called Darwin's finches) and mockingbirds and tortoises and lizards and plants of these isolated islands, his experiences finally crystallized his dawning thoughts and led him to the idea of evolution. He spent the next 20 years of his life confirming this hypothesis.

In July 1837, not long after his return to England, Darwin began a series of notebooks on the "transmutation of species." He was already aware of the full implication of this idea: the probable common ancestry of all living things on earth, including man. Though he soon saw how efficient human selection could be in creating new varieties and races of *domestic* animals and plants, he could not see how selection could operate in nature. And then, in October 1838, he "happened to read for amusement Malthus on *Population*"—I quote his own revealing phrase—and the idea of natural selection immediately flashed upon him. "Here, then," he continued, "I had at last got a theory by which to work."

The evolution of Charles Darwin as the creator of the master-theory of life was a slow one. He kept putting off publication of his work and kept piling up mountains of facts in support of his ideas and working out his arguments in ever fuller, more closely reasoned detail. Indeed, his procrastination verged on the pathological.

Not until 1842 did he give himself "the satisfaction" of writing a pencil abstract of 35 pages on his theory of evolution—which was found more than 50 years later in a cupboard under the stairs at his house in Kent. That year he also published his new and important theory of the origin of coral reefs based on *Beagle* observations.

Darwin was always reinforcing his general thought by particular investigation, and the reward of particular investigation was the discovery of lessons of general value. In 1844 he made an enlarged abstract of some 230 pages on the theory of evolution. If it had been published, it would have had the impact of the great *Origin of Species* 15 years later. Yet he procrastinated, discussing his ideas only with a few scientific friends, notably the geologist Charles Lyell and the botanist Joseph Hooker.

Darwin continued interminably to collect facts. In October 1846, starting to work on some barnacles he had collected on the *Beagle* voyage, he decided to devote himself to a monograph on the barnacles of the world. This was eventually published in four volumes between 1851 and 1854. Such painstaking, systematic work was typical of him. If he had not done it, he would have been another kind of man and it is not very apt to suggest, as Darwin himself once did, that he was wasting his time. Darwin's barnacle years were years of discipline. In 1854 he at last got down to whole-time work on the transmutation of species, and in 1856, under Lyell's influence, he began writing a vast treatise on the subject.

However, this was never published. Early in the summer of 1858 Charles Darwin got the greatest shock of his scientific life. Opening mail from the Malay Archipelago from his fellow naturalist Alfred Russel Wallace, he read an essay "On the Tendency of Varieties to

PORTRAIT OF DARWIN at the age of 66 now hangs in his grandson's home in Cambridge. Painted by Artist Walter W. Ouless, it depicts the great naturalist when he was in poor health, but still indefatigable in the pursuit of his scientific studies.

Depart Indefinitely from the Original Type." What Darwin read, point by point, was a summary of his own theory of evolution by natural selection. Wallace must always share with Darwin the glory of having thought of natural selection as evolution's chief agent. His idea was born of as many years of field natural history as those of the greater genius but was not backed by the same weight of evidence and argument. Wallace has left his mark on the vital though less fundamental study of geographical distribution, and the biologists, rather than the world at large, remember him today.

All came well. After much heart-searching on Darwin's part and the firm intervention of Lyell and Hooker, the views of Darwin and Wallace were communicated together to the Linnean Society on July 1, 1858 and published in the next number of the society's *Journal*.

The next and more important result was the publication of *The Origin of Species*. Strongly pressed by Lyell and Hooker, Darwin finished the book in just over 13 months. To the end of his days he called it "only an Abstract," though he acknowledged that it was "no doubt the chief work of my life," and this is certainly true.

The *Origin* was published on November 24, 1859. All of the 1,250 copies were sold the same day. It was received by the public with a horrified fascination that extended to many of Darwin's old scientific friends. His old teacher Adam Sedgwick found parts "utterly false and grievously mischievous." Sir John Herschel, the scientific philosopher, called it "the law of higgledy-piggledy." But many of the best brains were convinced. Lyell, Wallace and Hooker were all delighted. Alfred Newton, the distinguished ornithologist, was converted, and my own grandfather, the rising young biologist Thomas Henry Huxley, became Darwin's keenest protagonist.

IT is now difficult to imagine the vehemence with which emotion guided argument on evolution in those days. When the British Association for the Advancement of Science met in Oxford in 1860, Bishop Wilberforce, a mathematician and an ambitious prelate, announced his intention to "smash Darwin." Darwin was not present. After speaking "for full half an hour with inimitable spirit, emptiness and unfairness," he turned to Huxley, already known as an avowed Darwinist, and "begged to know, was it through his grandfather or his grandmother that he claimed his descent from a monkey?"

The exact words of Huxley's reply have been lost. But one of his hearers recalled it thus: "I asserted—and I repeat—that a man has no reason to be ashamed of having an ape for his grandfather. If there were an ancestor whom I should feel shame in recalling it would rather be a *man*—a man of restless and versatile intellect—who, not content with an equivocal success in his own sphere of activity, plunges into scientific questions with which he has no real acquaintance, only to obscure them by an aimless rhetoric, and distract the attention of his hearers from the real point at issue by eloquent digressions and skilled appeals to religious prejudice."

Since Huxley's cutting speech the educated world has come, with steady inevitability, to accept Darwin's conclusions. The theory of evolution has stood the test of time.

What is the significance of this? What was Darwin's particular contribution? How does Darwinism stand today? And what effect has it exerted on the progress of science and on general thought?

Darwin's essential contribution was twofold. By his patient accumulation and analysis of facts he made it clear that plants and animals could not possibly have been created in their present form but must have undergone a long process of development—in other words, that evolution was a fact. And by his discovery of the principle of natural selection and his brilliant working out of its implications, he gave a scientifically intelligible account of how that slow development could have occurred by natural means without supernatural intervention—in other words, of the *method* of evolution. "This

preservation of favorable individual differences and variations, and the destruction of those which are injurious," he wrote, "I have called Natural Selection, or the Survival of the Fittest."

To the question, How does Darwinism stand today, the brief answer is, "Very well indeed." No reputable biologist doubts the fact of evolution. In fact, it provides the foundation for the entire structure of modern biology. And natural selection, after a skeptical interlude from about 1895 to 1920, has now been firmly established as the main method by which evolution operates and the only one by which major changes can be brought about.

Almost all the main theses put forward by Darwin are still valid, though modified by later discoveries. In the first place, all existing animals and plants and most extinct species have certainly been produced from one or a few simple ancestral forms. Indeed, most scientists now believe that life has been produced from nonliving matter by natural process. The burning evolutionary problem is no longer the mechanism of the origin of species but that of the origin of life.

Darwin's next conclusion, that biological evolution was slow and gradual and demanded very long periods of time, has been fully confirmed. The fossils unearthed by paleontologists have shown no cases of abrupt transformation but many of gradual evolution. Paleontology has revealed the course of evolution in many kinds of animals, and we can now with considerable accuracy reconstruct its probable course in many others, including man himself.

Darwin led us to see man's place in nature in a new and more humble perspective. He did not himself examine the special features and future of human evolution. Now alone of the animals, man knows that he has evolved and begins to understand what evolution means. Through such understanding he may to a large extent be able to control the future of his own evolution and his progress in everything from population control and mental health to education and international development of the world's resources.

Darwinism has blown clean winds into virtually every branch of science and learning. It was Charles Darwin, more than any man, who unified the whole field of biology. Indeed, the scattered details of botany and zoology, phys-

LAMPOON OF DARWIN in a 19th Century German caricature poked fun at his theory of the descent of man by depicting him with a supposed primate ancestor. German scientific opinion, at first largely hostile to Darwin, soon swung his way.

iology and medicine, anatomy and behavior, could only be linked in the common framework of ideas provided by Darwinism. Many other subjects, often remote from biology, benefitted: astronomy, linguistics, archaeology, comparative religion, history, anthropology, psychology, all gained a new dimension. Every branch of study profited to a greater or lesser degree from adopting an evolutionary approach.

AN evolutionary approach: we may remind ourselves of what this means in Darwin's own words, in the immortal passage from the last paragraph of *The Origin of Species:* "It is interesting to contemplate a tangled bank, clothed with many plants of many kinds, with birds singing on the bushes, with various insects flitting about, and with worms crawling through the damp earth, and to reflect that these elaborately constructed forms, so different from each other, and dependent upon each other in so complex a manner, have all been produced by laws acting around us. These laws, taken in the largest sense, being Growth with Reproduction; Inheritance which is almost implied by reproduction; Variability from the indirect and direct action of the conditions of life, and from use and disuse: a Ratio of Increase so high as to lead to a Struggle for Life, and as a consequence to Natural Selection, entailing Divergence of Character and the Extinction of less-improved forms. Thus, from the war of nature, from famine and death, the most exalted object which we are capable of conceiving, namely, the production of the higher animals, directly follows. There is grandeur in this view of life . . . and that, whilst this planet has gone cycling on according to the fixed law of gravity, from so simple a beginning endless forms most beautiful and most wonderful have been, and are being evolved."

THE FACES AN APE MAKES were studied by Darwin to answer critics of evolution who said human emotions were an unbridgeable difference between man and animal. Insisting the difference was only of degree not of kind, Darwin cited four expressions of a chimpanzee shown here in quadruple exposure. They are *(left to right, top)* the pout of curiosity or distaste, a smile of pleasure, the mien of thoughtful anxiety and *(bottom)* a grimace of rage.

YOUNG DARWIN sat for a portrait by George Richmond in 1840, four years after the voyage.

EXPEDITION OF THE 'BEAGLE'

In 1831 Charles Darwin was an unsure amateur in biology. By 1836 he was a confident professional. What had changed him was his famous voyage around the world on the cartographic ship *Beagle*. The longest part of the trip, from England around South America, and the last leg of it from the Cape of Good Hope home are shown at right; the mid-part of the trip is mapped on the next two pages. Keyed by numbers into the list below are some of the animals studied by Darwin and depicted on the maps in or

1 Tortoise	37 Mountain vizcacha
2 Land iguana	38 Jaguar
3 Galápagos hawk	39 Morpho butterfly
4 Darwin finch	40 Gray's bat
5 Flightless cormorant	41 Cuttlefish
6 Marine iguana	42 Chaffinch
7 Scorpion fish	43 White wagtail
8 Albatross	44 Sea slug
9 Pipefish	45 Blenny
10 Parrot fish	46 Rufous sparrow
11 Megatherium	47 Brown booby
12 Darwin's rhea	48 Rock crab
13 Vicuña	49 Porcupine fish
14 Llama	50 Gallinule
15 Dog fox	51 Partridge
16 Black-necked swan	52 Ring-necked pheasant
17 Scelidotherium	53 Moray
18 Kelp goose	54 Flamingo
19 Tuco-tuco	55 Ant shrike
20 Darwin's lizard	56 Capybara
21 Vizcacha	57 Bottle-nosed dolphin
22 Marsh bird	58 Croaker
23 Firewood gatherer	59 Cape duiker
24 Tree frog	60 Salmon
25 Otter	61 Sandfish
26 Spectacled tyrant	62 Turkey vulture
27 Darwin's frog	63 Southern caracara
28 Pampas deer	64 Red ovenbird
29 Darwin's tanager	65 Agouti
30 Azara's opossum	66 Falkland Island plover
31 Rhinoceros beetle	67 Burrowing owl
32 Vampire bat	68 Jackass penguin
33 Armadillo	69 Zorrino
34 American rhea	70 American egret
35 Rufous tinamou	71 Brazilian lapwing
36 Jaguarundi	72 Sperm whale

AZORES

42

43

44

CAPE VERDE IS.

45

46

47

ST. PAUL ROCKS

48

RECIFE

49

50

ASCENSION

51

SAO SALVADOR

52

53

ST. HELENA

38

40

39

34

35

36

RIO DE JANEIRO

54

33

32

31

57

30

55

56

27

28

29

58

6

SANTA FE

25

60

59

24

MONTEVIDEO MALDONADO

BUENOS AIRES

Rio De La Plata

64

22

65

63

62

BAHIA BLANCA

Rio Negro

66

61

21

67

70

0

71

68

69

CAPE OF GOOD HOPE

Santa Cruz

FALKLAND IS.

TIERRA DEL FUEGO

72

A. Petruccelli

79

78

77

80

COCOS IS.

84

76

75

82

81

83

MAURITIUS

74

85

73

CAPE OF
GOOD HOPE

H.M.S.Beagle

near the regions where he found them. No single one of them was a revelation to him, but all of them together gradually persuaded his cautious mind that the diversity of life on earth had been created by a natural process of evolution.

The voyage was no pleasure tour. Aboard ship Darwin suffered agonies of seasickness. On land he suffered more than a tourist's quota of intestinal ills. But he soon learned to work on a queasy stomach and to hold the deck for hours observing porpoises or porcupine fish, sea gulls or sperm whales. His more important studies on land were made when the *Beagle*, in the course of mapping some little-known shoreline, could leave him in a place for weeks until she doubled back to pick him up.

The first long stopover was Brazil. In the tropic forest Darwin wandered "in a chaos of delight," netting so many insects that his shipmates dubbed him "the flycatcher." He hunted rheas with gauchos and staved off hunger on the pampas by smoking cigarets and drinking maté.

In Patagonia he met his first llamas and found he could attract their notice by lying on his back and kicking his legs. Here too he unearthed fossil monsters like megatherium and scelidotherium, two giant ground sloths of the Ice Age which could rear up on their hind legs and browse among the treetops. Sensing the kinship of such extinct giants with smaller living forms, he mused on their possible common ancestry. In the forests of Tierra del Fuego he saw a human female suckling her child while sleet melted on their naked bodies. The sight convinced him that human beings were not so far removed from animals as he had believed.

After the 90-foot *Beagle* rode out 24 days of terrifying tempests off Cape Horn he visited the Chiloe Islands where he captured a rare fox simply by walking up to it and knocking it on the head. In Chile he witnessed the great earthquake of 1835 and measured the two-foot rise in land level caused by it. Later when he found fossil seashells at 13,000 feet in the Andes he knew how they had been lifted there.

In the Galápagos, Darwin amused himself riding the backs of giant tortoises. He also noted that isolation had made the tortoises different from one island to the next—an observation essential to his later theories. In Tahiti he admired the people, in Australia the duck-billed platypus. The Cocos Islands, south of Sumatra, gave him a chance to study coral atolls.

By now he was sick of being seasick and eager to write up the ideas which possessed him. When the *Beagle* finally rounded the Cape of Good Hope and reached England, Darwin was tired and ailing, but he had sent ahead of him, crate by crate, one of the finest collections of rocks, plants and animals ever assembled.

73 Spade-footed frog	87 Jack
74 Flying fish	88 Eel
75 Shells	89 Gurnard
76 Long-toed frog	90 Live-bearing gecko
77 Cape pigeon	91 Kangaroo rat
78 Gannet	92 Platypus
79 Fairy tern	93 Gang-gang cockatoo
80 Hermit crab	94 Trigger fish
81 Butterfly fish	95 Trunk fish
82 Surgeon fish	96 Pink cockatoo
83 Swellfish	97 Crimson rosella
84 Shells	98 Goat fish
85 Giant toadlet	99 Albatross
86 West swamp rat	100 Frigate bird

HOUSE AT DOWNE where Darwin wrote *The Origin of Species* is kept as he left it by British Association. Here are the back porch *(left)* and wisteria-draped walls of central turret which houses the dining room and a bedroom.

GRAND PIANO on which Mrs. Darwin played stands in drawing room. Darwin had no ear for music but enjoyed it as a background for thought. Copy of portrait by John Collier shows Darwin in 1881, year before he died.

PLACID MEMORIES OF DAYS IN KENT

During the last 40 years of his life, Darwin published an amazing number of pioneering biological works and shook Western thought with his theories. But he lived in seeming leisure and deceptive calm. His retreat was an ungainly home amid beautiful gardens in the town of Downe in Kent, 20 miles from London. On returning to England he had at first lived in the city. But in 1842, after publishing the journal of his voyage and marrying Emma Wedgwood, of the wealthy pottery family, he had to move. Fame and his wife's charm had made his London life too much of a social whirl.

Even at Downe work came hard to him. Before publishing anything on an idea he was obsessive about collecting and experimenting until he had overwhelming evidence for his conclusions. Moreover, he suffered from nausea and headaches, tension and insomnia. But he was sweet-tempered. His 10 children, of whom three died in childhood, adored him, and his wife pampered him idyllically. Each day between his three 90-minute-long periods of intense study, she helped with his huge correspondence and endlessly read novels to him—he demanded happy endings and kind heroines he could love. At night she played backgammon with him which he frequently—and vociferously—lost.

SAND WALK *(right)* where Darwin strolled with his dog at least twice a day encircles a narrow strip of woodland. Here he often found contingents of his children playing and stopped for a romp or chat with them before going on.

WICKER CHAIR, a replica of the one in which Darwin liked to sit and think, stands on his back porch facing the rose gardens and wide lawns toward the Kentish chalk flats beyond.

STAFFORDSHIRE CHURCH *(left)* in which Darwin wed Emma Wedgwood overlooks the chimneys of Maer, her family home. He was her cousin, lived nearby, saw her often as a boy.

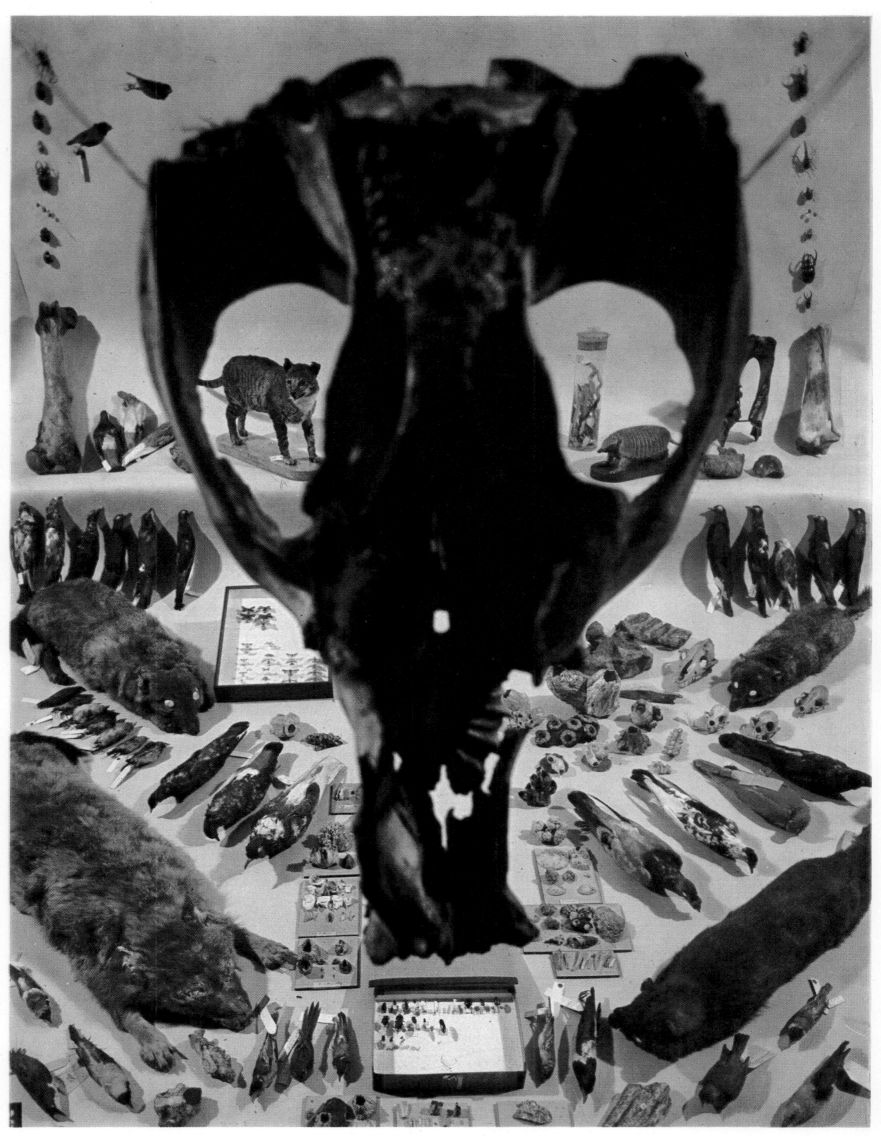

A COLLECTION OF SPECIMENS studied by Darwin is grouped around the skull of toxodon, a grazing monster of the pampas. A stuffed cat and armadillo are seen through its eye sockets. Two wild dogs crouch to left of its jaw. Between the dogs lie seven species of Galápagos finches, which Darwin suspected had evolved from a single species from the mainland. Other relics include a jaguarundi *(lower right)*, a Chiloe fox *(upper right)* and 26 forms of pigeons.

THE CLUTTERED STUDY where Darwin worked is packed with books, solvents and preservatives, much as he left them. His one-lens microscope stands on dissecting shelf before the window. On his low swivel stool he could quickly roll into reach of whatever he needed or rest his eyes on the garden outside. In this study he wrote all but two of his 17 books. Here or in the greenhouse he conducted painstaking experiments like those shown on the next two pages.

13

HIS EXPERIMENTS

POLLINATING BEE crawls from narrow neck of Malayan orchid in re-creation of Darwin experiment. He proved that orchids' adaptations for attracting bees and covering them with pollen helped keep species constant.

ELABORATE HORNS deck the heads of many male animals from a tiny stag beetle to the huge elk juxtaposed here. Darwin studied deer antlers and decided they evolved by selection because of their value to males in combat.

ILLUMINATED WORMS represent one of many small experiments which Darwin thought necessary for his last opus, a book on earthworms. By steal-ing up on unsuspecting colonies in the dead of night, he proved that worms

MEAT-EATING PLANT, the sundew, which Darwin studied for its animalistic behavior, traps fruit fly in sap exuded by its tiny red tentacles. Next, the longer tentacles under leaf will arch up to enclose the fly and digest it.

reacted to light only if bright. Here, night crawlers *(upper left)*, held on a glass plate, ignore the red glow of a bull's-eye lantern behind them. Candle flame emits degree of brightness he found would make worms go for cover.

TWINING TENDRILS were timed by Darwin for a book on movement of plants, a subject he explored for evidence of kinship between plants and animals. Here tendrils are symbolically superimposed on a watch like Darwin's.

A
LABORATORY
OF
EVOLUTION

THE giant tortoise (*galá-pago* in Spanish) survives today as the chief symbol of the lonely archipelago which took its name. There evolution, for centuries unimpeded by man, bred many creatures of mysterious origin, among them the Galápagos tortoise—a land creature living far from the mainland. "These huge reptiles," Darwin wrote on first glimpsing them, "seemed to my fancy like some antediluvian animals." In this painting a vermilion flycatcher perches above the tortoise's handsome shell.

LABORATORY OF EVOLUTION

Galápagos: Key to Darwin's Theories

Red-billed tropic bird

Red-footed booby

PINTA
(ABINGDON)

Blue-footed booby

Abingdon tortoise

Tree finch

GENOVESA
(TOWER)

MARCHENA
(BINDLOE)

Ground finch

Warbler finch

Galápagos dove

Galápagos hawk

Fur seal

Marine iguana

SANTIAGO
(JAMES)

Duncan tortoise

Short-eared owl

Land iguana

Flightless cormorant

RABIDA
(JERVIS)

Black-eared mockingbird

FERNANDINA
(NARBOROUGH)

SANTA CRUZ
(INDEFATIGABLE)

Land iguana

ISABELA
(ALBEMARLE)

PINZON
(DUNCAN)

Indefatigable tortoise

Pelican

SANTA FE
(BARRINGTON)

Lava lizard

Narborough tortoise

Galápagos penguin and young

Marine iguana

Flamingo

Waved albatross

SAN CRISTOBAL
(CHATHAM)

Ground finch

Sea lion

Barrington land iguana

Hood marine iguana

FLOREANA
(CHARLES)

Young albatross

ESPAÑOLA
(HOOD)

Cactus ground finch

Long-billed mockingbird

Green-footed booby

ROUTE OF THE "BEAGLE" *(dotted line)* took Darwin to four of the Galápagos Islands. He spent a month observing animal life and noting how creatures differed from island to island. The map, which gives both Spanish and English names of the islands, shows the kinds of life still found there, little changed from Darwin's day.

JAGGED CLINKERS OF BLACK BASALTIC LAVA STREW THE WESTERN SHORE OF JAMES ISLAND WHERE DARWIN ENCAMPED FOR A WEEK OF OBSERVATIONS

'Enchanted Isles' showed Darwin natural selection in action

IN July 1835 Darwin wrote a letter home from Lima, Peru, declaring, "I look forward to the Galápagos with more interest than any other part of the voyage." He had been with the scientific expedition aboard H.M.S. *Beagle* for more than three years as it rounded the South American continent; he had explored jungles and pampas, walked the wild shores of Tierra del Fuego, and scaled the high Andes. His notebooks teemed with thousands of observations which his mind was now piecing together into a vast new picture of the natural world. He was convinced of the *fact* of evolution, but he had not yet deduced how it worked. On the remote Galápagos archipelago he was to find the clue.

As a young man of 26, Darwin had good reasons for looking forward to the Galápagos. For this cluster of lonely volcanic islands, riding the equator 650 miles west of the mainland, lay shrouded in mystery and myth. Discovered in 1535, they had remained uninhabited for three centuries, save by whalers and buccaneers. The Spaniards had called them *Las Islas Encantadas,* or the Enchanted Isles, because of the capricious currents which seemed to endow them with magic power to attract or repel the ships that raised their shores. The *Beagle* arrived on September 15, and Darwin gazed with awe at a forbidding scene—bleak, black, basaltic mountains, pitted, cratered,

blistered, seamed with lava flows, littered with slag heaps, strewn with cinders, parched and prostrate beneath a sullen, smoldering sky. To his astonished eyes the landscape suggested "what we might imagine the cultivated parts of the Infernal regions to be."

Darwin remained in the islands for only five weeks, but they were crucial weeks in his life. Working with rapt intensity, he realized that he had stumbled on a living laboratory of evolution—"a little world within itself." Most of its inhabitants were unique, found nowhere else on earth. More remarkable, the individual species varied from island to island—*i.e.*, a finch or tortoise on one island was clearly different from a finch or tortoise on another island just a few miles away, though living under identical conditions. How did these differences arise? This was the "great difficulty" which Darwin sensed held the clue to a deeper mystery: the means by which new forms of life appear on earth. He pondered it for the next 20 years, and when he had found the answer and set it forth at last in *The Origin of Species,* man's concept of his place in the world was never the same again. Since Darwin's momentous visit, many of the Galápagos islands have been despoiled. Yet on a few the primeval populations, though waning in numbers, still survive in the same strange forms and curious diversity that baffled and inspired Darwin a century ago.

A COASTAL POOL on James Island is roiled by the sportive splashing of a sea lion enjoying a dip. Playful and tame, the sea lions have held their own against man's depredations, dwelling in herds on the rocks. Males often acquire harems of 10-20 females which they guard jealously.

KINGDOM BY THE SEA

Many wonders of the Galápagos world are creations of its curious climate. Though bisected by the equator, its islands are bathed by the Humboldt current which, surging up the continental coast, brings waters 15 to 20 degrees colder than the surrounding tropic sea. The combination of cool water and equatorial sun has produced a domain of nature like nothing else on earth. Except for a brief season of squalls from December to March, little rain falls. The trade wind blows, springs dry up, and the lava-laden lowlands sustain only a desert cover of thorny bushes and cactus down to the edges of the sea. The mountain slopes, however, rising to heights of several thousand feet,

are shrouded in veils of mist, and in these moist uplands tall trees grow, hung with moss and fern, and the giant Galápagos tortoise makes his home.

Yet it is amid the clefts and caverns of the coastal zone that the animal life which Darwin noted prolifically abounds. Here drought is no drawback, for its inhabitants live on the bounty of the sea. The cool Humboldt current conveys a never-ending supply of food to the keen-eyed watchers on the cliffs. And it has created, here on the very equator, a curious colony of *émigrés* from colder climes—sea lions, fur seals and, strangest expatriates of all, penguins, flightless exiles from a distant antarctic home.

A GIANT TORTOISE, SENSING DANGER, DRAWS IN

BABY PENGUINS, one month old, sprawl on a rocky roost on Albemarle. The Galápagos penguin is the northernmost member of its family.

When the young birds mature, they shed their soft brown down and put on the formal black-and-white attire of the well-dressed adult penguin.

A SCARLET ROCK CRAB squirts water in a moment of fright. Hosts of these crabs search the rocks for food, seldom entering the sea though

ITS HEAD WITH A HISS OF ALARM. IT WEIGHS MORE THAN 500 POUNDS, MEASURES 96 INCHES AROUND THE WAIST AND 53 INCHES DOWN THE LENGTH OF ITS BACK

always moistened by spray. Surprisingly nimble, they skitter into crannies before the winged shadows of their enemies, the predatory birds.

A YOUNG FUR SEAL suns itself on the rocks of James Island. At three months, it has been weaned and has learned to swim and forage for

itself. Implacably hunted for their fur, the tame, friendly Galápagos seals are in great danger of extinction. Today only a few hundred are left.

LAVA CLIFFS on Indefatigable Island, mounting above cool aquamarine waters, are mottled white with droppings from aquatic birds. The plant cover, characteristic of the arid coastal regions of the Galápagos, consists of varieties of cactus, Palo Santo (White Saint) trees, and other forms capable of existence with little rain. Sheer lava cliffs attest the volcanic origin of the island, which at some point in prehistory emerged from the depths of the sea.

PRICKLY PEAR CACTI attain tree size in the Galápagos, rearing their oval pads as high as 30 feet. Flourishing across the lowlands they provide food and drink for tortoises and iguanas which consume them spines and all.

TOWER ROCK, a 350-foot spire of jet black lava, born of some ancient volcanic upheaval and sculptured for centuries by wind and wave, points to the evening sky. Beyond lies James Island, scene of Darwin's main studies.

A LAVA LIZARD dines on a smaller member of his tribe, an unusual meal since lizards normally eat insects. Most abundant of local reptiles, lava lizards are found everywhere on the islands, including the homes of men. When angry they blow themselves up with air and spit their displeasure.

A WILD CUCUMBER, kin of the garden variety, produces seed pod *(above)* bearing red seeds *(below)*, which are eaten by Vegetarian Finches.

THE INLAND DOMAIN

Every visitor to the Galápagos who has ventured inland from the coast has painted a dismal picture of what he found. Darwin, after his first walk in the interior, wrote: "Nothing could be less inviting. . . . A broken field of black lava thrown into the most rugged waves and crossed by great fissures is everywhere covered by stunted, sunburnt brushwood, which shows little signs of life." A later visitor, the novelist Herman Melville, was even more repelled: "Little but reptile life is here found . . . no voice, no low, no howl is heard; the chief sound of life here is a hiss. . . . In no world but a fallen one could such lands exist."

Yet Darwin, ignoring discomfort, made repeated forays into the badlands. He counted 185 species of plants and ascertained that 100 were new types—"a proportion sufficient to make the Galápagos archipelago a distinct botanical province." For endless hot hours he studied the habits of the tortoise and timed its rate of progress, finding it to be 360 yards an hour or four miles a day, "allowing a little time for it to eat on the road." Observing a zoological vacuum in the absence of mammals, he hunted tirelessly and turned up two: a mouse, which he considered indigenous, and a rat, which he decided had jumped ship.

But it was from his cumulative perception of the variations within species from island to island that Darwin derived his most crucial insight. "I never dreamed," he wrote, "that islands 50–60 miles apart . . . would have been differently tenanted. . . . It is the circumstance that [they] possess their own species of tortoise, mocking thrush, finches and numerous plants, these species having the same general habits . . . and filling the same place in the natural economy of this archipelago, that strikes me with wonder."

GALAPAGOS HAWK SURVEYS A TERRAIN IN WHICH IT KNOWS NO FEAR, EVEN OF MAN

A GALAPAGOS PELICAN nests in a mangrove clump with two fledglings at its feet. Close kin to the familiar brown pelican of the U.S., it is the smallest member of its family, with a wing span of 6-7 feet. It feeds by diving on schools of fish with open bill and scooping them into its pouch.

THE GREEN GRASSY HIGHLANDS of Indefatigable Island roll down to the blue Pacific 15 miles away. It is only inland on the treeless slopes of the highest volcanoes surmounting the large islands that grass and leafy plants can grow. Cool, moist breezes, wafting in from the sea, are heated as they cross the arid lowlands, rise, and condense in clouds and mists about the mountain tops. At the highest elevations, of almost 5,000 feet, the

streamers of mist seldom disperse, and here lush meadows of ferns, grasses and mosses mantle the lava ridges. Moisture collects in the craters, forming clear, fresh-water pools, around which small flowers gleam and insects and birds make their home. Below, the vegetation fades away through zones of impenetrable brush and Scalesia trees (woody plants related to our daisies and sunflowers), down to the cacti and desert growth of the coastal plains.

PRIMORDIAL POPULATION is best preserved on Narborough Island. In this painting all major species are shown as they exist today in peaceable association on the spray-blown cliffs beneath Narborough's live volcano.

The time is November, start of the breeding season for marine iguanas, when the males put on their courting colors. The big, crested fellow atop the rock at left is defending his harem against an intruder. Nothing is likely to happen,

'A FIT SHORE
FOR PANDEMONIUM'

The island of Narborough, almost alone in the Galápagos, remains an untouched sanctuary. Man has never settled here nor loosed his dogs and other alien animals that elsewhere have upset the equilibrium of nature. To this day its ledges swarm with all the strange, improbable and antique island faunas that moved the master of the *Beagle,* Captain Fitz-Roy, to call the crawling cliffs of the archipelago "a fit shore for Pandemonium." The primeval aspect of Galápagos

for despite their formidable armament, iguanas dislike bloodshed; they prefer ritual fights in which they tense up, glare, and then butt their heads together, goat-fashion, until one gives way. Confirmed vegetarians, they tend to ignore the crabs that scuttle over their bodies hunting ticks, and live on algae and seaweed which they nibble from exposed rocks at low tide *(center foreground)*. On the guano-white rock at right a young flightless cormorant

life stems largely from the prevalence of iguanas. In the virtual absence of mammals, Darwin perceived that "the order of reptiles gives the most striking character to the zoology of these islands."

Nowhere else on earth have reptiles engendered such prodigies as the giant tortoise and the dragonlike marine iguanas shown above at left. Even the birds have hatched anachronisms—*e.g.*, the flightless cormorant *(above right)* which, like the extinct dodo, has lost the

use of its wings. Far from finding inability to fly a defect leading to extinction, the Galápagos cormorant proliferates exuberantly and is today the largest cormorant on earth.

With few exceptions these creatures include no predators and show no fear either of one another or of man. As one who in his youth was fond of shooting, Darwin wrote: "A gun here is almost superfluous; for with the muzzle I pushed a hawk off the branch

FOLD OUT: DO NOT TEAR

which is cracking a hard Cat-claw seed in its powerful beak. In the background, at right center, a Small Insectivorous Tree Finch hunts on the wing, while its mate perches on a nearer branch, and a Vegetarian Tree Finch plucks a berry from the tree at right. Lower on the trunk, a Tool-using Finch —one of the great rarities in nature—uses a cactus spine to dislodge insects from crevices too deep for its bill to probe. Above, at far right, a Warbler

DARWIN'S FAMOUS FINCHES are assembled in this painting of a low-land landscape on Indefatigable Island. At left a pair of Cactus Ground Finches inspect a vacant nest in an Opuntia cactus, while a Medium Ground Finch poises ready to probe for pollen and nectar in the yellow bloom above. In the center foreground, a Small Ground Finch pecks at an Opuntia fruit, watched by a Medium Ground Finch and a Large Ground Finch

enjoys a meal of regurgitated fish from its mother's throat. In the lower right-hand corner, beneath a clump of cactus, a Galápagos snake (one of few local predators) dines on a lava lizard. In the middle distance are pelicans *(upper left)*, sea lions and penguins *(right center)*, more iguanas and cormorants *(right)*. In the far distance a pair of blue herons perch atop some mangrove trees. Overhead, frigate birds soar on powerful wings scanning the sea for fish.

of a tree." Astonished by the tameness of the Galápagos birds, he decided that they had not yet learned that man is a dangerous animal and therefore "disregard him in the same manner as in England today shy birds disregard the cows and horses grazing in our fields. . . . We may, I think, conclude that the wildness of birds with regard to man is a particular instinct directed against *him,* and not dependent on any general degree of caution arising from other sources of danger; secondly, that it is not acquired by individual birds in a short time, even when much persecuted; but that in the course of successive generations it becomes hereditary."

Until now man's invasions of the Galápagos have been happily infrequent. This circumstance has preserved aboriginal life and endowed the Enchanted Isles with a look of eternity, as if the river of time had frozen in some peaceful epoch of the prehistoric past.

'A MOST SINGULAR GROUP OF FINCHES'

Until he came to the Galápagos, Darwin had thought of evolution in terms of vast reaches of time and major differences of natural environment. But here in a tiny island cosmos he saw to his amazement that species could diversify in identical physical conditions and a brief span of time. Discovering among the land birds "a most singular group of finches," he noted that "the most curious fact is the perfect gradation in the size of their beaks." There were 13 species in all, varying in both beak structure and habit *(chart below);* some hunted seeds on the ground or insects in the trees, some fed on fruits and flowers. Their plumage varied with their habitat, from lava black to leafy gray and green. Although it took Darwin years to understand this diversity within one group of birds, he surmised that an original family of finches had been early colonists of the Galápagos and had been "modified for different ends" —*i.e.,* they had seized divergent opportunities and diverged because of them. They had exploited varying ways of life left open by the absence of competitors. Had a true warbler preceded them, it is doubtful that the Warbler Finch would have evolved. But isolated in their domain the finches which were most successful—the fittest—survived.

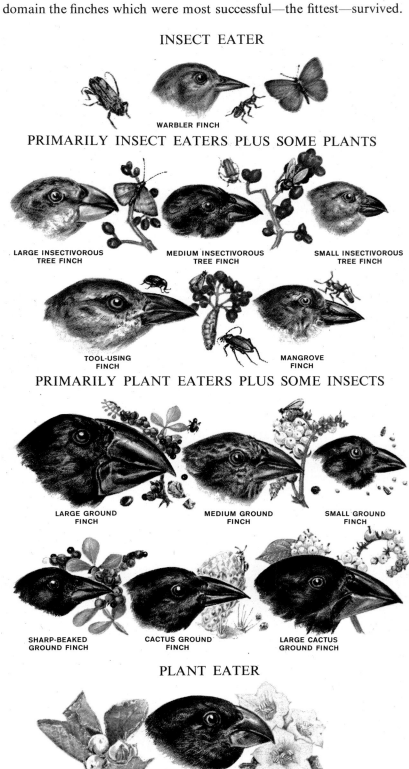

INSECT EATER

WARBLER FINCH

PRIMARILY INSECT EATERS PLUS SOME PLANTS

LARGE INSECTIVOROUS TREE FINCH

MEDIUM INSECTIVOROUS TREE FINCH

SMALL INSECTIVOROUS TREE FINCH

TOOL-USING FINCH

MANGROVE FINCH

PRIMARILY PLANT EATERS PLUS SOME INSECTS

LARGE GROUND FINCH

MEDIUM GROUND FINCH

SMALL GROUND FINCH

SHARP-BEAKED GROUND FINCH

CACTUS GROUND FINCH

LARGE CACTUS GROUND FINCH

PLANT EATER

VEGETARIAN TREE FINCH

Finch opens its bill to devour a luscious larva. In the lower right-hand corner a Large Insectivorous Tree Finch has descended to the ground to gobble a grub. In the center of the picture a land iguana munches an Opuntia fruit.

A LAND IGUANA climbs a tree in quest of greenery. Though these big sluggish lizards feed mostly on the ground, Darwin noted, "to obtain acacia leaves they crawl up low stunted trees. It is not uncommon to see a pair quietly browsing . . . on a branch several feet above the ground."

'IMPS OF DARKNESS'

Of all the animals on the Enchanted Isles, by far the most conspicuous and bizarre are the iguanas of land and sea. Found nowhere else on the planet, the big marine iguanas, warted, bossed and crenellated like dragons, armed with sawlike teeth and knifelike talons, seem incarnations from the age of dinosaurs. No other creatures of the Galápagos so perfectly embody their environment. The scales that stud their heads and spines are sculptured like volcanic cones. Their black and gray skins reflect the colors of lava and surf. Darwin, a writer who rarely indulged in imagery, called them "imps of darkness."

Yet for all their Plutonian appearance, they are essentially mild and torpid monsters which harm no other living things. The marine iguanas go through life basking in the sun and munching seaweed at low tide. Darwin found that despite their aquatic feeding habits they avoided the water when frightened. He proved this by heaving one bodily into a tidal pool several times in succession, and noting that each time it swam swiftly back to shore—and to him. "Perhaps this singular piece of apparent stupidity," he wrote, "may be accounted for by the circumstance that this reptile has no enemy whatever on shore, whereas it must fall prey to sharks. Hence probably urged by the hereditary instinct that the shore is its place of safety, it there takes refuge."

The land iguana differs from its aquatic relative only in habit and a few physical features of body and tail. It too is largely a vegetarian and a pacifist by temperament. One day, watching an iguana dig a burrow, Darwin pulled it out by the tail. "At this it was greatly astonished," he wrote, "and soon shuffled up to see what was the matter; and then stared me in the face, as much as to say, 'What made you pull my tail?'" As a field naturalist, Darwin decided that there remained one final question about the land iguana which he must answer. So he ate one and reported that they "yield a white meat which is liked by those whose stomachs soar above all prejudices."

SEA IGUANAS sprawl along the coast of Narborough where they propagate in greatest numbers. The only marine lizards in the world, they are graceful swimmers. Adults average three feet in length, 20 pounds in weight.

A LAVA-MONOLITH stands surrounded by crumbling clinkers, like the relic of some ancient idol, amid the sulphurous waters of the great crater lake of Narborough's main volcano. Behind it at left is the inner cone. In the distance rise the ramparts of the crater's outer walls.

THE GREAT CRATER

Although no one knows precisely when the Galápagos Islands were spewed upward by volcanic forces from the floor of the sea, traces of their violent birth are everywhere apparent. "I scarcely hesitate to affirm," Darwin wrote, "that there must be in the whole archipelago at least 2,000 craters." One of the largest dominates the island of Narborough. Here Darwin observed "immense deluges of black naked lava, which have flowed like pitch over the rim of a caldron." The pot whence the lava emerged was the enormous crater shown at right with its lake of hot sulphurous water and subsidiary cone of volcanic tuff and ash. Volcanic lakes often disappear and reappear unpredictably. Some months after these pictures were made in 1957, a Norwegian expedition looked over the crater rim and found that Narborough's lake was no longer there.

THE INNER CRATER contains a lake of its own, 500 by 300 feet. It stands at the same level as the outer lake, indicating a subterranean duct.

MAIN CRATER (right) of the volcano rings a lake 11 miles around, studded with an inner cone. The outer walls soar 4,900 feet above the sea.

CURIOUS RIDDLES OF THE

Darwin's visit inspired key questions which took him two decades to answer

ALTHOUGH Darwin's visit to the Galápagos Islands added an indispensable piece to the mighty mosaic of his theory, he discerned its outlines only dimly at the time. For, unlike other great geniuses of science, Darwin enjoyed no lightning flashes of revelation. Whereas Newton found the law of gravitation in the falling of an apple when he was 24 years old, and Einstein published his historic paper on relativity at the age of 26, Darwin had reached 50 before he finally synthesized the harvest of his observations into his masterwork *The Origin of Species*.

During his weeks on the Galápagos, Darwin saw and studied the curious animals and plants shown on the preceding pages. They raised key questions which he articulated in his account of the *Voyage of the Beagle,* published in 1839, three years after his return. The fact that even then he recognized them as crucial confirms the aphorism, *Prudens quaestio dimidium scientiae* (To ask the proper question is half of knowing). But he did not disclose his answers until he had fortified them with overwhelming documentation and detail two decades afterward.

At the outset of the section on the Galápagos in his journal of the *Voyage,* Darwin remarks: "The natural history of these islands is eminently curious. Most of the organic productions are aboriginal creations, found nowhere else; there is even a difference between the inhabitants of the different islands; yet all show a marked relationship with those of America, though separated from that continent by an open space of ocean, between 500 and 600 miles in width. . . . Seeing every height crowned with its crater and the boundaries of most of the lava streams still distinct, we are led to believe that within a period, geologically recent, the unbroken ocean was here spread out.

"Hence, both in space and time, we seem to be brought somewhat near to that great fact—that mystery of mysteries—the first appearance of new beings on this earth."

SWIMMING IN A VOLCANO, LIFE artist Rudolf Freund *(left)* and a guide reach Narborough's inner crater. In the course of their long swim they suffered cuts on lava rocks, but were amazed to find them soothed by the volcanic waters.

Thus in one pregnant paragraph Darwin states the essence of the problem that would haunt him for the next 20 years. If the Galápagos Islands had risen by volcanic action from the depths of the open sea, how did life arrive on their barren lava shores? Why were some Galápagos inhabitants unique to the islands while others appeared to be related to mainland forms? Why did the tenants of one island differ markedly from those on another island nearby? These were the riddles which, Darwin knew, held the key to the enigma of evolution.

The advent of life on the Galápagos, he reasoned, might be explained by supposing that at one time a land bridge connected the islands with the South American continent. But he rejected this explanation because of the freakish imbalance of the Galápagos populations—the virtual absence of mammals, the total absence of toads and frogs, and the extraordinary profusion of reptiles. Had a land bridge once afforded access from the mainland, more migrants would have used it. The small number of species, contrasted with

the richness of indigenous forms, pointed to the conclusion that life was conveyed to the islands haphazardly by sea and air. Such a theory would explain why the present population included no frogs but many lizards. "May this difference not be caused," he asked, "by the greater facility with which the eggs of lizards, protected by calcareous shells, might be transported through salt-water, than could the slimy spawn of frogs?" To support his theory of accidental transport Darwin performed many experiments in the years following his return to England. He immersed seeds in sea water for several months and found that some would still germinate. He grew plants from seeds that birds had ejected in their droppings, from seeds that had clung to mud on birds' feet, and from seeds in a half ounce of locust dung mailed to him by a friend in Africa.

But the most baffling riddle still remained. In his journal he reverts repeatedly to "the most remarkable feature in the natural history of the archipelago: it is that the different islands to a considerable extent are inhabited by a different set of beings." It was the vice-governor who first called his attention to this fact by remarking that he could tell by looking at a tortoise what island it came from. "I did not for some time pay sufficient attention to this statement," Darwin related, self-reproachfully. "I never dreamed that islands about 50 to 60 miles apart, placed under a quite similar climate, would have been differently tenanted." It was not the tortoises, however, but the finches that gave Darwin his ultimate insight into the mechanisms involved in the origin of species. Describing the variations in the 13 species of Galápagos finches, he made a revealing statement: "One might really fancy that from an original paucity of birds in this archipelago one species has been taken and modified for different ends."

Darwin apparently had already conceived the idea that competition could be as important as climate and geography in the development of new forms of life. It was only after 20 years of research and contemplation that he convinced himself that competition represented the missing piece in his theory of evolution. His difficulty had arisen, he wrote in *The Origin of Species,* "from the deeply seated error of considering the physical conditions of a country as the most important; whereas it cannot be disputed that the nature of the other species with which each has to compete, is at least as important. . . . Hence, when in former times an immigrant first settled on one of the islands, or when it subsequently spread from one to another, it would undoubtedly be exposed to different conditions in the different islands, for it would have to compete with a different set of organisms. . . . Undoubtedly if one species has any advantage over another, it will in a very brief time wholly or in part supplant it."

Thus all of the 13 species of finches on the Galápagos must have been descendants of a common ancestor which had migrated from the mainland—blown perhaps in an equatorial storm—at some time in the not-too-distant past. On the populous mainland the struggle

GALAPAGOS

and are still being investigated today

for existence amid a horde of competitors would have restricted them to a narrow niche in the economy of nature. But the absence of other land birds on the Galápagos enabled the finches to evolve in directions that otherwise would have been closed. Finding a wide-open domain of existence, they radiated into divergent types whose physical equipment in time adapted to their habits. Some developed slender, curved beaks for probing flowers, others evolved strong, parrot-like beaks for cracking seeds.

It was through his observations in the Galápagos, therefore, that Darwin could see evolution at work not in the antique fossil past, but in the living present. Here he beheld a domain unlike any other on earth, existing in isolation, unravaged by man, a miniature island cosmos where nature's processes could be clearly viewed in one small amphitheater.

In the years that have elapsed since Darwin sailed away from the archipelago the only major changes have been wrought by man. Evolution moves at tortoise pace, and all forms of life that Darwin studied are still there—in kind. But the ruthless depredations of man and of his domestic animals, gone wild, have reduced them in numbers so drastically that on some islands certain species have been annihilated utterly, and on others are threatened with extinction. Tortoises have been slaughtered for their meat and fat. The land iguanas have been hunted for their skins. And to this day, as in Darwin's, "sailors, wandering through the woods in search of tortoises, always take cruel delight in knocking down the little birds."

ALTHOUGH the Republic of Ecuador, which administers the islands, enacted conservation laws in 1934, they were not successfully enforced. In 1957 UNESCO, in collaboration with international conservation groups and LIFE Magazine, dispatched a survey team to the islands to see what creatures remained. The expedition included Dr. Irenäus Eibl-Eibesfeldt of the Max Planck Research Institute, West Germany, and Dr. Robert Bowman of San Francisco State College. In their reports they recommended the designation of certain islands as inviolate wildlife sanctuaries and the establishment of a biological research center to be known as the Charles Darwin Memorial Station. Their suggestions were approved in general at the International Zoological Congress in London.

The same year, Dr. Jean Dorst, assistant director of the National Museum of Natural History in Paris, was assigned to follow up the first expedition and make more specific recommendations as to the proposed Darwin Memorial Station. Of three sites suggested by Dr. Eibl-Eibesfeldt and Dr. Bowman in 1957, he recommended Tortuga Bay on the south side of Indefatigable Island by virtue of its biological diversity and semi-isolation from existing settlements. As a consequence of the Dorst report, the Charles Darwin Foundation for the Galápagos Isles was established at an international meeting in Brussels in July 1959. At the same time the Government of Ecuador passed a decree amending its obsolete 1934 laws, promising protection to rare Galápagos life, and setting aside Narborough and several other islands as sanctuaries forever. It was agreed that expenses for construction of the Charles Darwin Memorial Station would be divided between Ecuador and the Charles Darwin Foundation. Sir Julian Huxley was named honorary president of the foundation, with an executive council consisting of scientists from Ecuador, Belgium, France, Switzerland, Germany, Great Britain and the U.S. The president, Dr. Victor van Straelen, formerly of the University of Ghent, formulated an ambitious plan to explore the Galápagos methodically, island by island, including a full cartographical survey and a complete census of flora and fauna.

"The main purpose of our research," he said, "will be to understand better the problem of the origin of species. In the Galápagos we have a wonderful possibility of finding answers to the questions: how is a completely sterile land mass colonized under natural conditions; how did the different species arrive there? For many kinds of animals we can discover or deduce how they might have covered the distance from the mainland to the coast, but for others their mode of transport still remains a mystery."

In 1960 construction began on the world's first international biological station, to stand henceforth as a perpetual monument to Darwin's genius and a symbol of hope and determination that his living laboratory of evolution should not perish from the earth.

TAPING A TORTOISE, Dr. Irenäus Eibl-Eibesfeldt, member of the 1957 expedition to the Galápagos, takes the waist measurement of a giant resident of Indefatigable Island. Four men in the party tried in vain to lift it.

HOLDING A HAWK, Dr. Robert Bowman, the expedition's American member, inspects a bird that Darwin greatly admired. UNESCO yacht, *Odin*, lies in a cove of Duncan Island, which has been set aside as a sanctuary.

THE STRATAGEMS OF DEFENSE

WARNING off predators with the glow of its twin headlamps, the fire beetle of Brazil demonstrates one of the many subtle defense mechanisms evolved within the complex insect world. Its luminescent orbs are not eyes but body patches which simulate the menacing glare of a nocturnal prowler and thereby discourage birds and other enemies. Tropical insects observed by Darwin in Brazil protect themselves in a variety of ways: by artful camouflage, by mimicry, and by bad odor or taste.

THE BRAZILIAN FOREST shimmers in the golden haze of noon. On this very slope, near Rio de Janeiro, Darwin roamed during his visit, marveling at the splendor of the scene. He undoubtedly observed this giant ceiba tree which has been growing here for three centuries, its branches festooned with Spanish moss, orchids and the vines of other air plants. It was this spectacle which introduced him to the tropics and the first phase of his great adventure.

A BLUE MORPHO BUTTERFLY, MOST BRILLIANT OF ALL THE FOREST INSECTS THAT ENCHANTED DARWIN'S EYE, SPREADS ITS IRIDESCENT SAPPHIRE WINGS

THE STRATAGEMS
OF DEFENSE

Insects of the Brazilian forests disclose nature's hidden ways

BARELY two months after H.M.S. *Beagle* set sail from England on its epic five-year voyage, Darwin landed in Brazil and there looked wide eyed on an exotic land. The excitement he felt as a young man of 23, fresh from the rolling hills of Shropshire, still echoes in the words he wrote in his journal on Feb. 29, 1832: "Delight is a weak term to express the feelings of a naturalist who for the first time has wandered by himself in a Brazilian forest. The beauty of the flowers, the glossy green of the foliage, but above all the luxuriance of the vegetation filled me with admiration. To a person fond of natural history, such a day as this brings a deeper pleasure than he can ever hope to experience again."

Darwin's first ecstatic glimpse of the profuse and profligate life of the tropics provided a perfect prologue for his future work. He was at once bewildered and enthralled, for of all domains of life none is richer or more riotous than the equatorial forest with its hosts of animals, birds and, beyond all, insects, numberless as the leaves of the canopy above. His initial impressions remained vivid in his memory, and he often acknowledged their impact on the thinking of

his later years. At the end of his voyage, reflecting on Brazil and still enraptured, he wrote: "The land is one great wild, untidy, luxuriant hothouse, made by Nature for herself. . . . In my last walk I stopped again and again to gaze on [its] beauties, and endeavored to fix in my mind forever an impression which I knew sooner or later must fail. . . . Yet they will leave, like a tale heard in childhood, a picture full of indistinct but most beautiful figures."

Like all great scientists Darwin possessed an esthetic sense of the beauty of the natural world, both in its outer aspect and its underlying order. It was this sense which enabled him ultimately to penetrate the apparent chaos and diversity of the natural world and discover the harmony beneath. Not until he reached the Galápagos Islands did he begin to discern the mechanisms of evolution. But in the teeming, many-footed jungle of Brazil he first found clues that eventually gave him insight into nature's hidden artifices for survival and defense. In this chapter some of the bizarre and beautiful denizens of the Brazilian forest that Darwin saw are pictured, revealing in their diverse forms and habits the wondrous laws that govern life on earth.

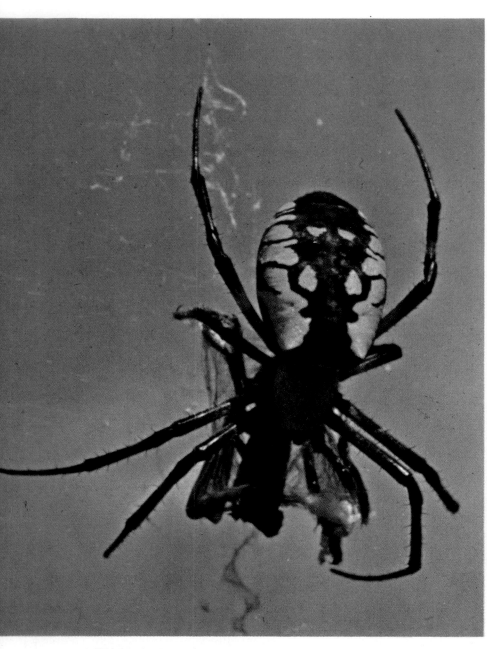

A TIGER SPIDER downs a small wasp which blundered into its web. As soon as its prey is ensnared, the spider envelops it in a cocoonlike case of silk and gives it a fatal bite. When the poison has taken effect, it dines at leisure.

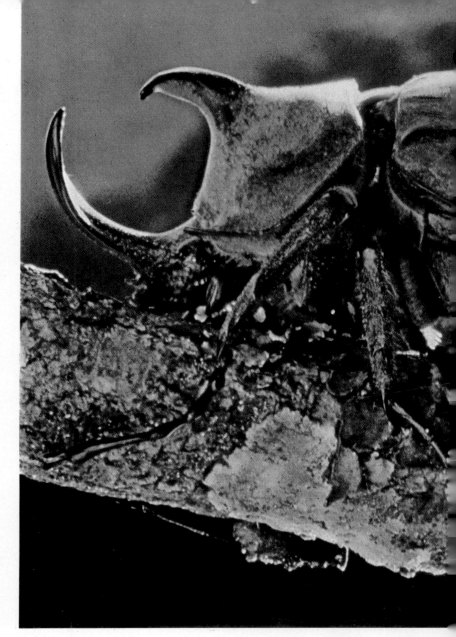

MALE RHINOCEROS BEETLE (above) wears fearsome horns apparently made for combat. Since Darwin never saw these beetles fight, he decided their horns were purely ornamental. The males sometimes do battle over females.

ENDLESS BATTLE TO SURVIVE

In Brazil, Darwin observed certain aspects of insect life which impressed him as dramatic instances of the endless struggle for survival in a hostile world. He noted the work battalions of the parasol ants laboring to harvest food supplies (right) and contemplated the horns of the male rhinoceros beetle (above right), a ferocious-looking pacifist that had never been seen to fight. Darwin's pursuit of the problem led him to the discovery that the horns of certain species are mere ornaments, worn for sexual attraction. Perhaps the grimmest example of nature's often ruthless ways Darwin found in the eternal warfare between wasps and spiders. He witnessed battles in which the spider was sometimes victor (above); at other times the wasp (far right).

Describing how certain wasps construct clay cells as incubators for their larvae, he wrote, "These cells they stuff full of half-dead spiders and caterpillars, which they seem wonderfully to know how to sting to that degree as to leave them paralyzed but alive, until their eggs are hatched; and the larvae feed on the horrid mass of powerless, half-killed victims. . . ." One day in Brazil, Darwin watched fascinated as a wasp attacked a spider for this purpose. "The wasp made a sudden dash," he related, "and then flew away: the spider was evidently wounded. . . . The wasp soon returned, and . . . inflicted two stings on the under side of the spider's thorax. At last, carefully examining with its antennae the now motionless spider, it proceeded to drag away the body." Darwin then ended the story with the cryptic comment, "But I stopped both tyrant and prey."

44

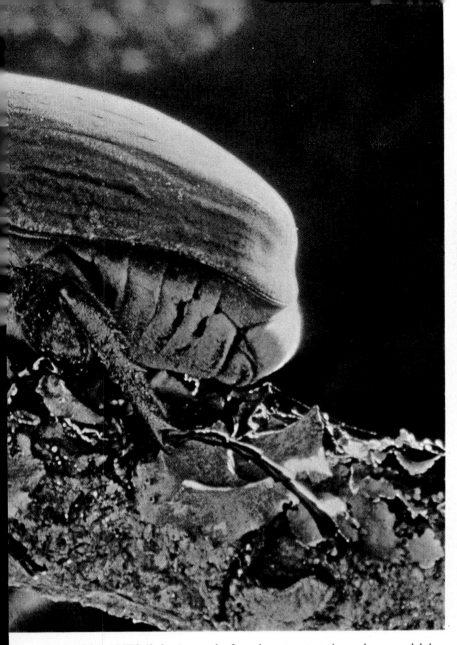

PARASOL ANTS *(below)* carry leaf sections to store in underground labyrinths. Darwin wondered at the tireless labors of the "never-ending foragers, burdened with pieces of green leaves often larger than their own bodies."

BATTLE TO THE DEATH takes place between a spider and a wasp. Here, as in the combat witnessed by Darwin, the attacking wasp evades the spider's legs *(top)*, implants its deadly sting *(middle)*, drags its paralyzed victim away.

45

DISGUISE, DEFENSE, DECEPTION

The pressure of life in the tropics is fiercer than anywhere else on earth. Here amid the dank green colonnades, insects swarm in every niche from the shadowed forest floor to the topmost spires of the canopy.

Infinitely diverse in form and habits, all have their enemies, all face death each instant in the feathered garb of some sharp-sighted, sharp-beaked bird, or in the livery of a long-tongued lizard, snake or toad. To survive they have evolved a vast repertoire of visual illusion, deceit, fakery and hoax.

In no other arena of life have processes of natural selection wrought greater diversity. In 1958 Dr. H. B. D. Kettlewell, Oxford geneticist, retraced Darwin's steps for the purpose of analyzing insect adaptations in the light of modern knowledge. Of 5,000 insects he collected, a sampling of the most important and bizarre is presented here in paintings by Swiss artist Walter Linsenmaier.

The most universal of all insect mechanisms of defense is camouflage, or protective coloration. At far left the Stink Bug and Longhorned Beetle both blend into the lichens on the tree. So does the giant moth, *Thysania Agrippina*, whose 12-inch wingspread makes it the largest moth on earth. An analogous device is exhibited by three smaller moths just right of the giant's lower wing. Above them other moths and butterflies match the tree bark. Next right, a long Phasmid Stick simulates a dead twig. Below, a green moth rests virtually invisible on a living leaf of matching hue. To its right, three more moths with windowed wings imitate dead leaves with holes.

The most consummate camouflage artists of the insect world are the Brown Leaf Mantid *(lower right)*, a carnivore seldom seen by the prey it devours; the Broken Twig Moth *(top, center)* which curls its wings into a single cylinder at rest; the Cossid Moth *(top, right center)* which looks like a fallen flower; and the Leaf Blemish Katydid *(right center)* whose green wings wear blotches of arboreal blight.

Such diversity of disguise derives from the variety of backgrounds provided by the Brazilian forest. For many species, however, camouflage is only a primary defense. The Brown Leaf Katydid *(lower right)* copies a dead leaf, but when discovered unfurls its wings, startling foes with a sudden flash of color *(far right)*. The Tan Camouflaged Saturnid Moth *(upper right)* resembles a faded leaf at rest; when threatened it displays alarming bloodshot eye spots which repel inquisitive birds. The Red-Flash Grasshopper below employs a similar defense of coloration and camouflage.

Quite different is the defense mechanism inherent in the garish warning colors of certain insects endowed with nauseating odor and taste—the Red-bodied Foul-smelling Moth and Yellow-winged Warning Moth *(top, right)*. Any bird that tastes them once will seldom sample them a second time.

LONG-HORNED BEETLE

LICHEN-COLORED STINK BUG

WORLD'S LARGEST MOTH

DISRUPTIVE WHITE-MARKED MOTH, WINGS FOLDED

TRIANGULAR-WINGED DISRUPTIVE NOCTUID MOTH

LARGE JEWEL BEETLE WAVY-PATTERNED BUTTERFLY BROKEN TWIG MOTH, WINGS FOLDED GREEN SPHINX HAWK MOTH FLOWERLIKE COSSID M
HUGE BROWN PHASMID STICK INSECT RUST AND WHITE PYRALID MOTH GREEN-SPOTTED GEOMETRID MOTH GREEN AND YELLOW VARI
PRAYING MANTID GIANT GRAY HAWK MOTH DISRUPTIVE-PATTERNED COSSID MOTH, WINGS FOLDED GRAY-GREEN TREE GRASSHOPPER BROWN-BLACK DISRUPTIVE M
DISRUPTIVE-STRIPED NOCTUID MOTH GREEN AND WHITE PATTERNED MOTH FOUR-SPOTTED LEAFLIKE MOTH ORANGE-COLORED DEAD LEAF M
WINDOW-WINGED MOTH

FOLD OUT, DO NOT TEAR

BLUE MORPHO BUTTERFLY   TRICOLORED DISTASTEFUL MODEL BUTTERFLY   WAXY-STREAMERED CICADA

UTTERFLY   TRICOLORED DISTASTEFUL HELICONIAN BUTTERFLY   TRICOLORED MELINIID BUTTERFLY   HORNED TREE HOF

         TRICOLORED NYMPHALID BUTTERFLY   TRICOLORED MECHANITIS BUTTERFLY   TRICOLORED EUEIDES BUTTERFLY   KNOBBED MEMBRACID BUG

PSIS WASP   RED-BEAKED TRUE WASP   RED-BEAKED WASPLIKE SYNTOMID MOTH   RED-WHITE-BLACK SWALLOWTAIL BUTTERFLY   CRESTED TREE HOPPER

   BLUE-BLACK TARANTULA HAWK WASP   ORANGE-BANDED WARNING SYNTOMID MOTH   BLUE-BLACK ASSASSIN BUG   THORNLIKE TREE HOPPER

50   ANTLIKE BUG   ORANGE-BANDED WARNING LYCID BEETLE   ORANGE-BANDED LONG-HORNED BEETLE

BIG-WINGED MASKED LANTERN BUG

BLACK AND YELLOW GRAY HAWK CATERPILLAR   MALE WHITE BUTTERFLY   ORANGE AND BLACK LEAF HOPPER   FEMALE WHITE BUTTERFLY   TRICOLORED LYCORID

GOLD-MARKED WARNING SYNTOMID MOTH   RED AND BLUE LEAF HOPPER   YELLOW-SPOTTED BLACK LEAF HOPPER   ORANGE-WINGED MYDAS FLY

YELLOW WARNING GEOMETRID MOTH   TWO-SPOTTED SYNTOMID MOTH   SMALL TWO-SPOTTED NOCTUID MOTH   ORANGE-WINGED PE

HEADLAMP CLICK BEETLE   GRAY TWO-SPOTTED ARCTIID MOTH

OTH   DARK-SPOTTED TWIG-HOLDING MOTH   RED-BODIED FOUL-SMELLING MOTH   TAN SATURNID MOTH IN EYE SPOT DISPLAY

GATED LEAF HOPPER   WEDGE-SHAPED MOTH, ON TWIG   TAN SATURNID MOTH, CAMOUFLAGED   YELLOW-WINGED WARNING MOTH

TH   GRAY SPHINX HAWK MOTH   GREEN LEAF BLEMISH KATYDID   BRIGHT TROPIC BEE   RED-FLASH GRASSHOPPER

OTH   BROWN LEAF MANTID   BROWN LEAF KATYDID   BROWN LEAF KATYDID IN FLASH DISPLAY   SNOUTED MOTH

                              YELLOW AND BLACK FLASH MOTH   HAIRY-BODIED MOTH

MUMMERY, MIMICRY AND MASKS

In the tangled mazes of the forest the simpler arts of camouflage shown on the preceding pages cannot alone protect the insect populations from their alert, ever-hungry foes. But the ingenuity of nature is limitless; hence bolder strategies—tricks of mimicry and mummery—have been devised.

Impersonation of other creatures represents a subtler form of masquerade than imitation of a leaf or flower. In the center of this painting flickers a swarm of black and orange butterflies. Although they look alike, they belong to different species and even different families. The two topmost specimens, the Distasteful Heliconian and the Distasteful Model butterflies, are unpalatable to predators. Others are edible but wear the same warning colors as their unappetizing models, seeking safety in similitude. But paradoxically the Male White Butterfly *(left)* lacks the protective coloration of his mate. Other creatures which sport orange and black uniforms to warn enemies away include the moths in the lower left corner, and the caterpillar above them.

An elaboration of this tactic is employed by insects which impersonate members of completely different—and usually dangerous —orders. Thus of the two big orange and black insects perched below the butterflies, the one at left is a harmless Mydas Fly, the other a venomous Pepsis Wasp. Hovering at their right are another wasp and its mime, a wasplike Syntomid Moth. At the bottom of the painting, the three similar orange and black insects are all of different families, a fragile moth and its hard-shelled models—two carnivorous beetles.

More exotic forms of mimicry appear in the cluster of insects on the tree in the upper right corner: moths masquerading variously as a spider, weevil, beetle and scorpion.

Transcending mimicry, some insects have features dramatically designed to cause fear, like the eye spots of the four small creatures at lower left, notably the Headlamp Click Beetle whose pseudo eyes are luminous at night. Still fiercer-looking adaptations are seen in the armaments of the Giant Horned Beetle and Horned Scarab Beetle *(lower right)* which are used in courtship battles and may also frighten predators.

The ultimate in horror defense, however, is worn by the Lantern Bug in the upper left corner. At rest this harmless creature is inconspicuous. In flight it exposes huge eye marks on its hind wings and its hideous head appears—an awful mask which bears the likeness of a tiny alligator complete with ravening teeth. As a final defense its body is coated with distasteful wax. Repellent white streamers of wax also protect the cicada flitting at upper right center.

By contrast the blue of the Morpho Butterfly, above, safeguards its fragile body not from predators but from heat, by reflecting ultraviolet waves from the sunlight gilding the higher pavilions in which it dwells.

SPIDERLIKE MOTH   SCORPION-TAILED MOTH   PALE BUGLIKE CICADA
KNOB-LEGGED GNATLIKE MOTH   WEEVIL-LIKE MOTH   GRAY-WINGED BEETLELIKE MOTH   PALE BUGLIKE MOTH
             LEAF-LEGGED SQUASH BUG   HAIRY BLUE-GREEN NOCTUID MOTH
      GIANT HORNED BEETLE   HORNED SCARAB BEETLE

SPHINX MOTHS rest motionless on trees by day, camouflaged by disruptive markings which blend with the bark. The moth above depends on coloration alone. The one below has other lines of defense: hidden underwings which flash a danger signal and leg spurs which inflict sharp stings.

PERFECTION OR DEATH

The perfection of camouflage evolved by forest insects to fool their enemies enabled many of them also to evade Darwin's eye. Today, with new techniques, scientists can study even such self-effacing creatures as the moths and caterpillars shown here. For nocturnal insects Dr. Kettlewell used a mercury-vapor lamp *(see page 58)*, whose ultraviolet radiation attracted thousands nightly.

The evolutionary interest of the Brazilian jungle lies in the fact that it has existed since prehistoric times. For millenniums the laws of natural selection have operated here, unaffected by the ice ages. The intensity of competition, moreover, has produced perfection in every artifice of mimicry and illusion. Since a single flaw means sudden death, survival of the fittest means survival of the craftiest, shyest and the most artful in this murmurous, implacable domain.

CAMOUFLAGED CATERPILLAR feeds clinging to the underside of a leaf. Its protective pattern of diagonal stripes and random splashes of blue-green and white reproduces the effects of light and shadow in the dappled foliage of the deep forest. This insect and those on the following page were photographed in Brazil by Dr. Kettlewell. The problem of illuminating small creatures in their dark places of refuge was solved by using large mirrors.

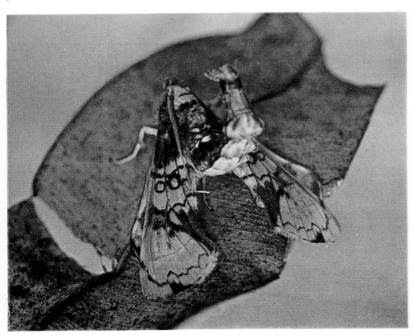

ACROBATIC MOTH disguises itself by throwing its abdomen over its head, thereby giving itself a most unmothlike appearance. No less than color, the position in which an insect spends the daylight hours is a factor in survival.

PSEUDO SPIDER is actually a species of hairy caterpillar equipped with eight false leglike appendages which if nipped off by some predator soon grow back. Confident in its disguise, it sits exposed by day on top of leaves.

WILY WEEVIL protects itself by the humblest of disguises. Its whitish shell, touched with brown, makes no attempt to blend with the green of the leaf on which it rests. Instead it simulates the excreta of its foes, the birds.

MOTTLED MOTH rests on the exposed upper surface of leaves, its disruptive pattern of light oval markings appearing, from the point of view of a passing bird, to be flecks of sunlight filtered through the foliage overhead.

TREE FERNS weave their lacy fronds into the canopy of the forest where Darwin conducted his investigation of Brazilian insects. They are among the largest of the fern family, their branches radiating treelike from a woody

HAIRY-LEGGED MOTH sits with its large black forelimbs outspread in an aggressive and unmothlike posture designed to confuse birds not deceived by its green protective coloration. In some positions its legs look spiderlike.

trunk. On first seeing this region Darwin wrote: "The forest abounded with beautiful objects; among which the tree ferns were, from their bright green foliage and elegant curvature of their fronds, most worthy of admiration."

PSEUDO-SPHINX CATERPILLARS promenade along a twig, disdainful of avian eyes. Their uniforms of orange and black, topped by shiny red helmets, are danger signals serving notice on enemies that they are foul-tasting.

ORIENTATION TO SUN is a protective mechanism employed by some insects in the tropic forest. Here a Draconia moth rests in its daytime hiding place. Instead of sitting with folded wings, like most moths, it stands erect with wings outspread at right angles to the sun, thus exposing only its thin wing edges and the long axis of its body to the sun's rays. This way it casts a minimum shadow, is least noticeable to hungry birds and other predators.

CONSUMMATE CAMOUFLAGE protects the Cossid moth which sits exposed by day, with its wings simulating petals of a fallen flower. Some insects have several means of defense, but the Cossid relies on artistry alone.

LONG WING-TAILS worn by this dawn-flying silk moth produce a slight rustling noise in flight. Dawn-flying bats, hunting by reflected sound, probably seize the tails, ripping them off, thereby permitting the moth to escape.

GAUDY COLORATION is used as a protective device by the Syntomid moth *(above)* as it is by some other unpalatable insects. Instead of attempting to blend with its background, it makes itself conspicuous to remind would-be diners of previous nauseating encounters. Among insects that rely on this defense, black, red and yellow are the most fashionable colors. Another kind of Syntomid uses a resemblance to a wasp *(page 50)* to scare off enemies.

THE EVIDENCE DARWIN

The process of natural selection in the insect kingdom has been both changed and

IN the long labor of creative thought that produced *The Origin of Species*, Darwin's visit to Brazil lingered in his mind like the opening sonorities of a symphony, a blend of brilliance and splendor whose individual motifs would be untangled only by future contemplation. It is evident in the contrasting passages of his early and later writings that his first dazzled entry into a lavish, new and complex domain of nature afforded him inspiration no less crucial than the insights he acquired from the sparse, insular fauna of the Galápagos. For in the lush Brazilian forest he viewed richer and more diverse forms of life, and more extreme patterns of specialization and behavior than may exist anywhere else on earth.

In the *Voyage of the Beagle*, published only a few years after his return, Darwin wrote purely as a keen-eyed and sensitive naturalist, imbued with the beauty and wonder of what he saw: "The day was powerfully hot, and as we passed through the woods, everything was motionless, excepting the large and brilliant butterflies that fluttered lazily about. . . . Various cicadas and crickets keep up a ceaseless shrill cry. Every evening after dark this great concert commenced; and often have I sat listening to it, until my attention was drawn away by some curious passing insect." Later, noting the attraction of certain insects to certain plants, a phenomenon he had observed in England, he wrote this portent-filled sentence: "We see here in two distant countries a similar relation between plants and insects of the same families, though the species of both are different."

Twenty years later, in *The Origin of Species*, Darwin set forth in detail the inferences he had drawn from his initial, fragmentary impressions of the insect world of Brazil. "Insects," he wrote, "often resemble for the sake of protection various objects, such as green or decayed leaves, dead twigs, bits of lichen, flowers, spines, excrement of birds, and living insects. . . . The resemblance is often wonderfully close, and is not confined to color, but extends to form, and even to the manner in which the insects hold themselves. . . . In all the foregoing cases, the insects in their original state no doubt presented some rude and accidental resemblance to an object commonly found in the stations frequented by them.

"Assuming that an insect originally happened to resemble in some degree a dead twig or a decayed leaf, and that it varied slightly in many ways, then all the variations which rendered the insects more like any such object would be preserved, whilst other variations would be ultimately lost; or if they rendered the insect less like the imitated object, they would be eliminated. . . . Insects are often preyed on by birds and other enemies, whose sight is probably sharper than ours, and every grade in resemblance which aided an insect to escape notice or detection would tend toward its preservation; and

COLLECTING INSECTS IN BRAZIL, Geneticist H.B.D. Kettlewell of Oxford studies specimens lured indoors by a mercury-vapor lamp. Emitting ultraviolet rays attractive to insect eyes, his light trap pulls in up to 10,000 insects in one night.

the more perfect the resemblance so much the better for the insect."

Here, in essence, is Darwin's explanation, which still holds true today, of the unending diversity of insect life in the Brazilian forest and of the inescapable process of natural selection which brought it about. Nowhere else in the world, not even in Africa, have insects diversified into so many different species; nowhere else have they evolved more polymorphisms (special forms within species); nowhere else have they invented more varieties of specialization and disguise. Today scientists can explain some of the reasons for the profusion and extreme specialization of insect life in Brazil. One reason is the diversity of plant life. Here in an equatorial climate, untouched by great climatic fluctuations either today or in the ancient past, the primeval forest has flourished for millions of years, without any interference save that of the casual, destructive hand of man. Today the eastern Brazilian jungle alone encompasses more than 400 species of trees, each with a different trunk texture or color, some brown, some red, but most of them white, as Darwin observed. Each tree has four zones of sanctuary against which camouflaged insects may rest during the daytime hours—the trunk, branches, leaves and buds—thus affording 1,600 different types of background.

Within the jungle may also be found 300 different species of birds, many of them insectivorous, as well as lizards, snakes, monkeys and other insectivores which hunt by sight. It is because of this diversity of background sanctuary and diversity of predators that Brazil's insects have specialized with such evolutionary perfection.

Darwin, lacking the tools of modern entomology, was unable to appreciate fully the enormous complexity of the forest's winged and crawling life. Nevertheless Brazil provided Darwin with a treasure trove of material which, however intricate, ultimately guided his thought to the theory of natural selection. From his observations he drew the very heart of his argument.

"Can it be then," he asked in *The Origin of Species*, "that variations useful in some way to each being in the great and complex battle for life should occur in the course of many generations? If such do occur, can we doubt (remembering that many more individuals are born than can possibly survive) that individuals having an advantage, however slight over others, would have the best chance of surviving and procreating their kind? On the other hand we feel sure that any variation in the least degree injurious would be rigidly destroyed. This preservation of favorable individual differences and variations and the destruction of those which are injurious I have called Natural Selection or the Survival of the Fittest. . . . Man can act only on external and visible characters; Nature, if I may be allowed to personify the natural preservation or survival of the fittest, cares nothing for appearances, except

58

MISSED

quickened by the works of modern man

insofar as they are useful to any being. She can act on every internal organ, on every shade of constitutional difference, on the whole machinery of life. Man selects only for his own good; Nature only for that of the being which she tends."

Ironically, Darwin might have obtained visible evidence of a dramatic evolutionary change within his own lifetime—not in the forests of South America but at home in England. Here, had his attention been attracted by a striking mutation in the coloring of certain familiar moths, he would have found an unmistakable confirmation of his theory that would have precluded all the arguments and controversies of his later years.

Although the change perfectly exemplified survival of the fittest, it is not surprising that it escaped even Darwin's percipient eyes, for he never dreamed that evolution could proceed at such a rapid pace. Nor did he know the power of modern man to transform the whole system of nature. Man's influence on his environment has been exercised for centuries, since the first farmers hacked clearings in the forests, sowed grain on scrubby moors and mountain meadows, and dug drainage ditches in marshy lowlands and muddy riverbanks. But these endeavors had heretofore wrought only local transformations in the character of the land and the balance of its wild inhabitants.

"Darwin's lifetime," says Dr. Kettlewell, "coincided with the first great man-made change of environment on earth." During the 19th Century the Industrial Revolution permanently transmuted great areas of the planet through the spread of stone, steel and smoke across the green, living landscape. Urbanization has affected the ecology of species most drastically in Britain, northern Europe and North America. There much plant and animal life has either perished or undergone profound adaptations as a consequence of the effluvia from factory chimneys, trains, heated buildings and automobiles.

ONLY recently have the insidious effects of this infection of the air been assessed by scientific study. It has been found that the foliage of trees and plants has been defiled, and the light-colored vegetative lichens that cling to their trunks and branches have been destroyed and washed away by corrosive rains.

As a consequence of these transformations in the flora, certain equivalent transformations have been observed in the fauna that inhabit them. In England, for example, there are 780 species of moths. A century ago most of these wore light colors which blended with the light tree trunks and lichen-covered rocks on which they passed the daylight hours. Today more than 70 of these species have exchanged their light attire for dark coloration. This phenomenon, which has occurred in urban areas elsewhere in Europe and in the U.S., is known technically as "industrial melanism"—the word "melanism" connoting an unusual development of black or nearly black pigmentation in the skin, hair or plumage of any animal.

One of the first observed specimens of this evolutionary product was the Peppered Moth (right), which has recently been the subject of a classic study by Dr. Kettlewell. In its melanic, or black, form, it was first espied in the English Midlands, near Manchester, in 1848 when it comprised less than one percent of the population. By 1895, however, the Peppered Moth population around Manchester was about 99 percent black. So profound a statistical revision in half a century could be achieved only through an overwhelming advantage of the dark form over its light-colored forebears—i.e., in its ability to blend with the blackened bark of the industrial Midlands.

In the course of a decade of research on the Peppered Moth, based on some 20,000 observations recorded by 170 voluntary watchers in various parts of Britain, Dr. Kettlewell concluded that 1) unless a moth adapts to a changing environment it is ruthlessly eliminated by predators (i.e., birds); and 2) once the mutation is achieved, natural selection accounts for its rapid spread. The correlation between industrial pollution and a preponderance of melanic moths is emphasized by the converse preponderance of light-colored species in nonindustrial western England and northern Scotland.

"Melanism," says Dr. Kettlewell, "enables us to appreciate the vast reserves of genetic variability which can be summoned when the occasion arises. Had Darwin observed industrial melanism he would have seen evolution occurring not in thousands of years but in thousands of days—well within his lifetime. He would have witnessed the consummation and confirmation of his life's work."

EVOLUTION IN PROGRESS is demonstrated by Peppered Moths clinging to soot-blackened tree in industrial Birmingham, England. The light moth is vulnerable to birds. The other, better camouflaged, is more likely to survive.

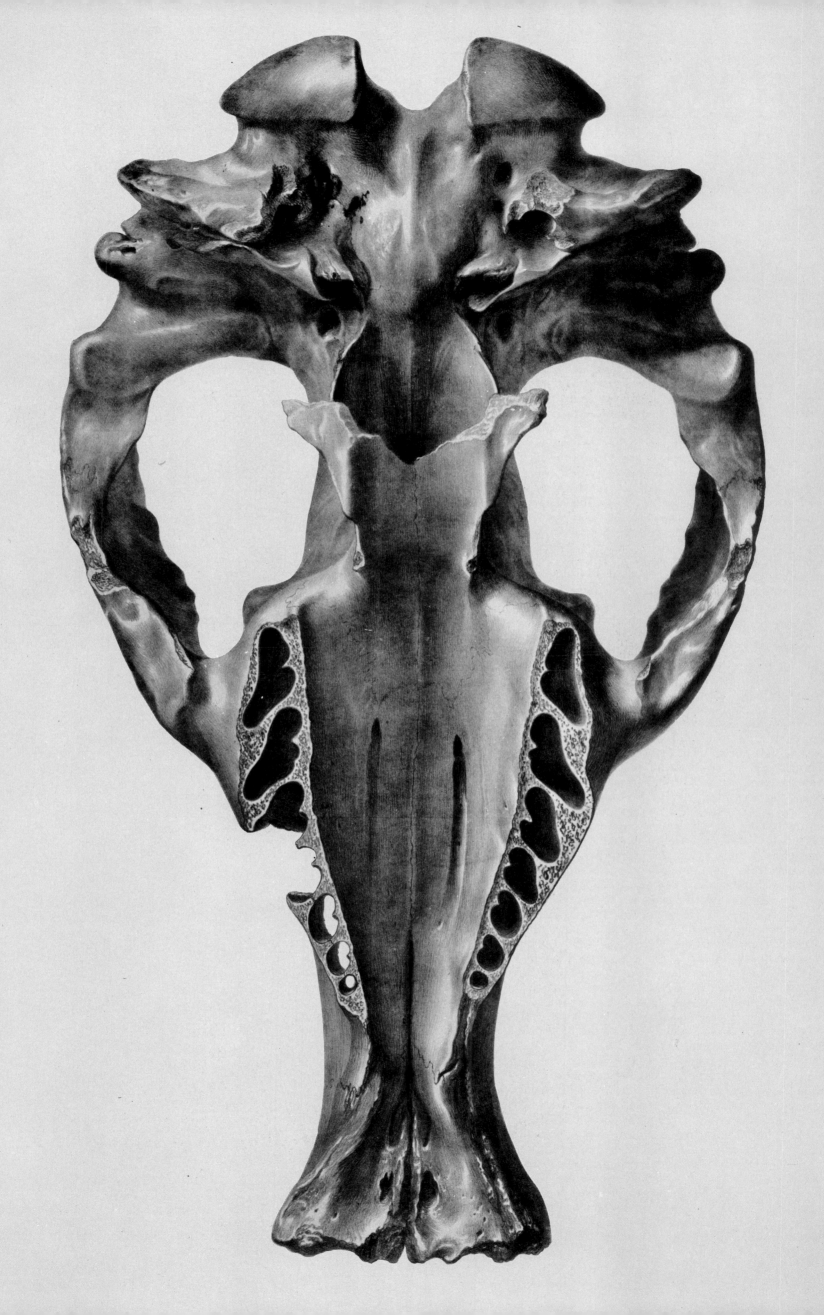

THE
CONTINUITY
OF
LIFE

THE extinct animal whose flesh mantled the weird skull shown at left was a toxodon, which flourished in South America one million years ago. Its enormous bones, engineered somewhat along the lines of the modern rhinoceros, were found by Darwin on the Argentine pampas and convinced him of the evolutionary ties uniting prehistoric and present animal forms over vast reaches of time. The skull shown here measures two feet, four inches in length and one foot, four inches across at its widest part.

DEER

DOG

MASTODONT

OPOSSUM

PORCUPINE

PUMA

MEGATHERE

ARMADILLO

RACCOON

TAPIR

EXTINCT
CAPYBARA

GLYPTODONT

RABBIT

TAYRA

EXTINCT HORSE

THE ENORMOUS
MIGRATION

The animals of the Americas are products of the
greatest migration in the recorded history of the
world. Since the Age of Dinosaurs the two continents had been separated by the sea. About one
million years ago the Isthmus of Panama arose,
creating a land bridge from north to south. Animals streamed across in both directions. From the
north came the varied species indicated on the
map by blue arrows. From the south came those
indicated by white arrows; those which got no farther north than the forests of Central America are
indicated by yellow arrows. Many of the migrants
became extinct in the great dying of the Pleistocene Age. Others, like the spectacled bear of
South America and the porcupine of North America, survive today only in their adopted homes.

PECCARY

SABERTOOTH CAT

GUANACO

TWO-TOED
SLOTH

SPINY
RAT

SQUIRREL

SPECTACLED
BEAR

GIANT
ANTEATER

TOXODONT

SPIDER
MONKEY

AGOUTI

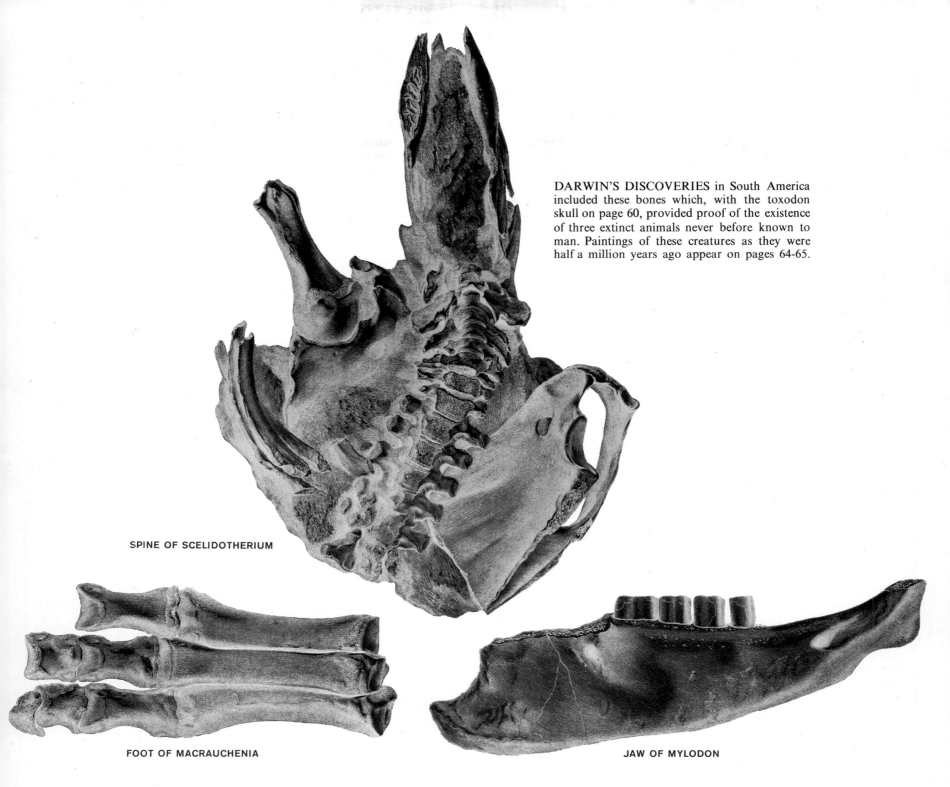

SPINE OF SCELIDOTHERIUM

FOOT OF MACRAUCHENIA

JAW OF MYLODON

DARWIN'S DISCOVERIES in South America included these bones which, with the toxodon skull on page 60, provided proof of the existence of three extinct animals never before known to man. Paintings of these creatures as they were half a million years ago appear on pages 64-65.

THE CONTINUITY OF LIFE

In Argentina, Darwin discovered strange relics of a lost world

LATE in August 1833, Darwin disembarked from the *Beagle* to explore the Argentine pampas and stumbled on one of the most dazzling discoveries of his voyage. Digging in the clay of a coastal plain, he uncovered the huge bones of some of the weirdest creatures that ever lived *(above)*. "It is impossible to reflect on the changed state of the American continent without astonishment," he wrote. "Formerly it must have swarmed with great monsters."

Monsters they were, for nowhere had more fanciful forms evolved in the twilight of prehistory. Their grotesque remains added another dimension to Darwin's widening horizons. In them he found evidence of the continuity of life in the immensity of time.

While the earth's antiquity is common knowledge today, in Darwin's era the science of paleontology had only begun to stir. The notion that unknown animals might once have ranged the earth and vanished clashed with belief in the separate creation of species.

Darwin was often asked: If extant species evolved from extinct species, why are fossil beds not filled with innumerable transitional forms? He replied: "The crust of the earth must not be looked at as a well-filled museum, but as a poor collection made at hazard." He knew that many species died without descendants in the struggle to survive. And he knew that the lands of earth rose and fell, now dividing populations, now creating land bridges across which animals migrated to new homes. Amazed by the archaic fauna of South America, he conjectured that the Isthmus of Panama might once have been submerged. His inspired guess has been confirmed. We know now that for 70 million years South America was an island where aboriginal species evolved in isolation. Then the isthmus arose, precipitating the great Pleistocene migration *(map at left)*. In the onslaught of the northern invaders on the native population, many wondrous creatures vanished forever, many new forms arose.

63

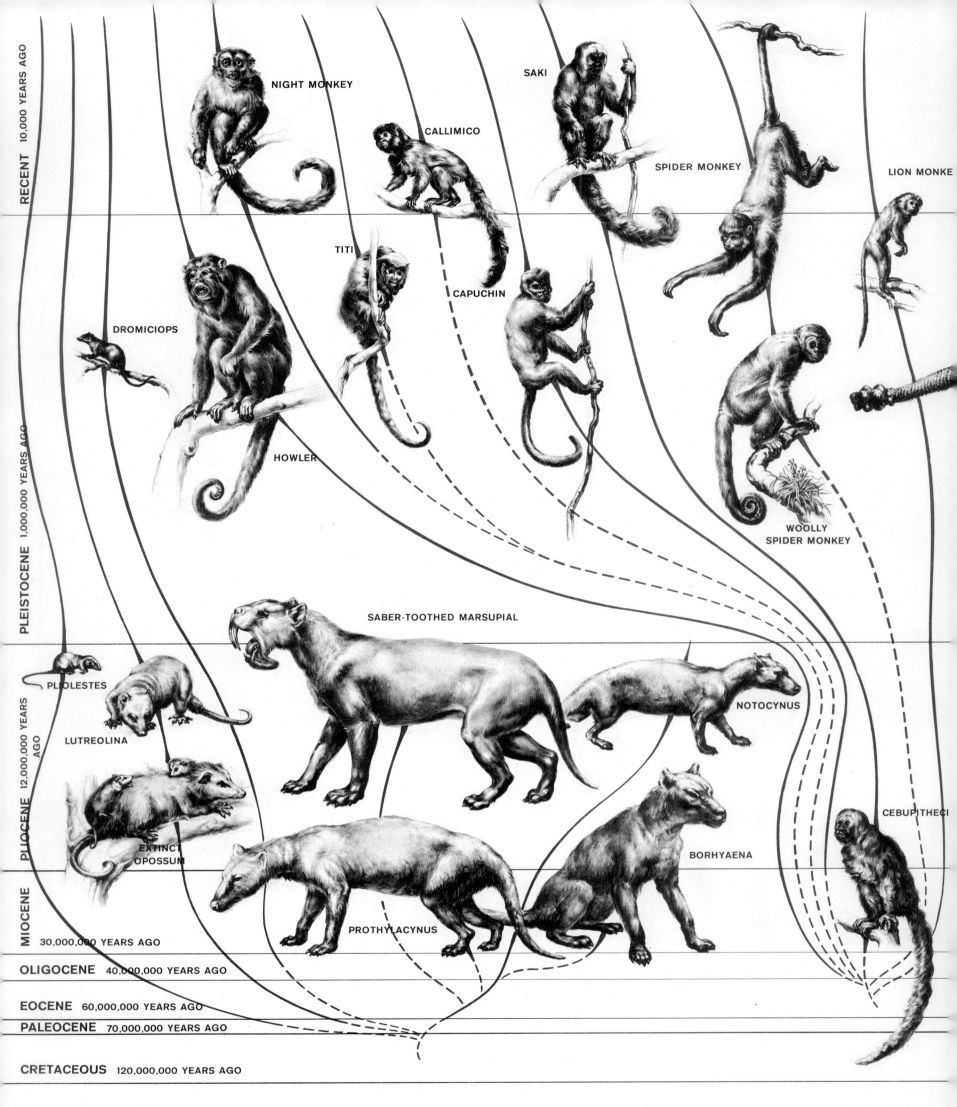

RECENT 10,000 YEARS AGO

PLEISTOCENE 1,000,000 YEARS AGO

PLIOCENE 12,000,000 YEARS AGO

MIOCENE 30,000,000 YEARS AGO

OLIGOCENE 40,000,000 YEARS AGO

EOCENE 60,000,000 YEARS AGO

PALEOCENE 70,000,000 YEARS AGO

CRETACEOUS 120,000,000 YEARS AGO

NIGHT MONKEY

CALLIMICO

SAKI

SPIDER MONKEY

LION MONKE

TITI

CAPUCHIN

DROMICIOPS

HOWLER

WOOLLY SPIDER MONKEY

SABER-TOOTHED MARSUPIAL

PLIOLESTES

LUTREOLINA

NOTOCYNUS

EXTINCT OPOSSUM

PROTHYLACYNUS

BORHYAENA

CEBUPITHECI

FAMILIES OF MARSUPIALS, MONKEYS,

Of the fantastic aboriginal populations that evolved in isolation during the millions of years when South America was an island continent, only a few lines survive to the present day. And all of these have undergone change in some degree. The charts on these five pages depict the evolutionary development of the native fauna as it has been reconstructed by means of the fossil record since Darwin's visit. Here history

flows from the bottom up, beginning at the end of the Cretaceous period when the giant reptiles died out and mammals became dominant. The curved lines indicate the evolutionary ascent from remote common ancestors, solid lines when the evolutionary record is clear, dotted when it is incomplete or based on conjecture. Where the same line actually touches two animals, those animals are closely related.

MATACO

SIX-BANDED ARMADILLO

NINE-BANDED ARMADILLO

TAMANDUA

THREE-TOED SLOTH

TWO-TOED SLOTH

DOEDICURUS

MYLODON

MEGATHERIUM

GLYPTODON

SCELIDOTHERIUM

STEGOTHERIUM

PLAINA

EXTINCT GIANT ANTEATER

HAPALOPS

PROZAEDIUS

PROPALAEOHOPLOPHORUS

UTAETUS

ARMADILLOS, ANTEATERS AND SLOTHS

Solid lines which reach the top of the page indicate that a related species still exists today, *e.g.*, monkeys, sloths, armadillos and the small marsupials at far left. Lines which end farther down indicate extinction at that point—as in the case of the catlike saber-toothed marsupial *(left center)* which died out in the Pliocene epoch. The two giant mammals shown in color are the ones whose bones Darwin discovered.

All these animals are of South American origin. The monkeys differ from those of Africa and Asia in that only they, in the whole world, can hang by their tails. Nowhere else have there evolved mammals so heavily armored as the herbivorous glyptodonts. Nowhere else has there evolved so perfectly adapted and single-minded a gourmet as the toothless anteater with its syringe-shaped nose and two-foot tongue.

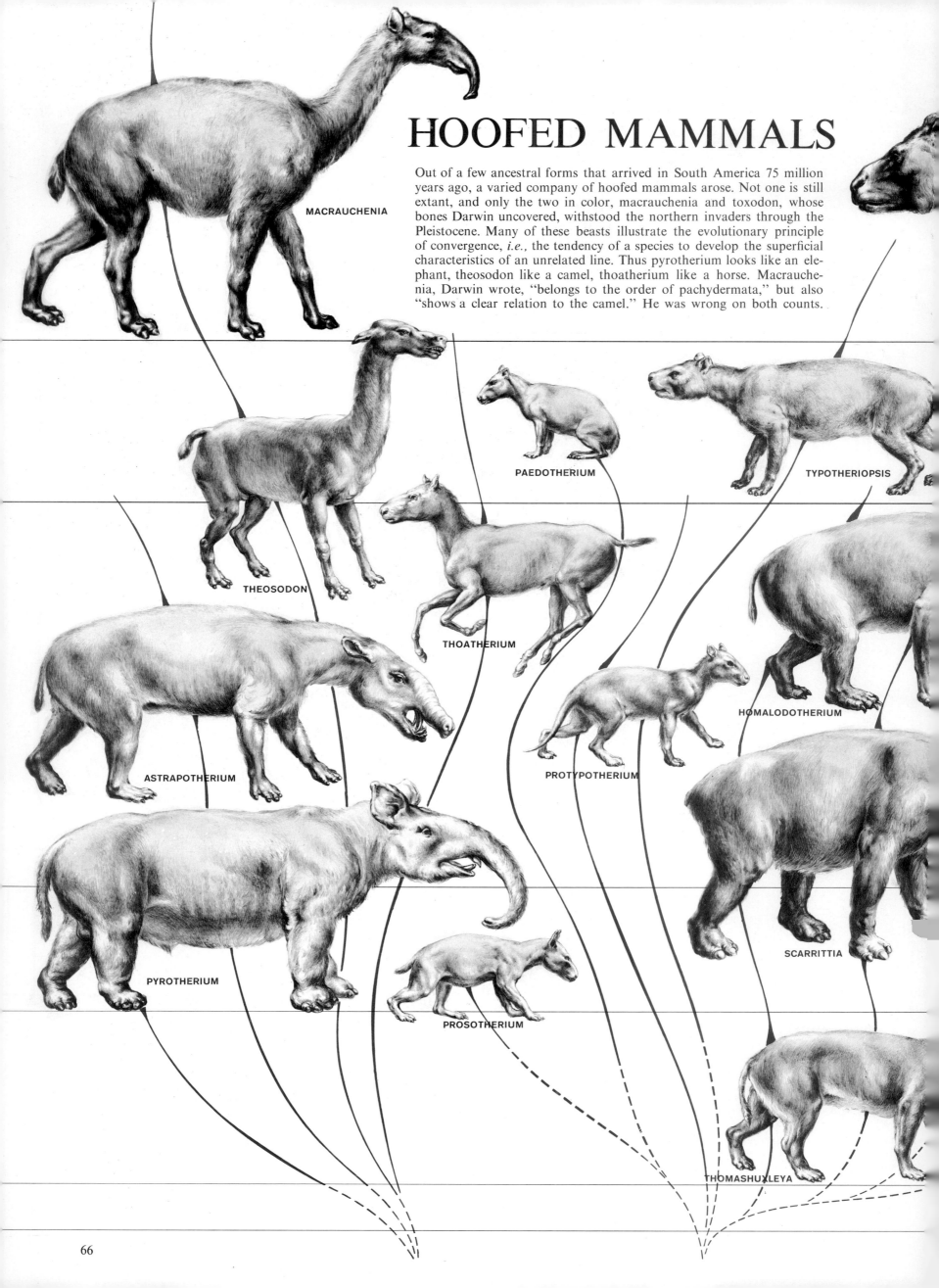

HOOFED MAMMALS

Out of a few ancestral forms that arrived in South America 75 million years ago, a varied company of hoofed mammals arose. Not one is still extant, and only the two in color, macrauchenia and toxodon, whose bones Darwin uncovered, withstood the northern invaders through the Pleistocene. Many of these beasts illustrate the evolutionary principle of convergence, *i.e.,* the tendency of a species to develop the superficial characteristics of an unrelated line. Thus pyrotherium looks like an elephant, theosodon like a camel, thoatherium like a horse. Macrauchenia, Darwin wrote, "belongs to the order of pachydermata," but also "shows a clear relation to the camel." He was wrong on both counts.

MACRAUCHENIA

THEOSODON

PAEDOTHERIUM

TYPOTHERIOPSIS

THOATHERIUM

ASTRAPOTHERIUM

HOMALODOTHERIUM

PROTYPOTHERIUM

PYROTHERIUM

SCARRITTIA

PROSOTHERIUM

THOMASHUXLEYA

PLEISTOCENE

PLIOCENE

MIOCENE

OLIGOCENE

EOCENE

PALEOCENE

CRETACEOUS

TOXODON

NESODON

RHYNCHIPPUS

RECENT

COENDU

AGOUTI

GUINEA PIG

CHINCHILLA

DINOMYS

NUTRIA

CAPYBARA

VIZCACHA

PLEISTOCENE

DARWIN'S TUCO TUCO

PRODOLICHOTIS

PLIOCENE

MIOCENE

NEOREOMYS

OLIGOCENE

STEIROMYS

PROTOCAREMYS

EOCENE

PLATYPITTAMYS

EOCARDIA

RODENTS

More successfully than any other animals, the versatile order of rodents weathered the upheavals of the Pleistocene. Southern rodents migrated north, northern rodents migrated south, intermingling so cozily that today the rodent roster of the Americas is a mixture of both stocks. The familiar porcupine of temperate woods waddled up from below the isthmus. Northern *émigrés* like the squirrel and meadow mouse settled contentedly in the south. A few less generalized types succumbed to time and change, among them the ancestral tuco tuco, a molelike creature whose remains Darwin unearthed, and the extinct relatives of dinomys, which grew big as calves—the largest rodents that ever lived.

CARNIVOROUS BIRDS

Of all the improbable inhabitants of South America, perhaps the most fantastic was a group of huge carnivorous birds. Flightless, ferocious, fleet-footed, fierce-beaked, they dominated the archaic faunas of the continent for millions of years, pursuing their prey across the plains and pampas until they gave way finally to the more efficient pumas, jaguars and giant dogs that came south in the invasion.

These birds were predators such as no other animals in the world had ever faced. Their only modern relative is the cariama *(right)*, which stands two feet high and, unlike his fearsome forebears, can fly short distances. In the glowering gallery below, the birds do not appear in actual proportion. Their respective heights: psilopterus, 27 inches; procariama, three feet; tolmodus and andalgalornis, five feet; hermosiornis, six feet; and finally gigantic onactornis, eight feet tall and armed with a massive, terrible 15-inch bill. Although Darwin never gazed on the fossils of these feathered flesh eaters, they perfectly exemplify, in their gradation by size, his principle of natural selection. For the size of each determined the size of its prey, thus limiting competition within the clan and allotting to each one a separate niche in nature's cruel economy.

CARIAMA

ANDALGALORNIS

ONACTORNIS

TOLMODUS

PROCARIAMA

HERMOSIORNIS

PSILOPTERUS

PLIOCENE

MIOCENE

OLIGOCENE

NATIVES OF THE NEW WORLD, guanacos graze on the flat pampas of Argentina, just as they have for countless ages past. Their ancestral family, the camels, emerged in North America during the Eocene epoch and evolved entirely in the Western Hemisphere before migrating to Asia and beyond. As recently as the Pleistocene many species of the camel family ranged the Americas. Today only two wild forms survive—the vicuña and the guanaco.

HORSE
DOGS
GLYPTODON
MASTODON

THE MINGLING
OF THE MIGRANTS

In a lush and parklike valley in Bolivia, migrant animals which had crossed the newly reared land bridge over the Isthmus of Panama met and intermingled with the ancient animals of South America sometime midway in the Pleistocene epoch about 350,000 years ago. Some dwelt peacefully together, many others had to struggle to survive. During flood periods when the valley floor grew swampy, some were engulfed in the clinging clay. As the land dried, their skeletons

MASTODON AND YOUNG   SABER-TOOTHED CAT
CRICETID RODENTS   GUANACO

were covered by shifting sands and entombed in time like the bones of Egyptian kings. The painting depicts this valley as it may have looked during the Pleistocene when intercontinental migration was in full swing and animals from north and south combined to create a curious convocation of mammals never seen before or since.

The most drastic effects of the invasion are seen in the activities of predators like the giant dogs at left, which are harrying a glyptodon, whose armor plate and retractable head render it virtually invulnerable. In the center of the picture a northern saber-toothed cat successfully attacks a guanaco, a species of llama related to the eastern camel. It is one of the ironies of evolution that descendants of the timid guanaco (which Darwin thought an "elegant animal") still live today on the Patagonian plains while its fearsome foe has perished forever from the earth. In South America, as everywhere else,

FOLD OUT, DO NOT TEAR

PECCARY

CRICETID RODENTS   ZORRINO

NUTRIA

OPOSSUM

lower left is quite similar to the smaller living armadillos which now range its lost domain. Two of the original South American rodents also exist today in slightly modified form: the nutria, well known for its luxurious fur; and the capybara, largest of the modern rodent family, which is sometimes called a water hog. One of the oldest mammals in the world to have persisted with little change is that hardy marsupial, the opossum. It spread to North America

and now flourishes on both continents, prolific and indestructible, just about the same old possum that first appeared on earth in the twilight of the dinosaurs more than 75 million years ago.

The invaders from the north—*e.g.,* the puma, peccary, deer, guanaco, tapir—have also been relatively successful in perpetuating their respective orders. The zorrino, or South American skunk, lives on, secure in its mastery of chemical warfare. Though Darwin

MACRAUCHENIA

ARMADILLOS

MEGATHERE AND YOUNG

Of all the aboriginal beasts of South America, perhaps the most grotesque was the macrauchenia. Endowed with the neck of a camel and an elephant's trunk, this "remarkable quadruped" (as Darwin called it) could forage for leaves on branches 10 feet above the ground. Yet in the Pleistocene carnival of animals, even so extended a creature was dwarfed by the giant of the region, the megathere, a species of ground sloth whose tallest members sometimes towered 20 feet high. While holding their own against the invaders, the megatheres migrated eventually to North America where they lingered on until the final great crisis of the ancient mammals.

Such unwieldy monsters as the macrauchenia and the megathere left behind no heirs, or even distant analogues. In the form shown here, all the animals above are now extinct. Yet many have recognizable offshoots in the modern world. The large armadillo at the

TOXODON

the Pleistocene was a time of mysterious, wholesale extinction of the larger and more spectacular mammals. Mightiest of these in South America were the mastodonts (the elephantlike group to which the mastodon belonged), which had evolved in Egypt 60 million years ago, then expanded east across Asia to the Americas.

Less spectacular creatures also vanished in the multitudinous dying: for example, the horse, which, having spread from North to South America, then disappeared from both continents until its European descendant was reimported by the Spaniards in the 16th Century A.D. All the archaic herbivores and most of the marsupials that had once thrived in isolation in South America for 75 million years became extinct. Their numbers included some extraordinary creatures—for example, the huge, swamp-wallowing toxodon, which Darwin has termed "one of the strangest animals ever discovered."

DEER **PUMA** **TAPIR AND YOUNG**

CAPYBARAS

thought the zorrino "an odious animal," he wrote, somewhat respectfully, that "conscious of its power, it roams by day about the open plain and fears neither man nor dog." The ancient peccary, while larger than its present-day descendants, is essentially the same. The tapir also survives but, where it once roamed vast areas of both hemispheres, today it is confined to three curiously dispersed habitats—Central and South America, and Malaya. In the course of his

South American field work, Darwin studied most of the animals shown here, either in fossil form or modern counterpart. Noting certain similarities between the bony relics of the ancient past and the familiar fauna of the present, he observed prophetically, "This wonderful relationship in the same continent between the dead and the living will, I do not doubt, hereafter throw more light on the appearance of organic beings on our earth and their disappearance from it."

A FABULOUS FIND OF

Unearthed in a remote Andean valley, an ancient bed of bones casts new light

FOLLOWING in Darwin's footsteps, an international team of scientists from Harvard University and the Museo Argentino de Ciencias Naturales happened upon one of the richest fossil fields ever revealed to questing man. They came across their great find in April 1958, imbedded in pastel-colored shale in a valley in the Western Argentine. Here, in a region known to Darwin, Dr. Bryan Patterson and Dr. Alfred S. Romer, both of Harvard, and their associates uncovered extensive fossil deposits of reptiles, fish and amphibians, dating from the Triassic period, 180 million years ago. They returned with a fabulous collection, nearly five tons of bones, to be assembled and exhibited in the Harvard Museum of Comparative Zoology *(right)*.

Darwin had been able to collect some specimens of the extinct animals that roamed South America during the Pleistocene era—such as the glyptodonts and toxodonts pictured on the preceding pages—but he knew nothing of the infinitely more remote forms of life from which they had evolved. The fossil record of the South American past may never be complete. But it has been greatly advanced by the 1958 Harvard-Buenos Aires expedition.

"Although we did not then know it," Dr. Patterson reported later, recalling the excitement of coming upon his Triassic trove, "we had taken our first look at one of the great fossil fields of the world. Like the ancient mariner and his shipmates, it was our incredible good fortune to be the 'first that ever burst into that silent sea.'"

The Triassic was one of the most eventful periods in the history of life on earth. In the plant kingdom the conifers of today began to evolve, supplanting the soft-tissued swamp trees and giant ferns developed in the Paleozoic. More important, there appeared the first dinosaurs which would rule the earth for 100 million years. This chapter in the story of evolution was still virtually blank in Darwin's day—for the fabulous fields of dinosaur relics in North America had not yet been exposed—and it is testimony to his genius that in the very infancy of paleontology, 125 years ago, his limited observations of a few fossil remains of South American mammals proved sufficient to convince him of the connection between living and long extinct forms of life.

Darwin had a few predecessors in the Western Hemisphere—observant amateurs, some priests, some adventurers, government officials, gauchos, business men, and officers of the British Navy and Argentine Army—who turned up interesting paleontological finds in the course of other vocations. As elsewhere in the world, these early mystifying discoveries were regarded as the relics of antediluvian

monsters which, for one reason or another, had not managed to obtain accommodations aboard the Ark at the time of the Great Flood.

The first American fossil—the huge bone of a Pleistocene mammoth or mastodon—was discovered in Mexico early in the 16th Century by Bernal Diáz del Castillo, a companion of Cortés, who sent it back to Spain. Some two centuries later a Jesuit priest, Father Falkner, came upon the shell of a glyptodon on the Argentine pampas and correctly deduced that it must have belonged to a giant relative of the modern armadillo. In 1789 the skeleton of a megatherium was turned up not far from Buenos Aires and, on order of the Spanish Viceroy, was shipped off to Madrid. King Carlos III acknowledged the gift with gratitude but added that he would appreciate a living specimen. His request was not incongruent with the knowledge of his time. Barely 14 years later, President Thomas Jefferson, when dispatching Lewis and Clark on the Louisiana Purchase Expedition, instructed them to note any specimens of the American mastodon or of the giant ground sloth megalonyx which they might happen to espy.

These finds were virtually all that was known about prehistoric America prior to Darwin. His classic observations inspired a wave of interest in the geologic past, both among South Americans and Europeans who were stationed on that continent.

It was not until the 1880s, however, that the researches of two remarkable Argentinian brothers, Carlos and Florentino Ameghino, laid bare the foundations of the prehistory of South America. The younger, Carlos, a hardy and intrepid man, was the field geologist who, in successive expeditions into the wilderness of Southern Patagonia, first discovered the rich deposits of the Santa Cruz formation, laid down in the Miocene period, in the Age of Mammals, 30 million years ago. From these field trips he sent back a stream of specimens and accurate geological records to his erudite brother Florentino. This older brother financed Carlos' explorations on the slender profits of a stationery shop and, writing at night in a small study in back of the store, described his findings in an extraordinary series of scholarly papers. In two decades the Ameghino brothers, between them, laid down our knowledge of the faunal succession of Cenozoic times (*i.e.,* the last 75 million years) with such accuracy and detail that no major revisions have been adduced by 20th Century research.

But in time the initial interest of the scientific world turned to skepticism. For though marvelously precise in matters of fact and description, the brothers erred in their interpretation and analysis.

A TRIASSIC TREASURE of fossil bones lies spread before Dr. Alfred S. Romer *(left)* and Dr. Bryan Patterson of Harvard, who unearthed them in South America in 1958. They are shown examining the skull of a 180-million-year-old reptile.

FOSSILS

on prehistoric life in South America

Florentino fell into two serious errors to which he stubbornly clung in the face of world-wide criticism. Many of the extinct South American mammals, shown in the paintings on the preceding pages, bear a superficial resemblance to mammals in other parts of the world. Pyrotherium *(page 66)* has an elephantine trunk; rhynchippus *(page 67)* has an equine head. To Florentino these analogies indicated lineal relationships, so he classified pyrotherium as a member of the elephant order, and rhynchippus as a horse. For like Darwin, who stumbled into a similar pitfall with respect to macrauchenia, Florentino ignored the concept of convergent evolution, described (with Darwin's error) on page 66. The principle was still new in his day, and he never accepted it. More seriously, he concluded as a result of misinterpreting Carlos' data that some mammals of the Oligocene (40 million years ago) had lived contemporaneously with dinosaurs, though it was known then as now that dinosaurs did not survive into Cenozoic times. From his misdating of these mammals, Florentino arrived at the notion that South American mammals evolved earlier than all others on earth, hence that South America was the primordial birthplace of mammals which then spread to the rest of the world. He defended this theory to the end of his days, defying all criticism, rebutting all new evidence.

WHILE nobody outside Argentina accepted Florentino's interpretations, the controversy he aroused engendered a lively interest in the paleontology of Patagonia and the pampas. Princeton University financed an expedition at the turn of the century, and the collection it obtained has never been surpassed. The material it educed was interpreted by the late Professor W. B. Scott. He established beyond doubt that the great ages assigned by Ameghino to the South American mammals were in error, that the resemblances between them and mammals elsewhere in the world must be the product of convergent or parallel evolution, and that the differences so far exceeded resemblances as to preclude all possibility of kinship.

"Today," Dr. Patterson declares, "the broad outlines of the Cenozoic age—the Age of Mammals—are clear. We know that the South American mammalian fauna was a unique assemblage, and it evolved in isolation. But with respect to earlier times we are almost as much in the dark as Darwin was when he first viewed the pampas in August 1833." A few dinosaurs and reptiles, however, had been found in Patagonia and Brazil, prior to the discovery of the extraordinary Triassic fossil field by the Harvard-Buenos Aires expedition. "A very little can be suggested," observes Dr. Patterson. "The Triassic reptiles of South America *do* appear to be related to those known in other parts of the world. From this it does not seem likely that the continent was then as isolated as it later became. It may be that at that time there was the possibility of fairly widespread faunal interchange all over the world, although the nature of the connections between continents cannot now be determined. At the present time there are too few contemporaneous faunas known from different parts of the world to give an adequate picture of similarities or dissimilarities between continents."

In a larger perspective, the new Triassic find is important because its relics of extinct amphibians and reptiles fill gaps heretofore lacking in the pageant of evolution in America. Among the reptiles whose bones lay in the ancient shale were the ancestors not only of the dinosaurs but of such extant forms as crocodiles. In the Triassic too, there evolved reptiles distinguished from their sluggish kinsmen by superior energy and, perhaps, warm blood—forebears of the great class of mammals. Some of the reptilian skeletons uncovered by the 1958 expedition exhibited definite mammalian characteristics, indicating that they were transitional forms, precursors of the viviparous, milk-yielding, intelligent animals that ultimately would supplant the dinosaurs as the dominant creatures on earth.

The accession of the mammals to the dinosaurs' domain has never been explained, nor has the subsequent great dying of the mammals in the Pleistocene. Darwin rejected all specific, catastrophic causes. He concluded, as most modern scientists now do, that man's brief span of life blinds him to the long workings of nature, within which rarity is an omen of extinction. "To marvel greatly when a species ceases to exist," Darwin wrote, "appears to me much the same as to admit that sickness is a prelude to death . . . but when the sick man dies, to wonder and to believe that he died through violence."

SEARCHING FOR SPECIMENS, paleontologists from Harvard and Buenos Aires seek Triassic fossils in a 175-million-year-old cliff of shale in the Andes Mountains, where Darwin made the crossing from Chile to Argentina.

THE
ANIMAL HEIRS
OF
AGES PAST

THE fierce, lissome jaguar is one of the most dangerous carnivores of the New World. From its habits Darwin noted its evident kinship to both the common house cat and the East Indian tiger. He was constantly struck in his explorations by the relationships he found between living animals and those of the past. The jaguar shown here swimming in a plant-clogged pool is a descendant of Old World cats that crossed the Bering Strait from Asia during the invasions of the Pleistocene.

THE SPOTTED TREE FROG VOICES ITS RHYTHMIC SONG BESIDE STILL WATERS IN THE SHADOWED FORESTS OF BRAZIL

THE ANIMAL HEIRS OF AGES PAST

Life of forest and pampas showed Darwin evolution's path

NATURE in these climes chooses her vocalists from more humble performers than in Europe," Darwin observed in Brazil, referring to the small frog shown above. "It sits on a blade of grass about an inch above the surface of the water and sends forth a pleasing chirp. When several are together they sing in harmony on different notes." This comment reflects the enthusiasm, acuity of observation and love of living things that made Darwin the great field naturalist he was. During the long voyage of the *Beagle* these qualities enabled him to discern every detail of the natural world within the framework of an unfolding panorama of life. Each creature he observed was both a wondrous living entity and the heir of ages past.

As he made his way down the coast of South America, Darwin passed through many realms of nature *(see map).* First there were the great forests. "No one can stand in these solitudes unmoved," he wrote, "and not feel that there is more in man than the mere breath of his body." Inland, he looked with delight on the Brazilian grasslands or *cerrados,* dotted with trees and etched with waterways. Farther south he rode for hundreds of miles across the pampas of Argentina and Uruguay—open, treeless plains—which looked to him like a sea bereft of color. The wild uplands of Patagonia stirred his imagination even more profoundly. "All was stillness and desolation," he wrote.

"One asked how many ages the plain had thus lasted, and how many it was thus doomed to continue."

In exploring these wastelands, Darwin made some of his most important discoveries. On the pampas and in Patagonia he found the fossil remains of prehistoric creatures that revealed the mutability of life in the immense span of terrestrial time. His observations of living animals made him aware of relationships between present and past. Noting similarities between existing and extinct species of armadillos, sloths and guanacos (llamas), he evolved his law of the "succession of types"—*i.e.,* in any given area on earth animals leave, in successive ages, similar though somewhat *modified* descendants. Darwin also discerned relationships in space as well as in time. Traveling southward, he was struck by subtle changes in allied species from one area to the next. Here he found the same principle at work—descent with *modification* due to natural selection and environment. In the light of this principle, he wrote, "We can understand how it is that the inhabitants of the plains and mountains, of the forests, marshes and deserts are linked together in so mysterious a manner, and are likewise linked to the extinct beings which formerly inhabited the same continent." The animals which Darwin studied and which brought him to his great conclusions are shown in this chapter as they exist today.

INLAND AREAS Darwin visited in 1832-34 included many varieties of habitat where he observed the animal populations of today and the fossils of their forebears.

THE PUMA is the lion of South America. Swift, stealthy, strong, it came down from the north during the Pleistocene migration and has flourished with little change. Prowling on cushioned feet from the equatorial forests to the wastes of Patagonia, it rules the widest domain of any carnivore in the Western Hemisphere. Darwin dined on puma one day while camping with gauchos. "The meat is very white," he reported, "and remarkably like veal."

THE THREE-TOED SLOTH, descended from the extinct species shown on page 65, is one of the slowest, dullest mammals on earth. Virtually defenseless (save for its long hair), it is nevertheless very powerful, lifting itself easily from one branch to another with three finger-like claws.

THE JAGUAR is the tiger of South America. Largest of the native carnivores, it measures six to eight feet in length- and weighs up to 250

HUNTERS AND HUNTED

Within the gallery forests that fringe the waterways, Darwin was only occasionally able to espy the wary creatures that dwell in the cover of the leafy canopy. But often he was made aware of their presence. One day, on the banks of the Uruguay, his guides called his attention to some trees which bore deep scratches and informed him they had been made by a jaguar. "I imagine this habit of the jaguar," he wrote, "is exactly similar to one which may any day be seen in the common cat, as with outstretched legs and exserted claws, it scrapes the leg of a chair." Despite this homely analogy, Darwin confessed "the fear of [the jaguar] quite destroyed all pleasure in scrambling through the woods."

THE TAPIR, kin of the rhinoceros and one of the most ancient of American animals, survives in its aboriginal form. Shy and gentle, it browses in rivers or lakes, drawing water plants into its mouth with its mobile proboscis. It is preyed upon by jaguars for food and by man for its hide.

THE NIGHT MONKEY is South America's only nocturnal simian. It sleeps by day in hollow trees. At night it hunts insects in the boughs.

pounds (as against the puma's 165). An excellent swimmer, it finds rivers no barrier to its roaming. An agile climber, it often hides in branches and leaps from above upon its prey. It assuages its appetite on varied delicacies from tapir to fish which it scoops adroitly from rivers with swift strokes of its paw. Unlike the more furtive puma, the jaguar is a noisy animal whose deep defiant roar resounds fearfully in the forests of the night.

THE PORCUPINE, a native of South America whose ancestors migrated north, now flourishes on two continents. The one shown here differs from its North American kin in the possession of shorter quills and a prehensile tail.

THE TAYRA, a wily, weasel-like marauder, can with equal ease invade a wild beehive for honey or climb a tree and plunder a bird's nest of eggs and young. A nocturnal prowler, it measures about four feet long, half of it tail.

PUMA   OVENBIRD

DEER   GUANACOS

CARIAMAS   CARACARA   GIANT ANTEATER   ZORRINO

BURROWING OWL   HAIRY ARMADILLO

GRASSLANDS AND OPEN SKY

"After being imprisoned for some time in a ship," Darwin wrote, "there is a charm in the unconfined feeling of walking over boundless plains of turf." On the pampas Darwin soon found an abundance of life, as shown in the painting above. As ever the birds caught his eye: the stately cariama, peace-loving descendant of giant carnivorous birds *(page 68)*; the carrion-fancying caracara and the burrowing owl; the ostrichlike rhea and the sociable ovenbird. He

84

BLACK VULTURES

TOCO TOUCANS

TOCO TOUCANS

TERO TEROS

GREEN PARAKEETS

RHEAS   MANED WOLF   CAPYBARA   SOUTH AMERICAN STILT

TUCO-TUCOS   THREE-BANDED ARMADILLO   SOUTHERN GREEN KINGFISHER

espied black vultures wheeling overhead, and, in a leafless tree, the gregarious toco toucans. He listened to the vociferous green parakeets and irascible tero teros screaming against trespassers. And he watched those anglers, the southern green kingfisher and South American stilt, poised patiently, waiting for fish. The tall grass was stirred by shy pampas deer, herds of wary guanacos, and the maned wolf—actually a timid epicure partial to rodents, frogs, figs and sugar cane. At the base of the grass Darwin noted smaller creatures —the zorrino, or South American skunk; the tuco-tuco, a molelike burrower; the hairy armadillo and the mataco, or three-banded armadillo; and the capybara, or water hog. Through this otherwise peaceable kingdom two creatures strode unmolested: the puma and the giant anteater, scourge of insects, slow but strong, toothless but clawed, and inedible by virtue of the acid it laps up with every meal.

THE GREEN TREE FROG is a one-and-a-half-inch-long individualist—an arboreal amphibian who prefers to live above water rather than in it, and seldom hops like other frogs. Equipped with suckers at the end of each toe, it promenades with deliberate speed among trees and reeds in search of insect fare. Although most amphibians lay their eggs in water, the female green tree frog deposits her eggs on the leaves of overhanging branches,

THE SCARLET IBIS, a rare and beautiful bird, dwells in colonies in marshy grasslands where shallow waters collect. Their curved bills are well designed for dredging worms, crustaceans and vegetable matter from bottom mud.

ON THE PAMPAS AND BY WATER

As he traveled southward Darwin emerged into sunlit country where the forests gave way to open pampas, watered by leisurely streams. In the summer of 1833 he spent a month on horseback, camping with gauchos. "There is high enjoyment," he wrote, "in the independence of the gaucho life—to be able at any moment to pull up your horse and say, 'Here we will pass the night.' " In this interlude he also found enjoyment in studying the less secretive animals of the open terrain. It is evident from his journals that Darwin's scientific objectivity was often tempered by his deep affection for animal life. He wrote fondly of many creatures, reporting that the ovenbird *(far right)* was known to Spaniards as the *casara*, or housemaker, because its nest was both stoutly built and exposed to the eye of man. He reported with chagrin that he dined one evening on a new variety of rhea *(right)* without realizing what he was eating at the time. And he wrote with special sympathy of the armadillo *(above, right)*. After describing its characteristics in detail, he added, "It seems almost a pity to kill such nice little animals, for as a gaucho said, while sharpening his knife on the back of one, 'Son tan mansos' (They are so quiet)."

THE ARMADILLO comes in various sizes but all have similar habits. They prefer dry country and feed on insects, roots and snakes. When in danger, they either burrow into the ground or crouch beneath their shells. The seven-banded armadillo above attracted Darwin's interest in Patagonia.

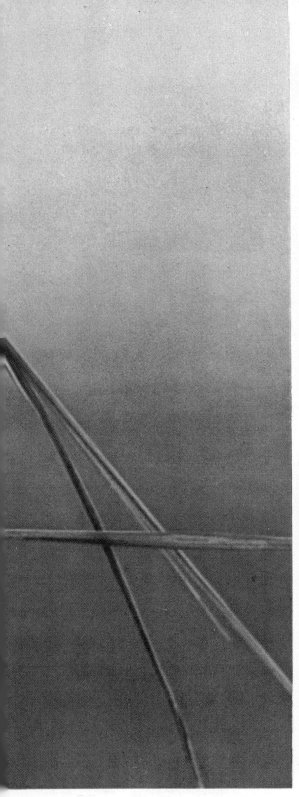

attaching them with an opaque jellylike secretion. The eggs hatch in rain and the emerging tadpoles are thus washed into the lake or waterway below.

THE CAPYBARA, or water hog, is the largest rodent in the world, measuring four feet in length and weighing up to 130 pounds. Struck by their tameness, Darwin concluded that man had not found it practical to hunt them, as "their skins are of trifling value and the meat is very indifferent."

THE RHEA or American ostrich (left) is the largest bird (four feet tall) in the western world. The male will attack men on horseback if threatened.

THE OVENBIRD takes its name from the shape of its nest of mud. An insect eater, it is sociable, extraverted and enjoys the proximity of mankind.

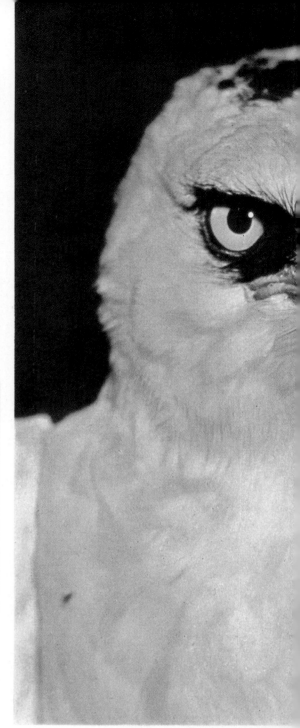

WINGED MARAUDERS

In childhood, recalled Darwin, "I took much pleasure in watching the habits of birds. . . . I remember wondering why every gentleman did not become an ornithologist." This passion never waned. He was fascinated by the carnivorous birds of South America—both allured by their bright plumage and graceful flight and repelled by the "disgusting habits" of the carrion feeders.

He wrote at length of the caracara *(left),* which he held in low esteem. It not only ate carrion, he reported, but forced other birds to vomit up food, which the caracara then downed. "They attempt also," he wrote, "to pick off scabs from the sore backs of mules and horses. . . . Their vulturelike necrophagous habits are very evident to anyone who has fallen asleep on the plains of Patagonia, for when he wakes, he will see on each surrounding hillock one of these birds, patiently watching him with an evil eye."

THE BRAZILIAN CARACARA is a member of the falcon tribe, distantly related to the goshawks and the peregrines of Europe. Its habits, however, differ from those of its hunting kin, for it is a carrion-eater. Darwin observed the caracara with distaste, finding it an "inactive, cowardly bird."

above the treetops or sitting amid the topmost branches, it bides its time till it spies a snake, lizard or rodent, then dives unerringly upon its prey.

THE KING VULTURE is the most bedizened member of a dynasty which has engendered the largest flying birds that ever cleft the skies. Its incredible eyesight enables it to discern food from great distances. When one descends for a feast, others notice and quickly gather from miles away.

THE BURROWING OWL intrigued Darwin by "standing like a sentinel" at the mouth of its abode. Tiny, it nests in tunnels drilled by armadillos and rodents, and lays its eggs at the very bottom. It feeds on mice, snakes, insects.

THE HAWK-HEADED PARROT, so named because of its ruff feathers and piercing eye, is a popular captive bird, easily tamed and facile in learning tricks. In its forest habitat it travels in groups of 10 to 12 individuals.

BRAZILIAN SWALLOW-TAIL   AMETHYST HUMMINGBIRD   CAYENNE WOOD-NYMPH   EMERALD HUMMINGBIRD

JEWELED BIRDS
OF THE WEST

Since hummingbirds—descended from the same forebears as the familiar swift—exist only in the New World, Darwin was captivated by these winged jewels poised above flowers in the perfumed air. He encountered them everywhere—near Rio de Janeiro, in deserts, in forests, and once in a snowstorm in Tierra del Fuego. "Male hummingbirds almost vie with birds of paradise in their beauty," he observed. It is known today that the iridescent colors of their plumage,

RUFOUS-THROATED SAPPHIRE   ANGELA STAR-THROAT   FRILLED COQUETTE   RUBY AND TOPAZ HUMMINGBIRD   BRAZILIAN VIOLET-EAR

shown in the painting above, are produced not by pigments but by the refraction of light from prismatic configurations of the feathers. The males of most species wear a bright bib. Some display patches of iridescence on breasts or bellies; others have bright head patches or crowns. Their darting, hovering, vibrating flight requires up to 80 wing beats per second and demands the highest energy output of any warm-blooded creatures on earth, hence they need 50 to 60 meals a day. Their food consists of nectar, which they sip through long tubular tongues, and of insects, which they often catch with their beaks. Vain, fearless, pugnacious, they fight constantly and defend their territory against trespassers as large as robins and crows. Skilled architects, they build delicate nests, some no larger than walnut shells, lined with down, decorated with lichen or fern and bound together with spider webs. In them they lay eggs the size of peas.

ARAUCARIA TREES march straight and tall up the valley slopes of southern Brazil. Their flat-crowned trunks can tower 100 feet high. Araucarias grow mainly south of the equator, but related fossils have been found in Arizona.

THE EMPTY LAND
OF BRAZIL

To Darwin's eye most landscapes of the world seemed inferior to the "picturesque beauty" of Europe. He made one exception: the exotic tropics, especially in Brazil, where he delighted in the untrammeled variety of an enormous, empty land. Even today, inland from the coast, Brazil still seems a country without people. Its heartland is the mysterious Mato Grosso—more than half a million square miles of wilderness which, until the last few years, lay virtually unknown. Although its name, in Portuguese, means "great, thick forest land," Mato Grosso encompasses primeval rain forests; *cerrados*, dry prairies dotted with gnarled bushes and cork-barked trees; and *pantanals (right)*, areas where summer rains convert arid grasslands into marshy plains, spangled with innumerable emerald pools.

TALL TERMITE NESTS stand like obelisks amid seasonal floods in the *pantanal*. Made of pulverized earth, cemented with salivary secretions, these structures, often eight feet high, become hard as stone under the tropic sun.

THE PANTANAL is a region of seasonally flooded grassland in the south-western reaches of Mato Grosso. During the three months of winter the land is bone dry and the vegetation flutters in the hot wind. Then sudden rains descend, inundating the land, creating small lakes and circular moats around green islands of vegetation. At this season, water lilies, water lettuce and other floating plants embroider bright patterns on the glistening flood plain.

GOLDEN MARMOSET

HARPY EAGLE

OCELOT ROYAL FLYCATCHER

HOWLERS

RED BROCKET DEER

TAPIR AND YOUNG

RED COATI-MUNDI

AGOUTI

SHRILL CLAMOR
OF THE FOREST DAY

"A most paradoxical mixture of sound and silence pervades the shady parts of the forest," Darwin observed. Most residents are secretive creatures, reluctant to reveal their presence. At dawn and dusk, however, the voices of the macaw, the guan and other birds betray the profusion of life. Periodically there is the resounding din of one of the noisiest animals in creation—the howler monkey. Dizzily acrobatic, howler monkeys are seldom seen but often heard

GREEN-WINGED MACAWS

HOWLERS

TAMANDUA

HOWLERS

HOWLERS

WHITE-HEADED GUAN

WHITE-LIPPED PECCARIES

VARIEGATED SPIDER MONKEY

—with acute discomfort, even terror—by invaders of their domain. The purpose of their uproar is to warn off predators, like the ocelot and harpy eagle at left, or rival monkey tribes *(right)* which have trespassed on their real estate. For all their sound and fury, howler monkeys seldom fight. Sociable, restless, they range the leafy galleries, with mothers carrying infants on their backs *(left center, above)* and providing living bridges across open space *(right center, below).*

Their tempo of movement, geared to the slowest member of the clan, rarely exceeds a quarter mile per day. The distress cries of an invalid will halt the entire band. Once set in a new resting place, the youngsters relax in play *(left center).* But howlers do not disturb the forest's quieter tenants—the tapir, the deer, the tailless agouti, the toothless tamandua, the red-coated coati-mundi, the surly peccary—who go about their business unmindful of the noisy neighbors overhead.

95

NECTAR-FEEDING BAT   GIANT TREE FROG   TAYRA   WOOLLY OPOSSUM   FOUR-EYED OPOSSUM

RIVER OTTER   SOUTH AMERICAN DOG FOX   WHITE BAT   JAGUAR   MARGAY

BULLDOG BAT   GRISON   CRAB-EATING RACCOON   BOA CONSTRICTOR

BLACK CHAMBERS
OF THE NIGHT

Although Darwin explored the river-girding gallery forests he could not fully discern the shifting patterns of their life. The forest has two populations—the animals which go forth by day to forage on the open pampas, and those which sleep by day and come alive at sundown. Nighttime is the hunting time of cats and bats. It is the good time for the hoarse-voiced jaguar, despot of the forest. And with him, on their own murderous missions, go many smaller carnivores

GIANT ARMADILLO PREHENSILE-TAILED PORCUPINE COMMON OPOSSUM FALSE VAMPIRE
JAGUARUNDI GREAT HORNED OWL NINE-BANDED ARMADILLO PAMPAS CAT
PACA

—the untamable jaguarundi, the savage margay, the sharp-clawed pampas cat, and those insatiable weasels, the grison and the tayra.

Only in the blackness of the forest night does the great horned owl, tyrant of the bird world, soar silently through dim arcades in quest of prey. Then, too, the sonar-guided bats wheel on leathern wings— the nectar-feeding bat, hummingbird of the night; the fish-eating bulldog bat; the tiny (3-inch) white bat and the false vampire, giant of its fearsome clan. But night protects prey as well as predator. In the dark many timid creatures go forth to feed. The giant tree frog croaks its diapason in the boughs. The river otter fishes in dim waters; the crab-eating raccoon hygienically washes its favorite hors d'oeuvre. The armadillo, opossum and paca go their humble ways. At their feet the immobile boa constrictor, largest of all nonaquatic reptiles in the western world, lies waiting to seize and strangulate.

HIDDEN HEARTLAND

The great green wilderness in the interior of Brazil has begun to surrender its

NO months of Darwin's odyssey were more adventurous than those he spent exploring the forests and savannas of Brazil and riding across the pampas and the desolate wastes of the Patagonian plateau in Argentina. In later years he often reflected on the strange faraway places he had viewed. "Among the scenes which are deeply impressed on my mind," he recalled, "none exceed in sublimity the primeval forests undefaced by the hand of man; whether those of Brazil where the powers of Life are predominant, or those of Tierra del Fuego, where Death and Decay prevail. Both are temples filled with the varied productions of the God of Nature."

Darwin's genius as a theorist has cast into shadow the fact that some of his greatest discoveries were made under conditions of excessive hardship and physical danger. During his journeys into the interior he endured extremes of heat and cold, fatigue, hunger and thirst; and he was exposed constantly to the threat of capture by marauding Indians or random death by gunfire in the incessant revolutions of the inchoate South American states.

There was one occasion when Darwin and a friend found themselves crossing a waterless, sulphate plain. By noon their horses had become dehydrated, and they were obliged to walk. "I had scarcely been 24 hours without water," Darwin related abashedly, "yet the thirst rendered me very weak. How people survive up to two or three days under such circumstances I cannot imagine; at the same time my guide did not suffer at all, and was astonished that one day's deprivation should be so troublesome to me."

Today the entire countenance of South America has been transformed. The coastal areas, both east and west, are studded with some of the largest and most modern cities in the world. The Andes and the pampas are crisscrossed daily by hundreds of airline flights; and a half dozen airports have been carved into the bleak, distant headlands of Tierra del Fuego. Yet one great region of the

MOUNTING SPECIMENS, Dr. Helmut Sick (*left*), naturalist of Brazil's Museo Nacional, and an assistant work outside their hut while natives look on. Dr. Sick works on a bird called a "grand potoo," his aide on a coati, kin to the racoon.

Grosso would retain its secrets for all time. Within recent years, however, a German naturalist, imbued with the same courage, far-ranging passion for observation and love of nature that inspired Darwin, succeeded in penetrating the very heart of Mato Grosso, and amassing a wealth of information about one of the few hitherto unknown regions left in the modern world. By an accident of history Dr. Helmut Sick, ornithologist at the University of Berlin, happened to be on a collecting mission in the Brazilian forest when World War II broke out. Interned as an enemy alien, he was asked, on his release at the end of the war, to join the staff of the Museo Nacional in Rio, and to accompany a government-sponsored expedition into the interior.

The principal purpose of the expedition was to survey a route through the states of Mato Grosso and Para to the Amazon, 750 miles northwest, as part of a long-range program designed to explore and develop the wilderness. To avoid the fate of former expeditions, they built and manned bases at intervals of about 100 miles. Connecting roads were planned and landing fields hacked out of the forest.

Like Darwin, who was the lone naturalist on a voyage devoted to cartography, Dr. Sick was the naturalist in a company of road builders and engineers. From 1945 to 1950 he advanced mile by painful mile through forests, *cerrados* and swamps. Intermittently he returned to Rio, to deliver his collections to the Museo Nacional. Then he would fly back to whatever far outpost had been established. Like Darwin, whose own first interest was birds, Ornithologist Sick cast his eager and all-embracing eye upon every perspective of the exciting new realm that lay disclosed before him. "I begrudged every hour I wasted in sleep," he wrote. "In the silent hours of the night the call of the mysterious, endless forest seemed more insistent than ever." His journal, published under the title *Tukani* in 1960, ranges freely over many domains of natural science—animals, birds, insects, fish, trees, flowers, geography, climate and the social customs of the aborigines. Many of the specimens he obtained for the museum represented new species and subspecies never seen or classified before.

continent remains virtually unchanged, untouched, untrodden by the bruising march of modern man. This is Mato Grosso, the enormous green wilderness in the interior of Brazil, where primeval trees still flourish as they did in the Pleistocene and some aboriginal Indian tribes subsist as they have since the Old Stone Age.

Since Darwin first gazed rapturously on the fringes of the Brazilian forest, a succession of scientists, explorers, rubber prospectors, fortune hunters and adventurers of various degree have ventured into Mato Grosso in pursuit of their special purposes. One of the few successful invaders was a Brazilian national hero, Marshal Cândido Rondon, who spent nearly half a century in the interior charting trails, stringing telegraph lines, pacifying Indians, and who in 1913 accompanied Theodore Roosevelt on an exploration of the River of Doubt (now the Rio Roosevelt). But many of his successors perished from starvation and disease; more than one fell dead with a poisoned arrow in his heart. In a few instances entire expeditions, like that led by the British Colonel Percy Fawcett in 1925 in quest of an ancient civilization and legendary gold, disappeared within the green curtain of the forest and were never seen again. It seemed Mato

Like Darwin he exposed himself cheerfully to hardships, hazards and danger. "One day, quite unexpectedly," he wrote, ". . . I found myself face to face with a female puma. She was a few yards in front of me in the depth of the forest and I did not, at first, realize the fact. My attention had been attracted by a flicker of yellow in the green foliage. Nature has given the puma a skin of one single color and the alternating deep shadow and little patches of sunlight had turned it into a mosaic which seemed . . . to be covered with a camouflage net—a camouflage, incidentally, that the spotted jaguar, who is much more of a forest-dweller, possesses as part and parcel of his normal equipment. The puma in front of me remained absolutely motionless. While I was still admiring the play of light and shade in the deep forest, something stirred on the ground, and a baby puma emerged; it wriggled out and squatted in front of its mother! Although these great beasts of prey will normally flee at

OF BRAZIL

secrets to modern scientific exploration

the slightest noise, there are two situations in which they are really dangerous—when they are cornered and when they have their young with them. . . . I began to withdraw just as cautiously as I had previously advanced. The puma never moved. I was probably the first human being she had ever seen."

The expedition averaged 100 miles a year. Its members established their first base in dry, bushy *cerrado* country on the outskirts of Mato Grosso. From there they advanced across the Rio das Mortes into the dangerous domain of the savage Chavante Indians, where constant fear of ambush was exacerbated by temperatures ranging up to 110° and a perpetual pall of smoke from brush fires set by the Chavantes to clear their land or stampede game. "The haze of these conflagrations enshrouds the whole country," Dr. Sick wrote. "It rises to a height of 10,000 feet and visibility at ground level is reduced to 20-30 yards."

Escaping attack, the expedition moved on to the shade of the *Hylaea Amazonica,* the great tropical rain forest that mantles the watersheds of the Amazon and extends northward to the sea. They crossed river after river, traversing alternate swamps, savanna lands and gallery forests. Here and there they encountered Indians who assisted Dr. Sick by collecting specimens in return for gifts of sugar.

At last, after nine years, the explorers emerged from the mouth of the Tapajós River into the great open highway of the Amazon. During his years with the expedition Dr. Sick discovered 84 new varieties of flora and fauna hitherto unknown to science, among them ten new species of plants and flowers, and 74 new species and subspecies of birds, lizards, insects, spiders, snails and worms.

ONE of his major studies concerned the courting dances of the *Pipridae* or manakin birds of the *Hylaea.* In all species of manakins, the male is brilliantly adorned while the female wears dull olive or gray. Their dance (which Dr. Sick observed but never was able to photograph) begins with a single male alighting on a conspicuous branch high in some tree—a special branch known to other manakins as a place of assignation. He sits there, singing, until he is joined by two or three other males, who perch beside him, all facing in the same direction. Eventually a female wings past, observes the stag line and lands beside them. She sits quietly, slightly removed, and pretends not to notice. The males then begin to rock and roll, singing in "a grave voice," blending in perfect harmony. The female pays no attention—she is bored. Suddenly the first male leaps into the air, flutters a few inches above her momentarily, then buzzes the other males and returns to his perch—but this time facing in the opposite direction. The other males, who have continued their rhythmical bobbing and weaving, now go through the same routine, each in turn. At the end of the performance the female, who has shown no interest whatever, selects the male of her choice (by some signal imperceptible to Dr. Sick) and flies off with him. The rejected suitors shrug their shoulders and look for another branch.

In concluding the journal of his great adventure, Dr. Sick observes, "Although the interior of Central Brazil, which we . . . traversed, had been completely virgin territory, it did not present us with as many surprises as we had expected. . . . Today it no longer holds any terrors as a vast and empty space." Distances which took a year to cover can now be negotiated in less than an hour by air, thanks to the new chain of airports extending from Manáus, the capital of Amazon province, to Rio.

One by-product of the expedition was a controversy as to whether areas of the great central heartland should be set aside as preserves for the protection of plant and animal life, and for the aborigines. Opposition was expressed not only by business and real-estate interests, but by the Church, which wished to convert the natives rather than isolate them as "museum pieces" in reservations.

Convinced that the untamable Chavantes face certain extinction by white settlers unless they are permitted to live in their ancient solitudes, Dr. Sick asserted, "Whatever happens, the fate of the original inhabitants of Brazil is sealed, and we must needs hurry if we are to learn anything more about them—the last survivors in an era of the human society of South America which has endured for many thousands of years. Let us hope the plans to create a large reserve in Central Brazil will come to fruition in spite of every opposition. . . . It will awaken the interest and admiration of the world."

FRIENDLY BIRDS perch on Dr. Sick's hand and arm. The little screech owl *(above)* hunts by night, emitting a gentle whistling call. The large macaw *(below),* easily tamed by man as a pet, is also killed by man for its feathers.

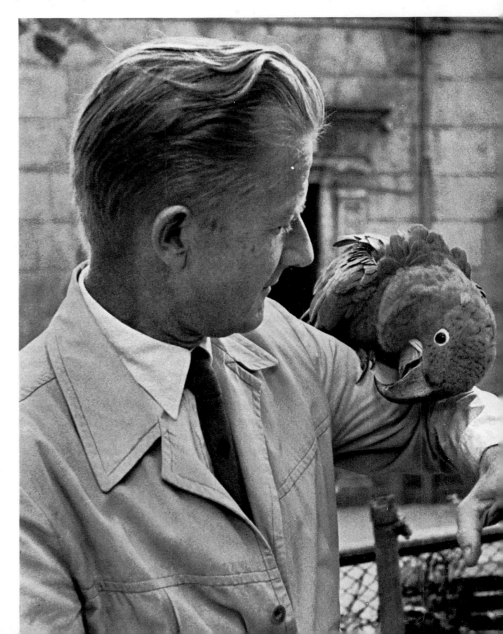

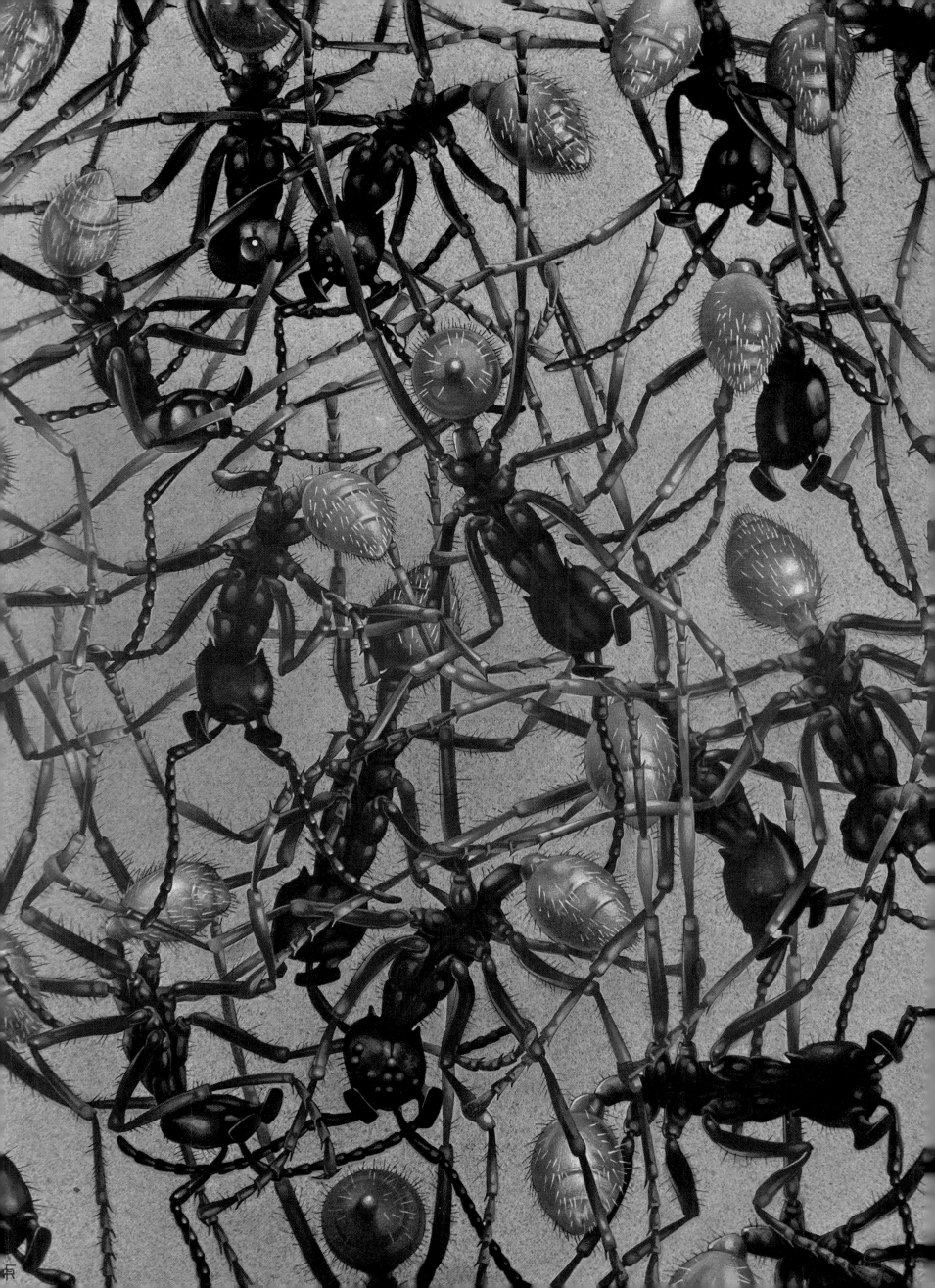

SUPREMACY
OF
THE
GROUP

ARMY ants, which struck Darwin as an astounding example of natural selection operating for the group, bivouac at night in a nest formed by their own interlocking bodies. Within their society, each ant serves as one unit in a superorganism—one fighter in an army, one link in a living nest. Here the nest is just forming as the ants lock themselves together with hooks on the terminal segments of their legs. Later a solid wall of ants will provide snug shelter for the queen and the brood of larvae.

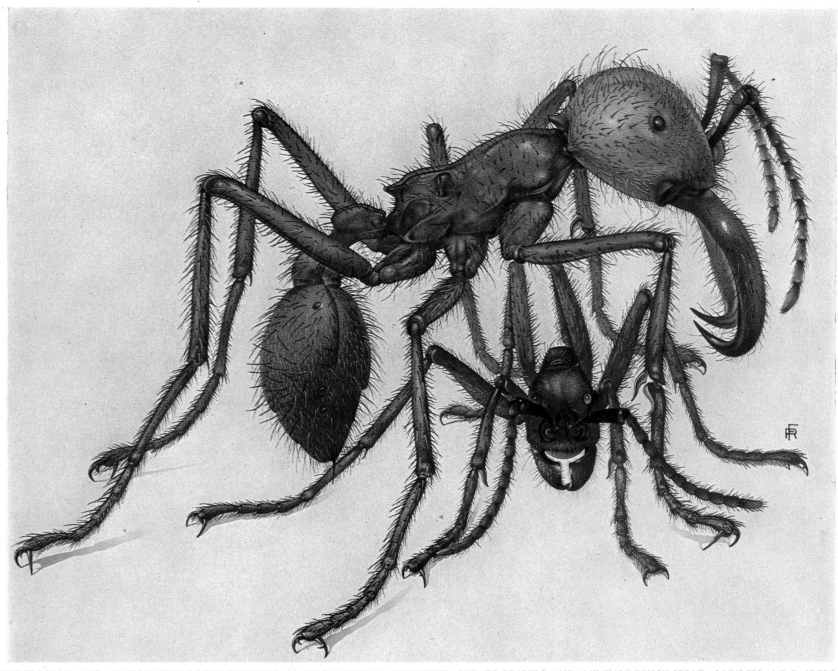

THE TROOPS IN ANT ARMIES INCLUDE BOTH FIGHTING "MAJORS," WHICH HAVE WICKED, CURVED PINCERS, AND "MINIMS," WHICH SERVE AS NURSES AND RAIDERS

SUPREMACY OF THE GROUP

Army ants show evolution for society instead of the individual

ONE day, at Bahia," Darwin wrote in Brazil, "my attention was drawn by observing many spiders, cockroaches and other insects, and some lizards, rushing in the greatest agitation across a bare piece of ground. A little way behind, every stalk and leaf was blackened by a small ant. The swarm having crossed the bare space, divided itself. . . . By this means many insects were fairly enclosed."

Thus in the autumn of 1832 Darwin chanced to witness one of the most curious and terrifying spectacles in the entire theater of nature—an army of ants on the march. In the communal world of ants, there are many social patterns: some groups engage in agriculture, some practice husbandry, some have evolved into degenerate societies which subsist on slave labor. But of the eight subfamilies in the ant kingdom the most militantly predatory are the carnivorous dorylinae—in the words of a famed entomologist *(page 111)*, "Huns and Tartars of the insect world"—which range the tropics and subtropics of both Eastern and Western Hemispheres. In the Old World they are called driver ants, in Central and South America army ants. But

their impact on forest life is the same. Advancing implacably, deploying in swarms of hundreds of thousands, they overwhelm and devour virtually every living creature in their path, save those agile enough to find sanctuary.

After studying the social structure of the ant empire, Darwin confessed perplexity that societies could flourish prolifically with so many sexless or neuter soldiers and workers like those shown above. "How is it possible," he asked, "to reconcile this case with the history of natural selection?" Darwin deduced that in their complex society "selection has been applied to the family, and not to the individual, for the sake of gaining a serviceable end." That end is the good of the colony, within which there really are no individuals. Each ant, deaf and almost sightless, functions as one cell in an insensate organism, powered by blind instinct. Even the queen is no leader, but a walking reproductive machine. Yet no other creatures on earth, below man, function in organized groups with the order, discipline and deadly efficiency of the marauding swarms of army ants.

FISSION OF THE COLONY occurs annually when the queen lays a brood including about six virgin queens and some 2,000 males. One new queen attains sovereignty and takes over half the army. The rejected queens, like the one in the foreground, are sealed off by workers while the army moves on, and then abandoned. The winged males *(top)* are held down temporarily and then released for flight. A few will mate with the queens, but all will soon die.

BLUNTHEADED TREE SNAKE

EMIGRATION COLUMN

OWL BUTTERFLY

ABANDONED BIVOUAC

MAJOR WORKER

THE ANT ARMIES MARCH BY NIGHT

Among many strange aspects of the savage society of army ants, one that baffled entomologists and other scientists for decades after Darwin's death was their mysterious disappearance and reappearance. Today it is known that the cyclical rhythm of their behavior is determined by the reproductive rhythm of the colony. The New World *Eciton burchelli* ants shown in these paintings spend two weeks in frenzied nomadism—raiding and plundering by day, marching each

CLICK BEETLE

MAIN EMIGRATION COLUMN

NOCTURNAL TREE FROG

QUEEN

MAJOR WORKER   GUEST BEETLE

MINOR WORKERS

night to a new bivouac—followed by three weeks in a quiet, settled phase. In an army of more than a million ants, one queen lays all the eggs, producing ten broods a year—enough to double the original population. Of these ten broods, nine bring forth only neuter (sterile female) workers. The tenth and smallest brood has about 2,000 males and six virgin queens, and it is the advent of this brood that effects the fission of the colony *(page 103)*. But whatever the character

of the brood, the three stages of its development shape the life of the entire army: 1) each egg hatches into a wingless, wormlike larva; 2) the larva spins a cocoon and enters a quiescent pupal stage; 3) the pupa matures and emerges a young adult insect.

As the maturing pupae begin to squirm and wriggle with increasing vigor, the worker ants are excited to a frenzy of activity; they pass the pupae back and forth, lick them, stroke them, nuzzle them

FOLD OUT, DO NOT TEAR

PARASITIC FLY   ANOLE LIZARD
BLOWFLY   ANT BIRD   PARASITIC FLY   EUGLOSSA BEE
VELVET ANT   GIANT WORKER ANT   VELVET ANT   THREAD-WAISTED WASP

FULGORID BUG   SOLDIER FLY   TORTOISE BEETLE   HELICONID BUTTERFLY

CHRYSOMELID BEETLE   HELICONID BUTTERFLY   SOLITARY WASP   TORTOISE BEETLE

ARBOREAL TARANTULA   STINGLESS BEE   SCORPION   STINK BUG

NEW BIVOUAC

LARVA-CARRYING SUBMAJOR WORKER   LARVA-CARRYING INTERMEDIATE WORKER

MAJOR WORKER   ANT LARVAE

WHIPLESS WHIP SCORPION

with their tactile organs. During the cocoon stage that follows, the twitching and stirring of the pupae augment the mass excitement. When at last the young workers emerge from their cocoons a charge is released and the colony explodes into its nomadic phase, stimulated on its travels by the similar stirrings of a second, later-maturing brood of larvae. When the second brood in its turn spins its cocoons, the colony again enters its settled phase—there to remain until the

process repeats itself. In this painting the army is revealed emigrating in darkness from its former bivouac at left to a new one at right. The column, more than 100 yards long, moves at a rate of 38 yards an hour. Many of the workers are shown carrying larvae. The various small forest creatures in the vicinity—the snake, the butterfly, the frog, the beetle, the scorpion—stay well out of the way, although the army here is intent on migration rather than fearsome plunder.

VESPID WASPS' NEST
TROPICAL FLY

HELICONID BUTTERFLY

WOLF SPIDER

FIERCE ONSLAUGHT BY DAY

Between emigrations the army ants erupt each morning from their bivouac and advance over a broad front, laying waste the forest floor in the sweeping attack depicted here. Their direction is set by chance, for ant armies have no leaders. In the crush of the emerging swarm a broad fringe of workers is thrust out ahead by the pressure of the multitudes behind. As these are swept forward, their anal glands lay down a trail of scent. The others blindly follow wherever this trail may lead—through tangled thickets, into swamps and steep ravines, over tenuous bridges spun of vines. Periodically fluctuations in the density of the swarm make it veer, including flanking movements that give an appearance of strategic planning and tactical skill.

The ants' massive onslaught spreads terror down the forest aisles, and all mobile creatures take desperate flight. Winged insects swarm into the air. Jumping insects leap frantically ahead of the advancing host. But slower terrestrial forms—as formidable as the tarantula, the scorpion, the lone giant worker ant, and the wolf spider—are overrun and ripped limb from limb. Clumsy efforts to escape are futile, for the ants, endowed with acute tactile perceptions, are driven to frenzy by an awareness of movement and ferociously attack anything that stirs. Fearing no foe they pour into the mazes of other ant societies and wage deadly battles underground. They penetrate the paper palaces of vespid wasps and divest them of their larvae. Such sieges exact their toll, and many combatants fall on either side. As the living prey is slaughtered by the fighting soldiers, platoons of foragers carry the dismembered meat to caches behind the battle front as a future feast for the queen, the brood and the nurse attendants which have remained throughout the raid secluded in the bivouac.

If crippled or helpless, even large animals may be suffocated by the great mass of the swarm, hence Indian tribes never leave new babies unguarded in their open huts. Yet some creatures remain unmolested by the voracious horde. The stink bug, for reasons implicit in its name, is left alone. So, because of their speed and strength, are the velvet ants, which are actually wasps. The anole lizard holds no interest for the army ants, nor do they for him; his attention is directed upon any fugitive insects which, in fleeing the army, pass within range of his long unerring tongue. Over the battlefield the air hums with the wings of many species of flies and other insects attracted to the scene by the frantic activity of both victims and predators. The commotion also explains the invariable presence of the little ant bird, whose sweet lyric cry recurrently sounds above the fray as it perches serenely on some observation post, surveying the carnage below and profiting, like camp followers everywhere, from the spoils of war.

NEW LIGHT ON A DARK

Research since Darwin's time has turned up 500 species of marauding army ants,

IN Darwin's day little was known of the secret world of ants, and virtually nothing of its most sinister family, the dorylinae—army or driver ants. It is not surprising, therefore, that he found himself baffled by the paradox of a prolific society made up almost entirely of neuters, incapable of reproducing themselves. And he saw an apparently "insuperable" difficulty in any attempt to explain by evolutionary process the enormous variations both in size and structure among the sterile majors and minims in the ranks of any one army.

"The reader will perhaps best appreciate the amount of difference in these workers," Darwin wrote, "by my giving a strictly accurate illustration: the difference was the same as if we were to see a set of workmen building a house, of whom many were five feet four inches high, and many sixteen feet high; but we must in addition suppose that the larger workmen had heads four times as big as those of the smaller men, and jaws nearly five times as big."

Brooding over these differences, he went on to observe, "If a working ant had been an ordinary animal, I should have unhesitatingly assumed that all its characters had been slowly acquired through natural selection. . . . But with the working ant we have an insect differing greatly from its parents, yet absolutely sterile; so that it could never have transmitted successively acquired modifications of structure or instinct to its progeny."

On the other hand, he reasoned, if evolution operates for the welfare of the family as well as for that of the individual then one could conceive of a family benefiting collectively by the creation of sterile workers of various sizes and functions. Hence, he wrote, "natural selection, by acting on the fertile ants or parents, could form a species which should regularly produce neuters, all of large size with one form of jaw, or all of small size with widely different jaws; or lastly, one set of workers of one size and structure, and simultaneously another set of workers of a different size and structure."

Contemplating "the wonderful fact" of distinctly defined castes of sterile workers existing together in the same nest, very different both from each other and also from their parents, Darwin added: "We can see how useful their production may have been to a social community of ants, on the same principle that the division of labor is useful to civilized man. Ants, however, work by inherited instincts and by inherited organs or tools, whilst man works by acquired knowledge and manufactured instruments. But I must confess, that with all my faith in natural selection I should never have anticipated that this principle could have been efficient in so high a degree, had not the case of these neuter insects led me to this conclusion."

Darwin's description of the army ants he observed in Bahia virtually initiates scientific annals on the subject, although accounts of their depredations have appeared in legend and literature for centuries. A millennium ago the Indians of Central and South America released army ants upon their victims in initiation and puberty ceremonies. From Africa have come many tales of legions of driver ants invading human habitations and suffocating the occupants by pouring into their nostrils and mouths, or biting them to death. And in recent years fossil discoveries revealed that the subfamily of army ants

shown on the preceding pages existed in America in its present form—very probably raiding, migrating, marauding as they do today—in mid-Tertiary times, 30 million years ago.

Against such horror stories, however, stands a considerable body of evidence that the dorylinae are at least partly beneficial to man, since they keep the insect populations down and periodically sweep entire areas clean of pests of every kind. The first written testimony to this effect appears in a journal kept by the secretary to Father Alonso Ponce, Commissary General of the Franciscan Order in Mexico from 1584 to 1589. Describing conditions at a parish in the bishopric of Guadalajara, he wrote: "There are many poisonous scorpions and flying chinches and other bugs, both dirty and painful, against which God has provided a marvelous remedy, which is that at certain times there come to town large bands of some ants which they call *arrieros* (muleteers), and they enter the houses and without doing harm to anybody they climb the roofs and from them and from holes they throw down, dead, all the scorpions and chinches which they find, and having done this in one house they go to the next and do the same thing, and then to the next, and in this way clean up everything."

ANT STUDENT Dr. Theodore Schneirla watches army ants he brought back from Panama's Barro Colorado Island. Here they bivouac in a cage at New York's Museum of Natural History, where he is curator of the Animal Behavior Department.

It was not until the late 19th Century, a good many years after the voyage of the *Beagle*, that scientists began serious observations of the army ants of the Americas and the driver ants of Africa. In 1874 an English naturalist named Thomas Belt noted the dorylinae of Nicaragua and fell into the common error of endowing them with human skill and Puritan virtue.

"When we see these intelligent insects," he observed, "dwelling together in orderly communities of many thousands of individuals, their social instincts developed to a high degree of perfection, making their marches with the regularity of disciplined troops, showing ingenuity in crossing of difficult places, assisting each other in danger, defending their nests at the risk of their own lives, communicating information rapidly to a great distance, making a regular division of work, the whole community taking charge of the rearing of young, and all imbued with the strongest sense of industry, each individual labouring not for itself alone but also for its fellows—we may imagine that Sir Thomas More's description of Utopia might have been applied with greater justice to such a community than to any human society."

This anthropomorphic view of army ants persisted well into the 20th Century. Since man is constantly torn between admiration of efficiency and distaste for ruthless efficiency, the ants gravitate in scientific literature between two roles—hard-working, self-sacrificing soldier-citizens, or sadistic emulators of Attila and Genghis Khan. In 1913 the famous American entomologist, William Morton Wheeler, inclined toward the latter view. It was he who called the army ants "Huns and Tartars of the insect world," and he remarked that their vast hordes of "exquisitely cooperating" and insatiably carnivorous warriors all suggest "the existence of a subtle, relentless and uncanny agency, directing and permeating all their activities."

It fell to a younger American to reveal in a quarter century of dedicated study the intricate life cycle of the army ant. In 1932 Dr.

SOCIETY

each of them different but all ferocious

Theodore C. Schneirla of New York's American Museum of Natural History first ventured into the dark and ominous jungles of Barro Colorado Island, off Panama. There, in the course of many subsequent field trips, he studied the activities of various species of *Eciton* (an American genus of dorylinae) with a devotion and thoroughness that established him beyond all doubt as the world's outstanding expert on army ants. By day he followed the raiding hordes, by night the migrations, wading through swamps, groping through labyrinths of lianas, stumbling into wasps' nests, narrowly evading the fangs of the fer-de-lance and other poisonous reptiles. More than once scorpions dropped down the back of his open collar and stung him grievously. He often felt the fiery, piercing mandibles of the subjects of his research. But out of his arduous adventures there emerged for the first time a clear picture of one of nature's most arcane societies.

Dr. Schneirla was the first to discover the alternating cycles of nomadic and settled existence on the part of army ant colonies, and to prove that they are governed by the reproductive cycles of the brood. He established the fact that the marvelous discipline of the marching armies was a product neither of intelligence nor of tactical skill, but simply a blind response to the olfactory stimulus of an anal odor trail and the tactile stimulus afforded by wriggling larvae. He plotted with mathematical accuracy the dynamic and repetitive relationship between the development of the brood, the vigor of the daily raids, and the retreat to the bivouac. He measured the volume of dismembered insect parts stored in a single cache after one raid and found it came to a full gallon. And his research led to solutions of many problems that had troubled Darwin—for example, the reason for gradations in size among the workers. Stature, Dr. Schneirla and his associates ascertained, was controlled by the amount of food received by the individual insect in its larval stage. In general the first eggs laid by the queen (in a week of prodigious output) are the first to hatch. The first larvae to emerge are most generously fed by the nurse workers, and these tend to become big-mandibled majors. Conversely, the last to hatch receive least attention, take less time to develop and tend to become minims. Between the two extremes intermediate forms arise.

TWO priests, the Belgian Jesuit, Dr. Albert Raignier, and his Dutch colleague, Dr. Joseph K. van Boven, began their observations of the driver ants of Africa in 1949. In the ensuing decade they made important discoveries revealing both similarities and dissimilarities between New World and Old World ant societies. Among the principal differences are: 1) American army ants live in colonies of 200,000 to one million or more while African driver ants assemble in colonies with a population sometimes reaching 20 million; 2) African driver colonies produce 12 to 30 potential queens each year, contrasted with the American varieties' five or six; 3) the nests of African driver ants are always underground, those of many American species above; 4) the mandibles of driver ants are more serrated, enabling them to fight and dismember their prey more effectively.

Other branches of the doryline family pillage the jungles of the Far East. An American, Dr. James W. Chapman, spent 35 years studying the *Aenictus* ants of the Philippines, and the varieties of parasites and camp followers that trail them in their endless columnar marches. Perhaps the greatest living taxonomist of army ants is a German Franciscan friar, Dr. Thomas Borgmeier, of Rio de Janeiro, who devoted 25 years to classifying 250 of the 500 known species that range the forest floors of earth today.

But many questions are still unanswered. No one knows, for example, how these rather terrifying and eminently successful insects originally spread around the planet, nor how they evolved into their extraordinary nomadic, carnivorous way of life. The Asiatic species have received little attention, and there are subterranean species in the United States that are so elusive as to be virtually unknown. Students of army ants are also profoundly interested in the nature of the ties that bind colonies numbering millions of individuals into societies as large, aggressive and well-organized as those of man.

Perhaps it is only by comparison with man that the mindless drive of the army ants can be really understood. Just as Wheeler compared the insects with Tartars and Huns, Dr. Schneirla found a ready analogy when asked if man could ever be drawn into a predatory society like that of the army ants. "Hitler came close," he replied.

ANT CLASSIFIER Friar Thomas Borgmeier stands in a banana grove in Brazil, where he spent 25 years not only studying army ant species but writing and illustrating the world's most extensive catalogue of the tiny predators.

THE
MYSTERIES
OF
MIGRATION

THE phenomenon of migration involves enigmas only partially understood by science. Here wild ducks, winging south for winter, inexplicably convene at Tule Lake National Wildlife Refuge in California, the stopping place for millions of migrating birds. The ducks shown in this picture are mainly pintails, which range the length of the continent, finding their way from their summer habitat in the subarctic to wintering grounds along the Gulf coast as if directed by a built-in compass.

Tristan Da Cunha

THE GREAT SHEARWATER COMMUTES ANNUALLY FROM ITS ROOSTS ON TRISTAN DA CUNHA TO ITS NORTH ATLANTIC FISHING GROUNDS

THE MYSTERIES
OF MIGRATION

On seasonal flights birds display uncanny feats of navigation

IN long days at sea aboard the *Beagle* as it traversed the oceans of the earth, Darwin marveled at the spectacle of migratory birds winging their way across the trackless watery wastes. From earliest boyhood he had been stirred by the biennial pageant. At home in Shropshire he had seen the skies dappled each spring and autumn with the multitudinous pinions of aerial travelers. By day the dissonances of honking geese and other diurnal flyers descended forlornly from above. After sundown the liquid chirps of little land birds cascaded like raindrops from the dark flyways of the night. And all around him meadows and marshes resounded with the discourse of winged transients at rest between their seasonal

homes. Darwin's studies of this phenomenon led him to conclude with astonishment that the migratory impulse took precedence over all other avian drives, even that of parental care. "Everyone knows how strong the maternal instinct is," he wrote. "Nevertheless, the migratory instinct is so powerful, that late in autumn [some birds desert] their tender young, leaving them to perish miserably in their nests." Despite Darwin's lifelong interest and patient observations, it was not until recent years that ornithologists, employing the techniques of modern science, solved the major mystery of migration— the mechanism by which birds find their way to specific destinations, flying for days over vast expanses of land and sea *(pages 122-123)*.

FLYING BY NIGHT, thrushes and warblers wing southward toward tropic climes in late September. The fact that some birds always make nocturnal flights on their migrations, while others invariably travel by daylight, provided an important clue to the secret of their navigation. Among the night flyers shown in this painting are a black-and-white warbler *(lower left)*, a Cape May warbler *(right center)* and a wood thrush *(upper right)*.

FLIGHT SOUTHWARD
IN THE AUTUMN

The advent of cool weather and bright autumnal skies annually incites the mass fall migration of North American birds, depicted in the painting at right which emphasizes water fowl and hawks. By the millions they stream down the five major continental flyways outlined above. Leaving their breeding areas in the north, some take the Pacific flyway (1), others the central flyway across the Great Plains (2). Another major artery follows the course of the Mississippi River (3), while East Coast breeders, joined by tributary streams of cross-country migrants, jam the Atlantic flyway (4). Certain hawks detour down the wooded ridges of the Appalachians (5). And a few birds which are shown here heading east or west are wanderers coming in from their maritime breeding places. They will turn south later in the year.

LOONS	1	Red-throated Loon
GREBES	2	Red-necked Grebe
ALBATROSSES	3	Black-footed Albatross
PETRELS	4	Great Shearwater
	5	Cory's Shearwater
STORM PETRELS	6	Fork-tailed Petrel
PELICANS	7	White Pelican
BOOBIES	8	Gannet
CORMORANTS	9	Double-crested Cormorant
	10	Pelagic Cormorant
HERONS	11	Egret
	12	Little Blue Heron
WATERFOWL	13	Whistling Swan
	14	Canada Goose
		a. Cackling
		b. Hutchin's
		c. Greater
	15	Brant
		a. Eastern
		b. Black
	16	Snow Goose
		a. Greater
		b. Lesser
	17	Blue Goose
	18	Mallard
	19	Black Duck
	20	Pintail
	21	Blue-winged Teal
	22	Baldpate
	23	Shoveler
	24	Redhead
	25	Canvasback
	26	Lesser Scaup
	27	Oldsquaw
	28	Eider
	29	White-winged Scoter
	30	Surf Scoter
	31	Black Scoter
	32	Ruddy Duck
HAWKS	33	Sharp-shinned Hawk
	34	Broad-winged Hawk
	35	Swainson's Hawk
	36	Ferruginous Rough-legged Hawk
FALCONS	37	Gyrfalcon
	38	Pigeon Hawk
CRANES	39	Whooping Crane
	40	Sandhill Crane
RAILS	41	Sora
JAEGERS	42	Pomarine Jaeger
GULLS	43	Glaucous Gull
	44	Heermann's Gull
	45	Laughing Gull
	46	Franklin's Gull
	47	Kittiwake
AUKS	48	Brunnich's Murre
	49	Rhinoceros Auklet
OWLS	50	Short-eared Owl

M—male F—female Imm—immature
In other species plumage of sexes is alike

A BLIZZARD OF GEESE flecks the crystalline air above a golden barley field at Tule Lake National Wildlife Refuge in northern California on a brilliant autumn afternoon. They have passed the summer months in their bleak breeding ground beyond the Arctic Circle in Canada and on the barren, rocky islands that stud the polar sea. Then early in September they start southward, down the Pacific flyway, heading for their winter roosts in

the lush valleys of central California. En route they habitually pause at Tule Lake to feed on the sunburned grain that gilds the land in early fall, remaining until the local waters freeze. Most of the migrants taking flight here are snow and white-fronted Geese. They are gregarious, loud-mouthed and swift, steady flyers, strong in soaring and agile in aerial acrobatics. In the spring warmth of early April they take to the sky again for the north.

A RETURN FLIGHT FOR THE SPRINGTIME

The return to northern regions in spring is a drive brought on by the impulse to breed. Unerringly most of the birds return not only to the same place year after year, but often to the same nest. In the painting at right some of the many species of song and shore birds are shown making their way to their summer abodes. Mapped in detail above are the main flyways, the Pacific (1), the Gulf Coast (2), the trans-Gulf (3), which is the most heavily used route, and the West Indian (4), the left-hand fork of which leads across 500 miles of ocean between Jamaica and South America—and is used chiefly by the bobolinks. Though most birds fly the same routes in spring and fall, there are exceptions, such as the golden plover which wings down the Atlantic oceanic route and returns overland up the center of the continent. Land and shore birds, normally active in daytime, do most of their migratory flying at night.

PLOVERS	1	Piping Plover
	2	Golden Plover
	3	Black Turnstone
SNIPE	4	Long billed Curlew
	5	Greater Yellow-Legs
	6	Knot
	7	Least Sandpiper
	8	Dunlin
	9	Dowitcher
	10	Wandering Tattler
	11	Western Sandpiper
	12	Marbled Godwit
AVOCETS	13	Avocet
PHALAROPES	14	Red Phalarope
TERNS	15	Arctic Tern
	16	Black Tern
CUCKOOS	17	Black-billed Cuckoo
GOATSUCKERS	18	Nighthawk
HUMMINGBIRDS	19	Rufous Hummingbird
WOODPECKERS	20	Red-shafted Flicker
	21	Sapsucker
		a. Yellow-bellied
		b. Red-breasted
FLYCATCHERS	22	Western Kingbird
	23	Scissor-tailed Flycatcher
	24	Olive-sided Flycatcher
LARKS	25	Horned Lark
SWALLOWS	26	Bank Swallow
	27	Cliff Swallow
NUTHATCHES	28	Red-breasted Nuthatch
WRENS	29	House Wren
MIMIC THRUSHES	30	Catbird
THRUSHES	31	Grey-cheeked Thrush
	32	Mountain Bluebird
SHRIKES	33	Northern Shrike
VIREOS	34	Yellow-throated Vireo
	35	Red-eyed Vireo
WOOD WARBLERS	36	Black-throated Blue Warbler
	37	Hermit Warbler
	38	Blackburnian Warbler
	39	Northern Water-Thrush
	40	Connecticut Warbler
	41	Redstart
BLACKBIRDS	42	Bobolink
	43	Bullock's Oriole
TANAGERS	44	Western Tanager
	45	Scarlet Tanager
FINCHES	46	Rose-breasted Grosbeak
	47	Lazuli Bunting
	48	Hoary Redpoll
	49	Savannah Sparrow
	50	Clay-colored Sparrow
	51	Fox Sparrow
		a. Sooty
		b. Eastern

M—male   F—female
In other species plumage of sexes is alike

Guy
Tudor

HOMING SECRETS OF

Ingenious experiments resolve an old enigma by proving that migrants chart

APOSTROPHIZING a realm of nature he deeply loved, St. Francis of Assisi said, "My sisters, the birds, ye are greatly beholden to God for the element of the air." Although man now depends on the air for the pursuit of his restless purposes, his ascent into the skies is such a recent event that he has spent vastly more time perfecting his own system of celestial navigation than speculating upon that of birds.

Yet long before Darwin's day the phenomenon of avian migration intrigued natural scientists, as well as poets and others sensitive to the natural world about them. The practice of bird watching is doubtless as old as man himself, for birds preceded man on earth and the first men were hunters. Aristotle had much to say about birds, although his theories were less accurate than his observations. He believed, for example, that the kingfisher, or halcyon, hatched its eggs in a floating nest at sea—hence the term "halcyon days" to describe calm, sunny weather suitable for nestlings.

Only within the last century have ornithologists begun to discern the patterns of bird migration. For the comings and goings of the birds are as sudden and dramatic as the entrance and exit of actors upon a stage. They swoop suddenly out of the sky, pause briefly, warily, and then move on. It has been through the joint efforts of an informal, international fraternity of scientists and amateur bird watchers that the sporadic flutterings of migrant birds have been etched into clear outlines of movement and behavior. Darwin, the greatest of observers, despite his insatiable curiosity about the processes of life and his innumerable studies of birds, lacked both the methods and equipment to perceive in detail the whole complex panorama of migration. Yet he not only recognized the migratory impulse as a powerfully recurrent one, he deduced that it played a role in the workings of natural selection. In addition to his personal observation that birds would leave their young behind at times of migration (page 114), he described instances of a confined bird during the migration season beating its breast against the bars of its cage till it was bare and bloody, and of a goose with clipped wings which doughtily started its long seasonal journey on foot.

"We can perceive," he wrote, "that an instinctive impulse, if it be in any way more beneficial to a species than some other or opposed instinct, would be rendered the more potent of the two through natural selection; for the individuals which had it most strongly developed would survive in larger numbers."

Although he expressed doubt that the migratory instinct in birds could be regarded as always stronger than the maternal instinct,

he added that "The great persistence . . . at certain seasons of the year during the whole day, may give it for a time paramount force."

In the decades after Darwin's death new techniques such as bird banding disclosed the main aspects of seasonal migration: the range and flight schedules of different species, their preferred routes, air speed and estimated times of arrival. They revealed such extraordinary facts as the endurance of the tiny ruby-throated hummingbird, which migrates each year from the U.S. Northeast down to its winter ranges as far south as Panama, a distance of about 3,000 miles; the incredible journeys of sea fowl like the great shearwater (page 114); and, perhaps most remarkable of all, the ability of the golden plover —a shore bird which nests in the Arctic and winters in the Southern Hemisphere—to fly for days over thousands of miles of open sea without food or rest.

Knowledge of the tremendous distances traversed by many species of birds naturally led to speculation as to how they navigate unerringly over strange landscapes and trackless seas. The difficulties of the problem were intensified when it became known that some species migrate by day, others by night, and that in many instances birds take off individually without a leader—each bird its own navigator. It was learned further that some adult birds depart from their breeding grounds before their young, leaving the latter to wing their way, without guidance or previous knowledge of the route, on unbelievable flights to distant destinations. In the spring they retrace their flight path to pinpoint objectives—the nesting place in a particular thicket or grove of trees where they first emerged from the shell.

Despite a vast body of research by the ornithologists of both Europe and America, the situation until recent years was such that no one could honestly conclude more than the late Werner Rüppell of Germany, who summed up years of research with banded crows and starlings by observing that the

TEST OF SOLAR NAVIGATION employs a caged starling (center), trained to feed by flying south toward the sun. Here, orienting itself to an electric light in the west (arrow, left), the bird now heads toward a westerly feeding station instead.

migratory birds appeared to depend on an inexplicable "sense of direction." In his last paper before he died, however, he wondered if perhaps birds, like human sailors, relied mostly on the sun.

The first spectacular breakthrough in the problem of bird navigation occurred in 1949, when Dr. Gustav Kramer of the Max Planck Institute at Wilhelmshaven, West Germany, initiated a series of controlled experiments with starlings.

Kramer decided to instill an artificial directional urge into the birds by Pavlovian methods—i.e., by rewarding them with food only when they sought it in a certain direction. To this end he designed an aviary with a ring of 12 feeding stations circling its inner wall. The bird being trained would find food only if it went to the feeding

BIRDS

their way by help of the sun and stars

station at the compass point selected by Kramer. The feeding stations were mounted on a rotating ring, so that by changing their positions regularly, the investigators could be sure that the bird was finding its reward only by sun orientation and not by any other visible sign. Within a month the average starling had been conditioned —*i.e.,* if it was being trained to migrate north, it went unerringly to the northernmost feeding station to obtain its food. But on cloudy days the starlings were lost.

The evidence was enough to convince Kramer that the birds gauged their direction with respect to the sun. To corroborate his first experiments he built another aviary, excluding all the sky save six small patches visible through six windows around the roof. One by one Kramer closed the windows, and found that the birds could still orient themselves until the last window was shut off. In hundreds of such experiments, Kramer established beyond doubt that the starling orients itself by the sun.

K RAMER'S epic discoveries left unanswered the mystery of the nocturnal migrants. It was a not unreasonable assumption, however, that if the day birds employed the sun, the night birds used the fixed stars. In 1956 Dr. Franz Sauer of Freiburg University began a series of experiments with European warblers, which migrate each autumn to Africa. The most astonishing aspect of the warbler's migration is that, flying mostly at night, it sets out without a leader or any companions and finds its way alone.

Dr. Sauer and his associates began their experiments by hatching warblers in glass-enclosed, soundproof cages where they matured in the illusion of everlasting summer. Despite their confinement the birds infallibly exhibited the migratory instinct each autumn. They would flit restlessly from perch to perch, night after sleepless night, for about the number of weeks required for the flight to Africa. And then when the imaginary flight came to its end they returned to sleeping. Dr. Sauer next placed his warblers in an outdoor cage with a glass top, so they could see part of the night sky. When autumn arrived they showed signs of unrest, but more significantly, they took up positions pointing in directions corresponding to the routes flown by particular species. In the spring their positions were precisely reversed. But when the sky was hidden from their view or the starlight diffused by screens, their directional unity dissolved.

As a final step in his investigation, Dr. Sauer took his birds to a planetarium in Bremen, where the projection of stars and constellations on the domed ceiling could be altered to correspond to any given longitude or latitude on earth. The warblers promptly responded to their artificially created geographical position. One bird, for example, while flapping its wings, supposedly flying from Germany to the Nile, was suddenly presented with an arrangement of stars such as would appear in central Siberia. It paused in doubt for almost a full minute, then changed its direction and pointed due west, heading back to its normal migration route.

Dr. Sauer's findings have been confirmed by actual observations with a new implement of ornithology—radar. A Swiss ornithologist, Dr. Ernst Sutter of the Natural History Museum at Basel, began following the movements of nocturnal passerine birds with the radar screen at the Zürich-Kloten airport in 1956. His findings confirmed graphically the conclusions indicated by Dr. Sauer's experiments—that is, that birds navigate successfully on clear starry nights, and become confused and bewildered in stormy weather *(right).*

No one can say how young birds come into the world carrying within their small frames a picture of the heavens and a knowledge of how the celestial panorama changes in time. In the light of Darwin's thought, it can only be surmised that what we call "sense of direction" may be an endowment deeply inborn in all creatures on earth through eons of evolution on this particular rotating planet with its ever-wheeling canopy of stars.

RADAR RECORDS OF MIGRATION *(right)* show paths of birds winging through the nocturnal sky. On a clear and windless night, when they can easily navigate by the stars, birds form a clearly defined pattern *(top)* as they unerringly fly in the same direction. When the wind blows them partially off course, they form a more diffused picture *(center).* When clouds obscure the stars, the befuddled flights of birds trace a helter-skelter pattern *(bottom).*

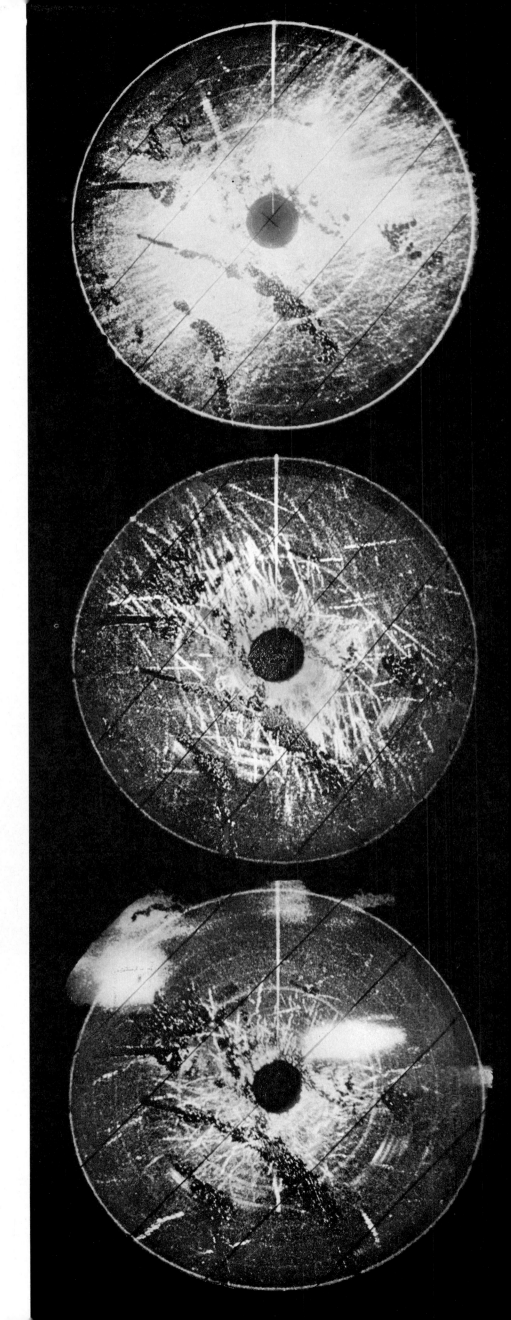

'MAN
IN HIS
MOST SAVAGE
STATE'

A YAGHAN Indian from Tierra del Fuego, 90-year-old Julie, was, when this picture was made in 1958, the oldest survivor of one of the most primitive people on earth. The Yaghans were wild canoe nomads dwelling on the bleak islands just north of the howling promontory of Cape Horn at the time of Darwin's visit there in 1832 and he wondered if modern man could truly have evolved from such as these. By the middle of this century nine Yaghans were left, all wards of the government of Chile.

'MAN IN HIS MOST SAVAGE STATE'

In Tierra del Fuego, Darwin found a race of primitive beings

A SINGLE glance at the landscape," Charles Darwin wrote, "was sufficient to show me how widely different it was from anything I had ever beheld." H.M.S. *Beagle* on its famous voyage had dropped anchor off the wild, forbidding coast of Tierra del Fuego in December 1832, shortly before the summer solstice. Few other white men had ever ventured to this uttermost region of the earth at the southern tip of South America. Magellan discovered the archipelago in 1520 and named it "Land of Fire" for the dancing flames of Indian camps along the darkened shore. Now on Admiralty orders, the *Beagle* was there to chart its islands and rock clusters, to study the labyrinthine channels and inlets of the foaming sea.

The very place names reveal the melancholy of the land—Desolation Island, Cape Deceit, Port Famine, Useless Bay. After Darwin first looked on Cape Horn, he wrote, "We saw this notorious promontory in its proper form, veiled in a mist, and its dim outline surrounded by a storm of wind and water. Great black clouds were rolling across the heavens, and squalls of rain, with hail, swept by."

Yet powerfully as he was affected by the somber scene, Darwin was even more excited on encountering the Fuegian Indians. "Nothing is more likely to create astonishment," he reported, "than the first sight in his native state of a barbarian—of man in his lowest and most savage state. One's mind hurries back over past centuries, and asks, could our progenitors have been men like these, men who do not appear to boast of human reason, or at least of arts consequent to that reason. I do not believe it is possible to describe or paint the difference between savage and civilized man. . . . It is greater than between a wild and domesticated animal."

Although the condition of the surviving Fuegians was later altered by contact with civilization, at the time of Darwin's visit they were surely the most wretched people on earth. Being dependent upon the sea for food, they ranged unceasingly by canoe from one temporary campsite to another. "Whenever it is low water, winter or summer, night or day," Darwin wrote, "they must rise to pick shellfish from the rocks . . . if a seal is killed or the floating carcass of a putrid whale discovered, it is a feast; and such miserable food is assisted by a few tasteless berries and fungi." Their only garments were skimpy guanaco hides or otter skins, laced across the breast by thongs.

Their habitations were crude wigwams consisting of long broken branches stuck in the ground, thatched on one side with tufts of grass and rushes or animal hides. At night, in these scant shelters, Darwin noted, "five or six human beings, naked and scarcely protected from the wind and rain of this tempestuous climate, sleep on the wet ground, coiled up like animals." He never ceased to marvel —and to shiver—at the spectacle of the Fuegians, stark naked at temperatures of 35-45°, paddling their canoes through wind-whipped waters or wading into icy surf to collect sea eggs and limpets. He particularly remembered one day when "a woman who was suckling a recently born child came alongside the vessel, and remained there out of mere curiosity, whilst the sleet fell and thawed on her naked bosom, and on the skin of her naked baby."

Darwin also reported—though modern observers have disputed this point—that in times of extreme famine the Fuegians practiced cannibalism, killing and devouring their old women. He cited several sources, among them a young Indian who "described the manner in which they are killed by being held over smoke and thus choked."

Speculating on the origins and destiny of the Fuegians, Darwin wrote that "Nature by making habit omnipotent, and its effects hereditary, has fitted the Fuegian to the climate and the productions of his miserable country."

But Darwin was scarcely able to foresee the devastating impact of the white man, who brought disease upon them and systematically slaughtered them for economic reasons. By the 20th Century the three Fuegian tribes were almost extinct. The Alacalufes, canoe people of the western channels *(opposite page),* numbered 10,000 at the time of Darwin's visit; by 1960 there were hardly 100. The Onas, an inland tribe, were massacred by sheep farmers in quest of grazing land; a modern count showed only seven alive of an original 4,000. The Yaghans once occupied the lower islands down to Cape Horn; out of 5,000, only nine purebred Yaghans remained in recent times. It was this tribe that Darwin knew best and that most impressed him with their hardihood. By the middle 1900s the Yaghans were receiving a modicum of food and clothing from the Chilean government and Catholic Church, of which they were nominal members. But lacking education, they had almost lost all ability to support themselves.

A FUEGIAN INDIAN stands before his wigwam in this drawing by an artist on the *Beagle*. Despite the climate the natives went virtually naked the year round. Darwin found their attitudes "abject," their expressions "distrustful, surprised and startled."

COASTAL NOMADS of the South Chilean archipelago, Alacalufe Indians gather for the funeral of a member of their fast-vanishing tribe. The coffin in the boat is being taken for interment on a nearby island. As they wander among the bleak islands of the archipelago they pause briefly at tiny settlements like the one shown here. The tent at left is made of sea lion hides, old sacks and old clothes. The hut at right was built by missionaries in the 1920s.

A FAMILY OF YAGHANS, SOUTHERNMOST PEOPLE ON EARTH, ENJOY A MOMENT OF SUN AT CAMP ON NAVARINO ISLAND IN BEAGLE CHANNEL. ASHORE

AN ONA INDIAN, 40-year-old Pappett, works for a white settler, cutting wood and tending sheep with a dog. Like most Indians on Navarino Island, where the Chilean navy maintains a base, Pappett receives free clothes from the government and a wage paid partly in money, partly in goods.

HALF-BREED CHILDREN, of mixed Yaghan-English ancestry, perch atop a sled in a summer meadow. Descendants of Old Julie, shown in the

YOUNG YAGHAN named Alberto draws lumber for navy personnel on Navarino Island, near the place where Darwin came ashore. As wheels are impractical in the rain-soaked forest, Alberto maintains eight oxen to drag logs. Wood is constantly in demand for fuel in this chilly domain.

THEY CONVERT THEIR BOAT SAIL INTO A TENT

frontispiece of this chapter, they live with their parents but receive most of their support from the Chilean government and Catholic Church.

GRANDMOTHER CHACON, an 85-year-old Yaghan matriarch, sits outside her hut on Navarino Island, looking across Beagle Channel to the snow-capped peaks of Tierra del Fuego. She makes models of the canoe used by her people long ago, and sells them to infrequent tourists.

HUNTING SHELLFISH, an Alacalufe Indian stands poised on the shore of Wellington Island, about to dive into an estuary of the Pacific Ocean. Although the temperatures of the air and water hover only slightly above the freezing point all year, Alacalufes regularly enter the chilly sea in quest of sea urchins, mussels and clams, and emerge after a leisurely swim into swirling mists and biting winds without exhibiting the slightest hint of a shiver.

NOMADS
OF THE
FAR SOUTH

Of the three Fuegian tribes indigenous to the stormy tip of South America, the Alacalufes, canoe nomads of the western islands, are the most numerous and secure. Unlike the nearly extinct Onas and Yaghans, who subsist on government aid, the Alacalufes retain their ancient culture. They still speak a complex language which, like the tongues of such other primitive people as the Bushmen and Hottentots, includes clicks and subtle sounds strange to civilized ears. By day the Alacalufe men hunt sea otters, sea lions, nutria and deer, while their women collect mussels and sea urchins at low tide.

Until relatively recent times these Indians fashioned canoes of wood and sea-lion skins, using stone chopping tools as crude as those of Peking Man 300,000 years ago. Later they resorted to a more efficient implement, the shell of a large quahaug or sea clam for which they dived 20 feet into icy water. (The word *Alacalufe* means "the people who use clamshells for tools.") Now they use modern axes to build dugouts like that shown below. But their whalebone harpoons and spearheads are similar in design to those made in Europe in Paleolithic times.

When first met by European travelers, the Alacalufes went naked save for otter skins fastened about their shoulders. Their bodies were smeared with sea-mammal grease and ochre. Today they wear castoff clothing contributed by sailors from passing ships. Despite a rigorous existence they are, unlike the wretched Yaghans, a pleasant people who, possessing almost nothing, want little.

IN MODERN DRESS, a little girl blinks at rare sunshine. Though they wear clothes when they can get them, children often play naked in snow.

IN A DUGOUT CANOE, hand-hewn with a modern ax, an Alacalufe heads for an island for a special beach evergreen good for boat building.

THE MARINELLI GLACIER is one of countless rivers of ice that flow down eternally from snow fields high on the cloud-veiled mountain peaks of the Tierra del Fuego archipelago into the intricate channels and estuaries of the antarctic sea. Darwin found the scenery desolate and "sublime." The glaciers, he wrote, "may be likened to great frozen Niagaras; and perhaps these cataracts of blue ice are full as beautiful as the moving ones of water."

JAGGED PINNACLES thrust skyward about 100 miles northeast of Beagle Channel—named for H.M.S. *Beagle*. These precipitous peaks form part of the bleak spine of the Andes which extends to the tip of Tierra del Fuego.

DESOLATE LAND OF ICE AND MIST

Tierra del Fuego overwhelmed Darwin. He was awestruck by the savage magnificence of the mountains and the perilous waterways that wound darkly among forlorn and nameless islands. The gloomy forests were cluttered with decaying trees. And everywhere the land was shrouded in mists and lowering clouds from which descended rain, sleet or hail, driven by violent winds. "In these solitudes," he observed, "Death instead of Life seemed the predominant spirit."

But occasionally the clouds lifted, revealing the grandeur of the mountain peaks. "They are covered by a wide mantle of perpetual snow," he wrote, "and numerous cascades pour their waters into the narrow channels below. In many parts magnificent glaciers extend from the mountainside to the water's edge. It is scarcely possible to imagine anything more beautiful than the beryl-like blue of these glaciers, and especially as contrasted with the dead white of the upper expanse of snow."

The profusion of mighty glaciers in a relatively equable, albeit stormy, climate puzzled Darwin. "I was astonished," he wrote, "when I first saw a range, only 4,000–5,000 feet in height, in the latitude of [northern England] with every valley filled with streams of ice descending to the sea-coast." Noting that the mean summer temperature of Tierra del Fuego was 50° and its mean winter temperature 33°, he compared these figures with records for Dublin, lying in precisely the same latitude north of the equator. Dublin's mean summer temperature was 59.5°, its winter mean 39°. Darwin concluded that the existence of glaciers depends less on very cold winters than on cool, overcast summers which prevent full melting of the winter's accumulations of ice and snow. His theory is accepted today.

THE AGOSTINI GLACIER discharges its icy burden into the Strait of Magellan. The *Beagle* traversed it in June of 1834—a passage so gloomy and forbidding that to Darwin it appeared "to lead to another and worse world."

MAGELLAN GEESE flash across a field in a valley of the Payne Mountains. They nest from August to November on the coastal islands down to Cape Horn. Most are permanent residents, though a few in the southernmost part of their range migrate a short distance in midwinter.

NORTH OF THE STRAIT

A bit north of the Strait of Magellan, near the Argentine frontier, a range of the continental Andes known as the Payne Mountains rises above the broken islands of the south Chilean archipelago, thrusting snow-capped peaks nearly 9,000 feet toward the frowning sky. Their lower slopes, dissected by an intricate maze of valleys, abound in waterfalls, streams and such wild life as guanacos and Magellan geese. In Tierra del Fuego and farther north, Darwin admired the guanacos, remarking that he "could not imagine anything more graceful than their actions." He noted that in breeding time the Magellan geese built their nests on small outlying islands, and conjectured that they did so from fear of mainland foxes. "It is perhaps from the same cause," he added, "that these birds, though very tame by day, are shy and wild in the dusk of the evening."

GUANACOS, pausing beside a mountain lake, thrive both in the high Andes and in Tierra del Fuego, where they swim from island to island.

IN THE PAYNE MOUNTAINS, above the Strait of Magellan, cataracts carry water from the high snowfields and lonely lakes down into the stormy coastal channels of the Chilean archipelago and the Pacific. From sea level to an elevation of 1,500 feet the mist-mantled mountainsides are covered with dense, dark forest. The trees then give way to a carpet of small Alpine plants which extend upward to 3,000-4,000 feet, where the perpetual snows begin.

THE RETURN OF THE

Darwin's strange tale of a trio who were abducted to England, then shipped home,

DARWIN'S studies of the Fuegian Indians were abetted by an extraordinary circumstance. He had the good fortune to observe at first hand the reactions of three young natives on their return to Tierra del Fuego after an absence of nearly three years among the English. Before his eyes there unfolded a strange and unhappy drama.

The chain of events began during a previous voyage of the *Beagle* to the Tierra archipelago in the years 1826-30. One day near the end of the expedition Captain Robert Fitz-Roy, commander of the *Beagle*, seized a group of Fuegians as hostages for a whaleboat which allegedly had been stolen. When the boat was not returned, Captain Fitz-Roy, a deeply religious man, decided to take four of the Indians back to England and provide them with a Christian education.

The four Fuegians—two men, a boy and a girl, all members of the Yaghan tribe—were fancifully named by the sailors. The oldest, and most intelligent, was called Boat Memory. The others were: York Minster, a surly young man of 20, named for a bleak mountain near Cape Horn; Jemmy Button, a boy of 14, supposedly purchased from his parents for a pearl button; and Fuegia Basket, a 9-year-old girl.

Shortly after their arrival in England, Boat Memory died of smallpox. The others were lodged at Fitz-Roy's expense in the home of a clergyman. They were sent to school and instructed in such useful crafts as carpentry and gardening. All three soon learned English. About nine months after their arrival, Fitz-Roy and his protégés were commanded to appear before King William IV and Queen Adelaide. Shampooed and shining, they were led into the royal presence and comported themselves well. The king asked many questions. When they left, the queen placed her lace cap on Fuegia Basket's head, and the king presented her with one of his rings.

Captain Fitz-Roy hoped that by educating the three young Fuegians and then resettling them in their homeland he would establish a friendly line of communication for future missionary work. In 1831, two years after their abduction, the Fuegians departed on the *Beagle*, laden with gifts of clothing, tools, seeds, books and chinaware. Also aboard were Darwin and a young missionary, Richard Matthews, who was to continue the instruction of the young natives en route and then remain in Tierra del Fuego and work for the betterment of the savage tribes.

In his journal Darwin wrote of the Indians: "York Minster was a full-grown, short, thick, powerful man: his disposition was reserved, taciturn, morose, and when excited violently passionate; his affections were very strong towards a few friends on board; his intellect good. Jemmy Button was a universal favorite, but likewise passionate; the expression of his face at once showed his nice disposition. He was merry and often laughed, and was remarkably sympathetic with anyone in pain: when the water was rough, I was often a little seasick and he used to come to me and say in a plaintive voice, 'poor, poor fellow!' Jemmy was short, thick and fat, but vain of his personal appearance; he used to wear gloves, his hair was neatly cut, and he was distressed if his well-polished shoes were dirtied. He was

fond of admiring himself in a looking-glass. Lastly Fuegia Basket was a nice, modest, reserved young girl. York Minster was very jealous of any attention paid to her; for it was clear he determined to marry her as soon as they were settled on shore."

When they reached Navarino Island, in the heart of Yaghan territory, Captain Fitz-Roy led a landing party ashore. It included Darwin, Matthews, the three Fuegians and all the possessions they had brought from England. A vegetable garden was sown and three wigwams constructed for Matthews, Jemmy Button, and York Minster and Fuegia Basket, who had been married by Matthews on their arrival. During the building of the huts scores of Yaghans paddled up in their canoes and watched with curiosity, but without any real friendliness. Fitz-Roy and his companions were disappointed, and Jemmy Button seemed ashamed of his countrymen. Not long after the landing a delegation from Jemmy's tribe turned up. With them were his mother and several brothers.

Darwin related: "Jemmy recognized the Stentorian voice of one of his brothers at an enormous distance. The meeting was less interesting than that between a horse turned out into a field, when he joins an old companion. There was no demonstration of affection; they simply stared for a short time at each other; and the mother immediately went to look after her canoe. . . . We had already perceived that Jemmy had almost forgotten his own language. It was laughable but almost pitiable, to hear him speak to his wild brother in English, and then ask him in Spanish '*No sabe?*' "

When the wigwams were completed, Fitz-Roy and Darwin took off with two boat crews to survey areas to the west, leaving Matthews alone with the Fuegians. On their return trip 12 days later they were alarmed to observe various articles of English clothing adorning the natives whom they passed on the way. At camp they found Matthews close to nervous collapse. No sooner had they departed than the Indians began a campaign of plunder, giving him no rest night or day. Fresh parties kept arriving, making an incessant clamor, demanding everything in sight and, when Matthews refused their demands, threatening him, making hideous faces and pulling his beard. His three charges lost many of their possessions, and Matthews was robbed of all he had not buried underground. Captain Fitz-Roy ordered Matthews back to the *Beagle*. "It was quite melancholy leaving the three Fuegians with their savage countrymen," Darwin wrote, "but it was a great comfort that they had no personal fears. York, being a powerful, resolute man, was pretty sure to get on well, together with his wife Fuegia. Poor Jemmy . . . would then, I have little doubt, have been glad to have returned with us. His own brother had stolen many things from him; he abused his countrymen, 'All bad men, *no sabe* nothing,' and though I never heard him swear before, 'Damned fools.' . . . I fear it is more than doubtful whether their visit will have been of any use to them."

About 15 months later the *Beagle* returned to Tierra del Fuego and anchored in the same familiar cove. All was silence and solitude.

FUEGIA BASKET AND YORK MINSTER were taken from their home by Captain Fitz-Roy, master of the *Beagle*, in 1829. Educated at his expense in England for two years, and returned to Tierra del Fuego, they reverted to savagery.

JEMMY BUTTON was the friendliest of the trio. But in old age he led a massacre of missionaries at Sunday service.

NATIVES

stirred modern interest in primitive man

Then a canoe, flying a little flag, approached down the channel. In the canoe was Jemmy—"Now a thin haggard savage, with long disordered hair, and naked, except a bit of blanket round his waist. . . . We had left him plump, fat, clean and well-dressed; I never saw so complete and grievous a change." Captain Fitz-Roy invited him aboard for dinner, and he told a sad tale of treachery. A few months earlier York Minster had decided to return to his tribal territory. He persuaded Jemmy and his mother to accompany him and his wife on the trip. One night, along the way, York Minster and Fuegia Basket deserted them, stealing every article of their property. Yet Jemmy's spirit was not dimmed. He contended that he was neither hungry nor cold and had no wish to return to England. "In the evening we found out the cause of this great change in Jemmy's feeling," Darwin wrote, "in the arrival of his young and nice-looking wife. Every soul on board was heartily sorry to shake hands with him for the last time. When Jemmy reached the shore, he lighted a signal fire, and the smoke curled up, bidding us a last and long farewell, as the ship stood on her course into the open sea."

Although Darwin ended his narrative here, there are postscripts to the chronicle of Fitz-Roy's Fuegian protégés. In subsequent years several missionary expeditions attempted to educate and civilize the Yaghan tribes. All failed, and a number of brave Englishmen lost their lives. The most tragic episode occurred on Nov. 6, 1859 when a group of missionaries and sailors were massacred while holding Sunday service in a half-finished church being erected on the site of Fitz-Roy's original encampment. The planner and chief instigator of the massacre was Jemmy Button.

Yet the missionaries persisted, and the Rev. Thomas Bridges, who devoted his life to the Yaghans, ultimately mastered their intricate language well enough to win their confidence. One day in 1874, some 40 years after the *Beagle*'s departure, Bridges encountered Fuegia Basket, now more than 50 years old, nearly toothless and remarried to a youth of 18. York Minster had been killed in retaliation for a murder. Bridges saw Fuegia Basket for the last time a decade later, on Feb. 19, 1883. She was extremely frail physically and dreadfully unhappy. Bridges tried to cheer her by holding forth the radiant hope of the Christian faith. But Fuegia Basket did not appear to understand. For although she had received two years of religious instruction, all traces had vanished from her mind.

As a result of the observations and writings of Bridges and his son Lucas after him, much is known about the primitive culture of the Onas and Yaghans, now virtually extinct. Their neighbors, the Alacalufes, who still maintain their marginal ways of life in the westward channels of the archipelago, have received far less attention. To remedy this a team of U.S. and Chilean scientists spent part of the winter of 1959 with them on Wellington Island.

Anthropologists, including Dr. Carleton S. Coon of the University of Pennsylvania and Dr. Alberto Medina of the University of Chile, studied their cultural habits and took tape recordings of their language. Physiologists, led by Dr. H. T. Hammel, also of Pennsylvania, studied the mechanism enabling Alacalufes to tolerate the cold of their harsh environment.

They noted that, unlike the Onas, who slept in open lean-tos, winter and summer, the Alacalufes have always lived in skin-covered huts with a fire burning on the earthen floor and dogs lying about for added warmth. During the day, however, they expose themselves to the chilling effects of snow, sleet, rain and raw sea winds. They wear no protection for feet, legs, hands or arms. And while the men go forth in their canoes to hunt, the women and children wade into the icy sea to gather shellfish at low tide.

The scientists obtained nine male Indian volunteers who agreed to spend an eight-hour period at night sleeping beneath a single blanket in an unheated tent with thermocouples taped to various parts of their bodies, to measure their body heat, and their heads in a ventilated plastic hood to record their oxygen consumption and metabolic rate. The temperature in the tent ranged from 32° to 41°F. Analysis of the data immediately disclosed one fact: both the body temperatures and metabolism of the Alacalufes stood considerably higher than those of white men in temperate climes. Darwin was thus proved correct in his conjecture that nature, by adaptation, had fitted the Fuegian Indians to the conditions of their cheerless land.

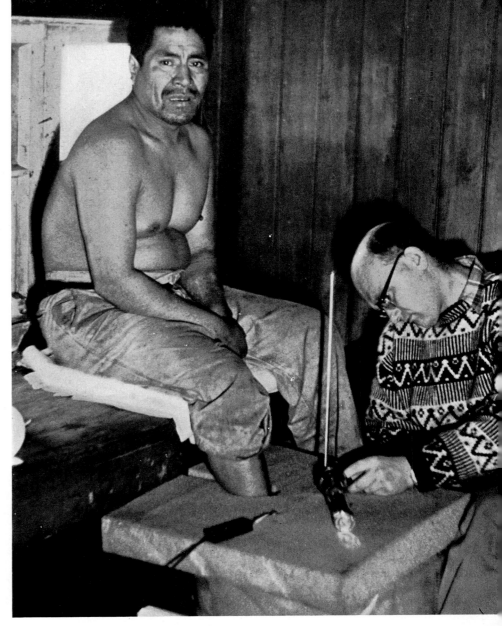

SKIN TEMPERATURE TEST, designed to explain the amazing resistance to cold of the Alacalufe Indians, is conducted by Dr. Christian Lange-Anderson of Oslo University. The subject's foot is held submerged in a tub of ice water.

INSPECTING THE ISLANDS, Drs. Carleton S. Coon *(left)*, anthropologist of the University of Pennsylvania, and Per S. Scholander, University of California physiologist, watch birds in the Strait of Magellan from their ship.

CREATURES
OF
THE
HEIGHTS

THE guanaco, which Darwin found ranging throughout South America, is one of the many creatures which have mastered the art of survival at high altitudes. This adaptability accounts for its continued existence while its camel-like forebear has become extinct. Here in the Andes, a sentinel stands guard as its companions graze. Domesticated guanacos were the main beasts of burden in America up to the time Cortés brought horses to Mexico in 1519. They remain important as bearers and for their wool.

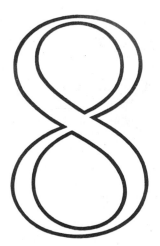

ALONG THIS PLEASANT CHILEAN SHORE, 1,500 MILES ABOVE CAPE HORN, DARWIN LEFT THE SEA AND HEADED INLAND TO SCALE THE MIGHTY ANDEAN RANGE

CREATURES OF THE HEIGHTS

In the Andes, Darwin found a new and harsh domain of life

LEAVING the tempestuous headlands of Tierra del Fuego, the *Beagle* cruised north up the Chilean coast, emerging from mists and raging winds into gentler latitudes where white sands and flowered shorelines beckoned. "How opposite," Darwin exclaimed, "are the sensations when viewing black mountains half-enveloped in clouds, and seeing another range through the light blue haze of a fine day!" Yet this interlude of clement weather and repose was but a prelude to a rigorous year (1834-35), during which he hacked his way through the dank Valdivian forest on the lower slopes of the Andes, traversed 500 miles of the lifeless Atacama coastal desert, and audaciously crossed and recrossed the cordillera—the great Andean range—via perilous passes more than 14,000 feet high.

Scaling the cordillera Darwin added important fragments to the great mosaic of his theory of evolution. By discovering fossil shells embedded in sedimentary rock nearly three miles above sea level he confirmed again his awareness that "nothing, not even the wind that blows, is so unstable as the level of the crust of the earth." Comparing marked differences between the flora and fauna of the eastern and western slopes of the Andes, he concluded that "these mountains have existed as a great barrier, since the present races of animals have appeared; and therefore . . . we ought not to expect any closer similarity between the organic beings on the opposite sides of the Andes, than on the opposite shores of the ocean." Finding at the high altitudes distinctive creatures, he marveled at the many ways in which they could adapt themselves to the cold and sparse air.

Though his mountaineering adventure was gruelling, Darwin nevertheless thrilled to the ecstasy of the explorer. "When we reached the crest and looked backwards," he wrote, "a glorious view was presented. . . . Neither plant nor bird, excepting a few condors wheeling around the higher pinnacles, distracted my attention from the inanimate mass. I felt glad that I was alone: it was like watching a thunderstorm or hearing in full orchestra a chorus of the Messiah."

140

LARGEST FLYING BIRD in the world, the South American condor has a wingspread of more than 12 feet. Nesting in high, rocky eyries the length of the Andean chain, condors are scavengers and birds of prey which may swoop down on lambs or even full-grown llamas in times of extreme hunger. Darwin, fascinated by their ability to soar, reported, "Except when rising from the ground, I do not recall ever having seen one of these birds flap its wings."

BEECH TREES stand in a solemn grove deep in the Chilean forest, 1,000 feet above the sea. Darwin, who had seen beeches up to 13 feet in circumference in Tierra del Fuego, thought these by comparison "poor, stunted trees."

'SUBLIME SILENCE OF THE FOREST'

Before ascending to the heights, Darwin made several trips into the rain-drenched forests on the lower slopes of the Andes. "No one can imagine so entangled a mass of dying and dead trunks," he wrote. "I am sure that often our feet never touched the ground. At other times we crept one after another on our hands and knees, under the rotten trunks." In the great Valdivian forest, which he explored in 1835, he discovered a long-nosed frog that now bears his name and a shy, cold-weather parakeet. After describing the discomforts of the terrain, he added, "Yet with the true spirit of contradiction, I cannot forget how sublime is the silence of the forest." However, all was not entirely sublime, for Darwin's visit coincided with a violent earthquake. "A bad earthquake," he observed, "destroys our oldest associations: the earth, the very emblem of solidity, has moved beneath our feet."

THE VALDIVIAN FOREST cloaks some 4,000 square miles of rain-soaked hills with a steaming growth of ferns, mossy trees and plants like the red copihue at left. The alerce trees at right are related to pines.

142

DARWIN'S FROG is unique in both its pointed nose and its domestic life. The male tends the eggs. When they hatch he takes the tadpoles in his mouth and harbors them until they are ready to hop out as complete froglets.

THE CHILEAN PARAKEET dwells on the high Andean slopes, nesting in stunted trees and hunting seeds on the ground. Though most parrots are tropical, this rather conservatively dressed bird has adapted to mists and cold.

AN ANDEAN WATERFALL, the Salto del Laja, cascades down from the snow-crowned cordillera on the river's path to the Pacific. Only in central Chile is precipitation favorable to civilized man. Northern Chile is a desert; southern Chile is one of the rainiest regions on earth.

THE CHILEAN SLOPES

In his travels through Chile, Darwin crossed many a foaming cataract and invaded many a mountain realm. He found central Chile, where birds and game abound, much to his liking. And in the cordillera one day he saw "some snowwhite columns," which proved to be the petrified remains of araucaria-like trees. "It required little . . . to interpret the marvelous story," he wrote. "I saw the spot where a cluster of fine trees once waved their branches on the shores of the Atlantic, when that ocean . . . came to the foot of the Andes. I saw that subsequently this dry land . . . had been let down into the depths of the ocean . . . but again the subterranean forces exerted themselves, and I now beheld the bed of that ocean, forming a chain of mountains more than 7,000 feet in height."

ASHY-HEADED GEESE dwell on both flanks of the Andes down to Tierra del Fuego, mostly in interior grasslands protected from the sea.

ARAUCARIA GROVE studs a hillside with unusual trees that grow in only two areas of South America—in the Andes and the east *(page 92)*.

A MALE GUANACO LEADS ITS DUTIFUL HAREM DOWN A TREELESS RIDGE IN THE HIGH ANDES. THIS WILD LLAMA FINDS ITSELF EQUALLY AT HOME IN THE CAPE

ROCKY BACKBONE OF A CONTINENT

The jagged Andes, marching the length of South America from the Antarctic to the Equator, are the rocky backbone of the continent. They are also a habitat and highway for hardy, high-altitude animal life. Hence some of the Andes' more restless denizens range the wind-whipped heights foraging on sparse, scrubby slopes or in chilly tarns from Patagonia to Peru. The most ubiquitous tenant of this unfriendly domain is the guanaco *(above)*, the camel of the New

THE HAIRY ARMADILLO, which dwells both on the pampas *(page 84)* and in the Andes, sleeps by day, feeds by night and if in doubt burrows.

BLACK-NECKED SWANS live only in southern climes. In summer they breed in streams and estuaries of Tierra del Fuego and Patagonia. In winter they migrate northward into the pampas and up the coast. Their young are born white and develop their high black collars only in maturity.

HORN REGION, WHERE IT SWIMS THROUGH ICY WATERS, AND IN THE UPLANDS OF PERU WHERE IT STEPS SURELY AMONG JAGGED CRAGS THREE MILES HIGH

World, cousin of the smaller vicuña and brother of the llama and alpaca, which man employs as beasts of burden and walking repositories of food and fur. Temperamental and wary, the male guanaco fights jealously in defense of his multiple mates with flailing foot and tooth. In minor emergencies he resorts to a more specialized weapon—a blinding, bad-smelling jet of saliva which he ejects with deadly accuracy. Darwin was beguiled by the guanaco, the beautiful

black-necked swans and many other residents of the Chilean uplands *(below)*. He was particularly taken with the hard-shelled hairy armadillo, a prodigious digger, and remarked that "it often tries to escape notice, by squatting close to the ground. . . . The instant one was perceived, it was necessary, in order to catch it, almost to tumble off one's horse; for in soft soil the animal burrowed so quickly that its hinder quarters would almost disappear before one could alight."

THE PAMPAS CAT, though not much larger than a house cat, is a coldly efficient predator. For all its soft coat and nonchalant air, it is very hardy, ranging from the coastal regions to the ramparts of the Andes. Nocturnal, it hunts on the ground but takes to the trees in emergency.

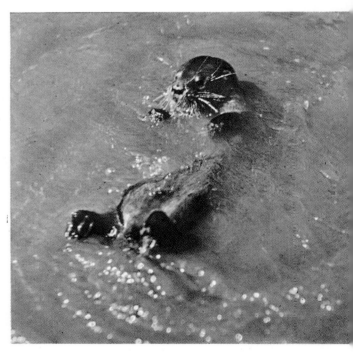

THE FRESH WATER OTTER is hunted by the Indians for both its meat and its pelt. This one is floating on its back, a state of utter otter repose.

147

ANDEAN FLAMINGOS

JAMES'S FLAMINGO

CHILEAN FLAMINGOS

ANDEAN CRESTED DUCK

VICUNAS   ANDEAN GULL

HORNED COOTS

ANDEAN AVOCET

R. T. PETERSON

BIRD LIFE
ON A SALT LAKE

Of all enclaves of life, there are few less hospitable than the salinas, or salt lakes, of South America, where Darwin recurrently encountered that shy and beautiful bird, the flamingo. The lake depicted in this midsummer scene—Laguna Verde—lies in a pass of the Andes, some 15,000 feet above the sea. Here in cold, green, briny water the three main species of South American flamingo convene each summer. Chilean flamingos, distinguished by gray legs with red joints,

ANDEAN CONDOR

JAMES'S FLAMINGO   ANDEAN CARACARA   CHILEAN FLAMINGOS

SHARP-WINGED TEAL   ANDEAN GULL

are shown at right, nesting on bare lava ledges, and at left, engaging in nuptial display—thrusting out their wings, stretching their necks, and wagging their heads from side to side—while others fly gracefully away. Nearby, Andean flamingos with yellow legs dredge for mollusks, crustaceans and algae. Also present, at right center and lower left, are two James's flamingos, smallest of the South American species, characterized by their dark red legs and eye patches. In

addition to flamingos, Laguna Verde provides a chilly sanctuary for other residents of the Andean heights, notably the horned coot, one of the world's rarest birds, seen at left center defending its nestlings against a marauding Andean gull. Another gull *(right foreground),* having raided a flamingo nest and opened an egg, screams imprecations at a big caracara, or carrion hawk *(pages 84-85),* that has just expropriated its loot. Overhead a condor soars on mighty wings.

149

JAMES'S FLAMINGOS, smallest, rarest, most delicate of the New World flamingo species, nest in summer on salt banks in Laguna Colorada, a shallow, saline lake with cold, red, algae-tinted water, 14,800 feet high in the Bolivian Andes. Until recently ornithologists believed James's flamingo to be extinct. Then in 1958 flocks numbering in the thousands were discovered in this remote breeding ground. Here, even in summer, the lake freezes at

night, and regularly every afternoon it is roiled by thunderstorms, rain, sleet, snow and violent winds. Despite the isolation of their habitat, James's flamingos suffer depredations from the Andean Indians, who raid their nests for eggs. In winter when the lake is locked in ice the birds migrate, but where they go no one yet knows. This remarkable photograph was taken by Artist Roger Tory Peterson from a blind hollowed in the mud of the shallow lake.

151

REDISCOVERY OF RARE

An elusive species, which some experts feared had been extinct for half a century,

"HOW surprising it is that any creatures should be able to exist in brine!" Darwin exclaimed after visiting a South American salina, or salt lake, and noting the varied forms of life, great and small, that thrived in its brackish waters. "Flamingoes in considerable quantities . . . breed here; throughout Patagonia, in Northern Chile, and at the Galápagos Islands, I met with these birds wherever there were lakes of brine.

"I saw them here wading about in search of food—probably for the worms which burrow in the mud; and these latter probably feed on infusoria [minute organisms found in stagnant water] or confervae [a kind of algae forming green scum on ponds]. . . . Well may we affirm, that every part of the world is habitable! Whether lakes of brine or . . . warm mineral springs, the depths of the ocean . . . even the surface of perpetual snow— all support organic beings."

The adaptability of the flamingos, one of the most remarkable attributes of these lovely and seemingly delicate birds, may account for many of the legends associated with them since earliest times. The three South American species, shown on the preceding pages, can endure temperatures of five degrees above zero in their high Andean habitats. Their Old World cousins can proliferate exuberantly in the blinding heat of salt lakes in the Rift Valley of equatorial Africa.

In view of the flamingo's prevalence and the beauty of its rosy-red plumage it is no surprise that the bird has enchanted the eye of man since the dawn of human imagination and art. The first known representation of a flamingo was painted on the wall of a Spanish cave by a Neolithic artist probably in the fifth millennium B.C. In ancient mythology the flamingo became associated with the legendary phoenix (from the Greek word *phoinix,* meaning "red"), the miraculous bird which every 500 years was immolated in fire by its own act, only to rise anew from its funerary ashes. In Egyptian hieroglyphics, the flamingo is the sign for the color red. The Phoenicians traded the dried skins of flamingos to the Celts of Britain and Europe in exchange for tin and amber, passing them off as the vestments of the fabled phoenix, thus able to endow their owners with a measure of infectious immortality.

In the First Century A.D. the pagan legend of the phoenix was absorbed into Christian mythology as a symbol of physical resurrection. In its earliest representations in religious imagery, it was depicted fancifully, as a bird that never was—an eagle clad in peacock plumes. But at some point early in the Christian era, the concept of the undying phoenix was attached to the flamingo—perhaps because in soaring flight the flamingo's outstretched wings and long trailing legs, silhouetted against the sky, etch the sign of the cross.

Of the six species of flamingos recognized by American ornithologists (Europeans contract them into four), one variety has recently manifested phoenixlike endowments by returning from supposed extinction. This is James's flamingo, known scientifically as *Phoenicoparrus jamesi*—the dainty, elusive bird shown on pages 148-151. The

PROBING WITH A POLE, Roger Tory Peterson makes his way across the oozing mud flats of Laguna Colorada, the blood-red Andean lake where the rare, rosy-red James's flamingo dwells. He led an ornithological expedition there in 1957-58.

first specimen of *jamesi* was obtained in Chile and sent to the British Museum more than a century ago. But its variance from the larger Andean flamingo was not recognized for 36 years, when an Anglo-Chilean expedition organized by H. Berkeley James, a British financier, procured a number of specimens. This time their characteristics were more carefully studied; the birds were classified as a separate species and named after James, the sponsor of their discovery.

A few more observations were reported by South American naturalists, a few skins collected for museums. But in the first decade of the present century James's flamingo dropped out of sight, and thereafter the suspicion arose that it might be extinct. In 1956, in a scholarly study of flamingo populations around the world, the ornithologist Robert Porter Allen of the National Audubon Society set down some provocative ideas: "The most astonishing fact concerning *Phoenicoparrus jamesi,*" he wrote, "is that its habits and nidification [nest building] have never been described. No actual breeding sites, past or present, are known. . . . Although the fact *jamesi* has not been observed for many years may be a result of its isolated range . . . we cannot but wonder if James's flamingo still survives. . . . This would seem to be one of the outstanding mysteries of the avian world."

These words inspired three expeditions which resulted in the discovery of *jamesi* nesting grounds in a brackish, incredibly inaccessible and inclement lake in the Bolivian Andes and, after many vicissitudes, in the securing of the first living specimens.

The first expedition was organized by several Chilean ornithologists, A. W. Johnson, F. Behn, and W. R. Millie. Setting forth in January 1957, they planned to visit every possible flamingo habitat in the mountains of northern Chile. In the course of their 3,125-mile journey they made a side trip across the nearby border of Bolivia. There in a mountain fastness 14,800 feet high, ringed by volcanic mountains, they looked for the first time on the red expanse of Laguna Colorada *(pages 150-151).* Dappling its shallow waters like rose petals in a bowl of claret, Chilean and Andean flamingos were feeding in great abundance. And then, Johnson reported, "we noticed that in a small group of about 30 flamingos, one bird seemed to be somewhat smaller and whiter on the back than the others." It was a *jamesi,* with characteristic brick-colored legs and a wide yellow band on the bill. Later the same year Luis Peña, a Chilean entomologist, visited Laguna Colorada and confirmed the presence of *jamesi.*

Late in 1957 Peña and the American ornithologist Roger Tory Peterson embarked on an expedition to observe and photograph *jamesi* flamingos both on Laguna Colorada and on Laguna Verde, another salina to the south *(pages 148-149).*

The third and most recent expedition, sponsored by the New York Zoological Society and led by Peña and William G. Conway, Curator of Birds at the Bronx Zoo, set forth in January 1960, and after many arduous adventures in one of the wildest and most desolate

FLAMINGO

has now been found in the high Andes

regions on earth managed to capture 19 *jamesi* flamingos alive, of which 18 survived the trip to New York and adjustment to captivity.

All three expeditions confronted great hardship, for Laguna Colorada and Laguna Verde are in the puna region of the Andes, nearly three miles high. "The puna," Conway wrote on his return, "is a desolate, treeless, pastoral zone of the high central Andes . . . typified by widely scattered clumps of vegetation, either grasses or low bushes. . . . The morning following our arrival several of the crew found themselves victims of 'puna sickness' with the splitting headaches and nausea induced by that altitude."

Just 125 years earlier Darwin had reported some slight discomfort from this illness of the Andean heights. "The short breathing from the rarefied atmosphere is called by the Chilenos 'puna,'" he wrote in *The Voyage of the Beagle.* "The only sensation I experienced was a slight tightness across the head and chest, like that felt on leaving a warm room and running quickly in frosty weather." He added, however, that on discovering some fossil shells on the highest ridge, "I entirely forgot the puna in my delight. Certainly the exertion of walking was extremely great, and the respiration became deep and laborious. . . . The inhabitants all recommend onions for the puna; as this vegetable has sometimes been given in Europe for pectoral complaints, it may possibly be of real service—for my part I found nothing so good as the fossil shells."

IT was not only the altitude which beset the ornithologists at Laguna Colorada, but an unspeakable climate. Each day between noon and 1 p.m. clouds gathered, lightning played around the mountain-tops, and rain descended, turning to hail, sleet or snow as the afternoon progressed. Gale-like winds swept across the lake, making work in the afternoon virtually impossible. Toward evening the winds subsided and the skies cleared. But the temperature fell abruptly from its noonday high of about 70°, descending during the night to barely a few degrees above zero.

After failing to capture flamingos in accessible areas, Conway and Peña decided to try their luck on the birds which nested in the shelter of the narrow salt islands or on mud bars far out from shore. The intervening water was in many places too shallow for rowing, yet a boat was necessary for the transportation of 300 pounds of equipment. The ornithologists, therefore, were compelled to wade out to the roosts, towing the boat behind them.

"Lucho [Peña] had warned us," reported Conway, "that it was impossible to wear hip boots in the mud, for the suction would anchor us firmly, so [we] merely donned heavy socks and waded into the water, despite a thin glaze of ice which the sun had not yet fully dispelled. . . . The frigid water and occasional sharp salt crystals soon made our feet ache terribly so that we welcomed the numbness eventually induced by the cold. Gradually the water became shallower and . . . [the mud] became deeper and stickier making the withdrawal of each foot a major effort. . . . The bottom . . . seemed to consist of successive layers of plasticine-like mud and crystallized salts. As our feet slid through mud to rest on what felt like a solid bottom, the shifting of our weight to take another step caused us to crash down through painfully abrasive layers of salt. The bottom was riddled with apparently bottomless holes where subterranean geysers pour into the lake. . . . Progress became a series of short struggles punctuated with rest periods while we stood covered from head to foot with mud and gasped at each other. . . . The colony itself rested upon the most incredibly impassable muck of all."

Despite these difficulties, equipment failures, and nights wracked by splitting headaches, muscular cramps, nosebleeds and violent chills, the expedition managed in the end to lay snares and capture their timid quarry. Since their arrival at the Bronx Zoo, the *jamesi* flamingos have demonstrated the amazing ability of their family to adapt to a new climate and a new way of life. They have shared the flamingo pond with the other five known species—two from the Old World, one from the West Indies, and the Andean and Chilean varieties—with equanimity, and have even shown some slight interest in nest building. Instead of their accustomed diet of microscopic lake organisms they have accepted a mixture of baby food, poultry feed and assorted vitamins plus carrot oil to keep their plumage red. By the summer of 1960, Conway was confident that his precious *jamesi* would live and thrive.

STRUTTING PRIZES, leggy James's flamingos, least-known of the world's six species, sun on a rocky island in New York's Bronx Zoo. They are among the 18 survivors of 19 airlifted by William Conway from the Andes in 1960.

A
FORM
WITHOUT
FUNCTION

DAWN dispels the morning mists on South Island, New Zealand, 2,000 years ago as a flightless giant moa cranes down from its 12-foot height in search of gizzard stones. It was only in safe, remote areas like this that birds were able to shed the protection of their wings. This change was, however, a fatal evolutionary error. Not long after the arrival of man in New Zealand the awesome giant moa had disappeared forever—a fate paralleling that of most of the strange flightless birds of earth.

FORM WITHOUT FUNCTION

Flightless birds gave up their wings for life upon the ground

THERE is no greater anomaly in nature," Darwin wrote, "than a bird that cannot fly." If these flightless birds should vanish from the earth, he wondered, who could envisage such oddities as the penguin, which employs its wings as fins for swimming, or the ostrich, which spreads its wings as sails while running, or the kiwi *(below)*, whose vestigial wings serve no purpose whatsoever?

In point of fact *all* birds are simply glorified reptiles, upholstered with feathers instead of scales. Their ancestors took to the air in Jurassic times, midway in the age of dinosaurs, 135 million years ago. As millenniums passed they developed warm blood and high body temperatures to sustain the energy demands of flight; they acquired powerful chest muscles, superb eyesight and enlarged brain centers governing balance and coordination. Instead of abandoning their eggs, like reptiles, to the vagaries of weather and circumstance, they learned the arts of building nests and caring for their young. Why then did some birds, engineered for aerial existence, mysteriously

revert to life upon the ground? Darwin supplied an explanation that is accepted by most ornithologists today. Certain birds which fed and nested on the ground found no use for their wings except to flee from danger. Until man arrived, no dangerous carnivores despoiled the peaceful fastnesses of Australia, Madagascar or New Zealand. And so, in the absence of predators, certain heavy birds—like the emu, moa and cassowary—abandoned flight. As their wings shriveled, their legs grew longer and stronger. Similar adaptations altered the form of the African ostrich and the South American rhea. For, though dwelling with predators, both birds graze in open country where ambush is impossible; both have developed spectacular vision and running speed. Of these clear manifestations of his law of natural selection, Darwin wrote: "Many animals possess structures which can best be explained by the effects of disuse. . . . The structure of each of these birds is good for it, under the conditions of life to which it is exposed, for each has to live by a struggle."

THE KIWI OF NEW ZEALAND

Clad in feathers that resemble hair, preceded by a six-inch beak with sensitive nostrils at the tip, the tailless and nearly wingless kiwi waddles through the woods by night, probing for earthworms. The only bird in the world that guides its foraging by smell, the kiwi has extremely poor vision. Its olfactory gift and nocturnalism have enabled it to survive, virtually unchanged, for thousands of years in the New Zealand forests.

THE CASSOWARY OF INDONESIA

With slashing strokes of its three-pronged claws, a male cassowary rakes a rival in a territorial fight in its Aru Island habitat west of New Guinea. Fiercest of all flightless birds, the violet-necked cassowary attacks by leaping feet first and striking with saberlike talons that can eviscerate a large animal or man. Its head is protected by a bony helmet worn like a crown. In combat its feathers bristle, its wattles swell and glow with violent color.

THE OSTRICH OF NORTH AFRICA

His neck blushing pink with the ardors of wooing, a male ostrich drops to the ground in abject
supplication. Rocking back and forth, exhibiting
his tail feathers, displaying one wing, then the
other, he then recurrently sounds the courtship
call of his species—two short "booms," followed
by a long, protracted "boo-oo-oo-oom." After

mating, the pair will take turns incubating the
three-pound eggs—a deviation in behavior, for
within the order of flightless birds the male usually attends to this chore alone. Largest of all living birds, the African ostrich may attain a height
of eight feet. It traverses its desert terrain with 15-
foot strides, speeding as fast as 40 miles an hour.

COMMON EMUS

A pair of emus watch alertly over their brood of
striped fledglings. Second in size to the ostrich,
the emu stands five to six feet tall. Similar to the
cassowary in form and habits, it lacks its savage cousin's bony helmet and lethal talons. The
female is the aggressor in courtship, but lets the
male take on domestic duties once the eggs are

OF AUSTRALIA

laid. He incubates them for eight weeks, longer
than most other birds. He leaves the nest only
for a little food or water. If disturbed, he feigns
injury, attempting to draw off the intruder by
staggering and stumbling like a drunken man.
When the chicks are hatched the female returns
from her vacation and rejoins the family group.

DARWIN'S RHEA

A male of a small species, discovered by Darwin and found from Bolivia south through Argentina, tends his nest. The half dozen members of his harem lay their eggs together. He hatches them and rears the young. A fiery father, he will attack both horse and rider if they disturb him.

CRESTED TINAMOU

A tasty game bird hunted for sport in western Argentina and Patagonia, the tinamou has some ability to fly, though weak wing muscles limit its aerial range to only a half a mile. While the male is incubating and educating the young, his larger mate may take off with another male.

AMERICAN RHEA

A covey of "noble rheas," as Darwin called them, hiss in fear as one stands entangled in the bolas of South American gauchos. Largest birds of the New World, rheas stand five feet high. In the 19th Century, when feathers were in demand, a half million rheas were killed yearly.

THAT 'TERRIBLE BIRD'

New facts cast light on the mysterious disappearance of a flightless giant which

ON the morning before Christmas, 1835, Darwin went for a walk in one of the famed evergreen forests of New Zealand. He noted the height and grandeur of the kauri pines and their density of growth, remarking, "Some of the New Zealand forests must be impenetrable to an extraordinary degree. [I was informed] that one forest only 34 miles in width, and separating two inhabited districts, had only lately, for the first time, been crossed." He commented briefly on the poverty of bird life and the absence of indigenous animals. Then he made a most astonishing suggestion: "The several species of that gigantic genus of birds, the Dinornis, seem here to have replaced mammiferous quadrupeds in the same manner as the reptiles still do at the Galápagos archipelago."

The remarkable fact about Darwin's statement was that at the time of his visit virtually nobody in the civilized world had ever heard of the dinornis (from the Greek *deinos,* "terrible," plus *ornis,* "bird"). Not until three years later, a year before publication of *The Voyage of the Beagle,* did the scientists of Europe become interested in the enormous giraffelike bird, 10 to 12 feet tall, which had formerly ranged the plains of New Zealand in numbers comparable to the antelope herds of the African veldt. But in the years that followed, New Zealand's big dinornis—popularly known as the moa—became famous all over the earth. The controversies that raged about its towering head derived from the fact that it had apparently become extinct, not in the far-off Pleistocene age, but in relatively recent times. What circumstances led to the extinction of the moa? Even more piquant was the question: Is the moa really extinct? Torrents of rumors, augmented by the legends and folklore of the Maoris, New Zealand's aborigines, encouraged the notion that a few survivors of the ancient line still lurked in the dark forests that cloak the desolate fiordlands of South Island.

Darwin's stopover in New Zealand lasted only between December 21 and December 30. Yet in these nine days he somehow learned—he never told how—of the giant, vanished moa. Sailors and sealers had picked up native tales of "dreadful birds" on South Island, and in 1823 a few huge bones, with flesh still adhering to them, were uncovered at the mouth of a river. But the bones were subsequently lost and the stories discounted. Darwin, however, apparently gave them credence, and with his uncanny insight deduced that in an island habitat free from predatory mammals flightless grazing birds might flourish and fill the ecological niche occupied elsewhere by hoofed animals like zebras, giraffes and buffalo.

Today zoologists know that the isolated islands of New Zealand have provided sanctuary for the evolution of many creatures without

counterpart anywhere else in the world. Here birds are the dominant group. Until man arrived with his dog the birds of New Zealand had enjoyed complete seclusion, unmolested by mammalian predators of any kind. So secure was their refuge that many lost the urge to fly. New Zealand, more than any other place on earth, became the land of flightless birds.

Of these the reigning giant was *Dinornis maximus,* largest of all moas, which stood taller than any animal of modern times, except the giraffe and African elephant. Despite their Greek name, the great moas probably were not very "terrible." They were herbivores, ranging the grasslands, and incessantly browsing and cropping the shrubs and herbage with massive, rounded beaks. From the size and the weight of their bones it has been estimated that an adult moa required as much grass each day to sustain his energies as a full-grown ox.

The first published reference in Europe to a moa appeared in 1838 in a travel book on New Zealand written by an amateur naturalist named J. S. Polack. In the course of six years' wandering about the islands, he had heard of a giant ostrichlike bird that had been exterminated on North Island but which the Maoris believed still survived in remote regions of South Island. More important, Polack had acquired possession of several moa bones, and one of these was shipped to the great English anatomist, Sir Richard Owen. Owen refused to believe that any bird could have evolved such a massive bone and identified it first as the thighbone of an ox, then of a horse. But on closer examination he concluded that "there existed and perhaps still exists in New Zealand a species of running bird, which must have been taller and bulkier than any known species of ostrich."

At almost this same time several other amateur naturalists became interested in moas. They interviewed the Maoris, collected bones, and dispatched several baskets of remains to England. In 1843

DWARFED BY MOA BONES, three New Zealand scientists hold upright the massive leg bones and pelvis of a fossilized giant moa found in a swamp in 1949. This extinct 700-pound bird grew 12 feet tall on a diet of grass, twigs and herbs.

Owen noted that there were several species of varying sizes and weights. Today some ornithologists recognize as many as 37 species.

During the ensuing century, thousands of moa bones were disinterred, along with moa feathers and dozens of moa eggs 10 to 12 inches in length. But the burning question remained: Does the moa still exist? Eager scientists from all parts of the world came to New Zealand and questioned the Maoris. They imaginatively responded with the sort of information their questioners wished to hear: tales of moa hunts and moa feasts, moa footprints, moa mating calls and moa habits, including the story that moas hid their heads in the sand—which is not true of the moa, the ostrich or any other bird. Even Darwin's old associate, Captain Fitz-Roy of the *Beagle,* became

–THE MOA

inhabited New Zealand 700 years ago

involved in the great moa hunt. While serving as governor of New Zealand in 1844, Fitz-Roy questioned a number of ancient Maori tribesmen. They informed him that one way to kill a giant moa was to toss it a red-hot stone which it would voraciously swallow and thus grill itself from within. Thereafter Fitz-Roy was an ardent advocate of the living moa school.

The mystery of the moa remains bemisted today by a mass of ambiguous evidence. On the one hand the Maoris were certainly familiar with moa remains. They wore moa feathers in their headdresses. Their traditions include tales of a "down-covered demon in the shape of a bird." But cultural anthropologists have failed to discover any credible record of actual encounters with *living* giant moas. It would seem, therefore, that the great birds were already extinct when the Maoris arrived. Relative latecomers by comparison with other aborigines, the Maoris immigrated to New Zealand from eastern Polynesia around 1350 A.D., barely three centuries before discovery of the islands by civilized man. The question thus arises: If the Maoris did not exterminate the moas, who did?

One clue has been supplied by archaeological studies conducted during the last decade on South Island, revealing that the Maoris had not pre-empted an empty land, as once supposed, but had evicted and exiled or expunged a still earlier population. Little is known of these shadowy first settlers, who came to New Zealand centuries before the advent of the Maoris. They are known today simply as "the moa hunters," for excavation of their graves and camp sites provides incontrovertible evidence that they hunted, slew and feasted on the moas. They caught fish with hooks fashioned from moa bones. They shaped these hooks with moa-bone chisels and knives. They wore moa-bone necklaces. And they buried their dead with moa bones and moa eggs. Whether these hunters alone caused extinction of the moa is a question anthropologists cannot answer with assurance. Having no knowledge of agriculture, and hence being completely dependent on hunting and fishing for survival, they must have taken a huge toll of the moa population.

Moa remains have been found all over New Zealand. The oldest bones thus far uncovered lay 75 feet down in a stratum no less than two million years old. Other bones were exhumed from a dried-up swamp in which a flock of the great birds had somehow become mired. The technique of radiocarbon dating was applied to the contents of one bird's stomach. The analysis showed that this particular dinornis downed its last meal on earth sometime around 1290 A.D., toward the end of the pre-Maori culture. Since the great moas had prospered and proliferated in their island solitudes for such an enormous span, it is significant that their reign terminated not long after the arrival of other smaller but relentlessly carnivorous bipeds.

THROUGHOUT most of the world, wherever birds allowed their wings to atrophy from disuse, the mutation succeeded only in the absence of man. The giant ostrichlike aepyornis or roc of Madagascar is as dead as the famous dodo of Mauritius. It was early in the 16th Century that Portuguese sailors first landed in the Mascarene Islands and there found huge flocks of a fat flightless bird which became known as the dodo—either because of its cry or from the Portuguese *doido,* meaning idiot. But with the colonization of Mauritius, the depredations of man—plus those of his dogs, his pigs and stowaway rats from ships—decimated the dodo population. A single century after their discovery, no Mauritius dodo remained alive in the world.

In his studies of flightlessness, Darwin concluded that the use of wings would be a disadvantage in the case of birds and insects living on oceanic islands where sudden storms might blow them out to sea. Natural selection would thus favor species that remained mostly on the ground. It is indeed on islands that flightless birds have most frequently evolved. In February of 1960 an important discovery was made on the island of Bermuda, when excavations revealed a cave that had apparently been sealed since prehistoric times. Inside, a rich store of fossil birds of many species lay embedded in the walls. The specimens which most intrigued ornithologists were 40 to 50 flightless rails of a hitherto unknown genus. Since rails tend to live in freshwater marshes, and since Bermuda has none, their presence on the island posed many questions of the changing relationships between land and sea—as well as adding one more to the growing list of strange birds which once walked the earth.

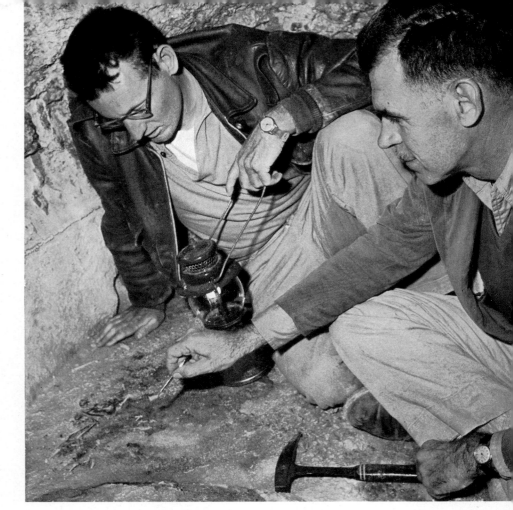

EXCAVATING A FOSSIL in Bermuda, Dr. Pierce Brodkorb *(right)* indicates the atrophied wing structure of a flightless rail to David Wingate, the Bermuda naturalist who identified it in 1960 as a member of a new genus.

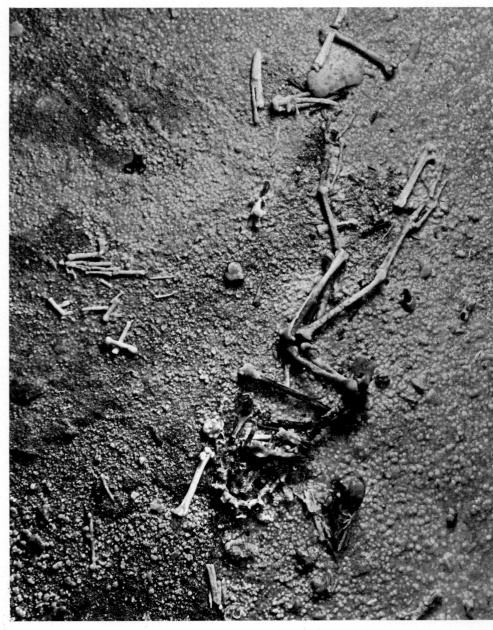

EMBEDDED IN A CAVE, the intact bones of the extinct rail rest in the stone floor where the bird died more than 100,000 years ago. It was probably trapped while fleeing a storm which might otherwise have swept it out to sea.

163

EARTH'S MOST PRIMITIVE MAMMALS

HALFWAY up a eucalyptus tree with a baby clinging to her back, this little koala also stands halfway up the ladder of evolution. Koalas are marsupials, an order of primitive mammals which nurse their young in an abdominal pouch. Though elsewhere marsupials have succumbed to the competition of higher placental mammals, whose young develop more fully in the womb, they have thrived in isolated Australia in many forms. Koalas, once ruthlessly killed for their pelts, are now protected by law.

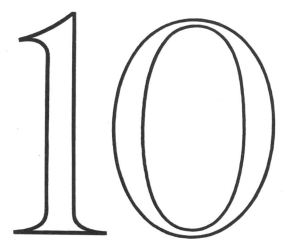

10

A KOALA, the engaging "teddy bear" of Australian forests, leaps between gum trees with a baby clinging to its breast. Despite its bearlike appearance the koala is actually a marsupial, related to the possum. At birth the infant, barely an inch in length, wriggles at once into its mother's pouch, where it remains for about six months. Adult koalas, full grown at four years, weigh up to 30 pounds. They dine on the leaves of gum trees, mainly the eucalyptus.

A GOLDEN POSSUM surveys the morning sky before retiring to sleep for the day. A nocturnal prowler, it dwells mostly in the trees, using its long bushy tail to maintain balance, feeding on foliage, flowers and honey. Prolific and highly adaptable, the familiar possum thrives anywhere.

PRIMITIVE MAMMALS

Marsupials of Australia resist evolution

In the slow, unending stream of evolution certain strains are carried into backwaters where they lie becalmed, age after age, unmoved by the main currents of their time. One such quiet eddy is Australia, where the most primitive mammals on earth survive, little changed in form and habit from their progenitors 75 million years ago.

These strange "living fossils" crept into the world in the twilight of the dinosaurs. The monotremes, including the duck-billed platypus and spiny anteater *(pages 174-175)*, are transitional creatures with both reptilian and mammalian characteristics. Slightly higher in the evolutionary scale are the marsupials—koalas, possums, kangaroos—all of which carry their young in pouches. Spreading over the earth in the earliest dawn of the Age of Mammals, they may have reached Australia via some land bridge from Asia that sank about 60 million B.C. On other

continents the higher placental mammals came into ascendancy and drove the marsupials into extinction (save for the persistent American opossum). But on the huge island of Australia, which produced virtually no placental mammals until they were imported by man a few centuries ago, the marsupials flourished, some becoming carnivores, others vegetarians.

Although little scientific study had been attempted in Australia previous to Darwin's arrival in 1836, he was aware of a few fossil finds which revealed striking resemblances between extinct and modern marsupials. He had already been impressed by the similarities in living and dead creatures of South America. These twin observations convinced Darwin that "the wonderful law of the long endurance of allied forms on the same continent . . . is intelligible, for the existing and the extinct will be closely allied by descent."

RING-TAILED ROCK WALLABY springs gracefully through the air in a 12-foot leap from crag to crag. Wallabies, junior members of the kangaroo family, are dainty, attractive creatures often as small as rabbits. Residents of the southern plains regions of Australia, they wander widely like their larger cousins. They roam abroad in the morning and evening, feeding on foliage, bark, roots and grasses, and often go without water for long periods of time.

AIR-BORNE MARSUPIALS

SUGAR GLIDER nibbles upon grasshopper in a she-oak tree *(above)*, then takes off in flight *(right)*. A member of the possum family, it gets its name from its taste for honey and the parachute-like membranes between its limbs which enable it to glide 100-150 feet from the treetops.

During the hottest part of the day they seek shelter in the shade of rock promontories or caves. Astonishing leapers, they are equipped with padded, granulated soles on their hind feet which prevent them from slipping on the rocks. Their main enemies are wild dogs, imported by the prehistoric ancestors of the aborigines, and foxes. If hotly pursued, rock wallabies sometimes take to the trees, clinging to the branches by their prehensile middle toes.

The order of marsupials boasts some of the most agile acrobats of the nonsimian world. But owing to their hazardous mode of gestation, they have a slimmer chance of survival than higher mammals whose young remain longer in the womb. Newborn marsupials blindly grope their way into their mother's pouch. Those that miss are never retrieved; those that make it often find there are not teats for all.

They are also handicapped by inferior intelligence. Only a few evolutionary rungs above reptiles, they are no match for quick-witted, aggressive placental mammals. Yet marsupials have expanded into every niche of the land. Grazing herbivores like kangaroos and wallabies have appropriated the open plains and grasslands populated in other lands by hoofed mammals. And in the absence of squirrels the gentle sugar glider sails through the colonnades of the trees.

THE GREAT KANGAROO: MAIN MARSUPIAL

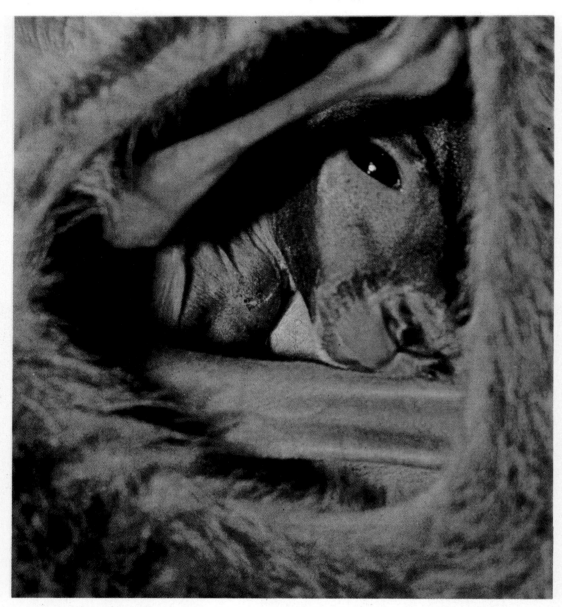

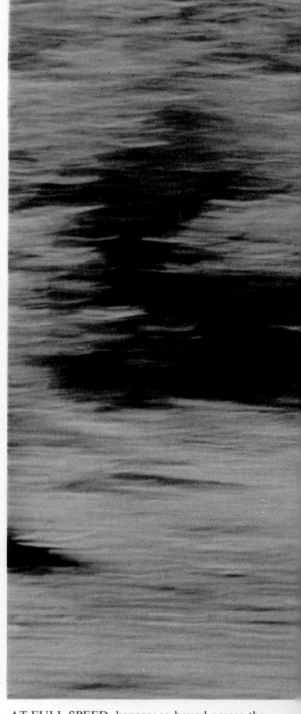

IN MOTHER'S POUCH, an infant kangaroo lazily regards the world with bland and liquid eye. Born prematurely by mammalian standards, helpless infant kangaroos spend their first six months in snug and sedentary ease. This baby is four months old—not yet ready to venture forth.

AT FULL SPEED, kangaroos bound across the open plain at 30 mph. Among all different models of the species the largest—and largest of all

HEADING FOR HOME, a young kangaroo insinuates itself into its mother's marsupium, or pouch. Though apparently a tight fit, the pouch is elastic and affords a two-way stretch as the youngster—known as a joey—noses in.

TAKING IT EASY, the baby kangaroo lolls upside down as its mother washes her face with forepaws. When in danger, mother kangaroos often eject their young, lead their enemies a merry chase, and then return to baby.

marsupials—is the Great Kangaroo, shown here disdaining gravitation with leaps of 15-20 feet. Its acceleration is generated by muscular hind legs, augmented sometimes by the propulsion of its powerful tail. Kangaroos continue growing as long as they live. An elderly male, or boomer, may stand seven feet high and weigh 200 pounds. As they age, they become more and more short-tempered—and are dangerous to meddle with.

BREAKFAST IN BED is relished by the baby kangaroo when its mother pauses to graze. The weaning process begins this way. As the joey develops toward independence it spends more and more time outside the pouch.

NOONDAY SNOOZE in a sun-bathed grassy glade relaxes mother and child. Kangaroos are nomadic in their habits: they have no homes and range over the countryside as the spirit moves them and nature beckons.

THE WOMBAT, like many Australian marsupials, reveals diverse traits. Its appearance suggests a small beaver, but its habits are those of a badger. It is a formidable burrower, whose idea of a dream home is a tunnel 100

THE VARIETY OF

To the first white settlers, the most puzzling aspect of the Australian animals was their near resemblance to cats, bears, rodents and other familiar mammalian forms. Though the Australian marsupials differed from the fauna of Europe in carrying their young in a pouch, they exhibited an equally wide range of behavior; some dwelt in trees, others in desert burrows; some nibbled leaves by day, others hunted prey by night. Today naturalists explain these parallel habits as examples of adaptive "radiation." The vast island of Australia

THE TASMANIAN DEVIL owes its name to its dark coloration, bad temper and occasional appetite for domestic fowl. Actually this marsupial is no more wicked than any carnivore, and invades the chicken coop of man

THE TREE KANGAROO is the only arboreal member of its family. About three feet tall, it has limbs more evenly proportioned than those of its terrestrial cousins. Using its tail as a rudder it executes 70-foot leaps to the ground.

feet long leading down to a spacious, subterranean bedchamber. It lives on grass, roots and the inner bark of trees, a rugged diet for which it is endowed with teeth that grow continuously, as fast as they are worn away.

MARSUPIAL LIFE

represented a zoological vacuum in which the marsupials radiated, or diversified, into every domain of existence without competition from more efficient species. Families like the possums branched out into many forms, ranging from the big brush-tail *(right)* to the tiny pygmy possum *(page 177)*. Even the kangaroos diverged. Originally arboreal, their ancestors climbed down to the ground at some point in prehistory. Most remained there, but one strain, the tree kangaroo *(left)*, reverted to life in the murmurous boughs.

only when its normal prey—rats, mice, frogs—runs seasonally low. Once prolific in Australia, it now survives only in nearby Tasmania. It is catlike in cleanliness, lives in a burrow and can swim long distances under water.

THE BRUSH-TAIL POSSUM remains in the treetops at night, where it browses on leaves, fruit and nuts. When confronted by its archenemy, the fierce tree goanna lizard, it freezes in fear and sits waiting to be devoured.

DUCK-BILLED PLATYPUS snuffles along a pebbly bottom, dredging for worms, crayfish, grubs and other aquatic delicacies with its flat, capacious bill. Though it fills the same function as a duck's bill, a duckbill's bill is not hard, but soft and leathery and charged with sensitive nerves. The young use their bills in suckling to press on their mother's abdomen, for the female platypus has no nipples, only tiny, sieve-like pores. Lying on her back, she

OLDEST MAMMALS
IN THE WORLD

Since the aim of science is to find order in the apparent chaos of the natural world, it came as a shock to zoologists 160 years ago to confront a small furry animal with a beaver-like tail and a duck-like bill, which paradoxically laid eggs but suckled its young. The duck-billed platypus and its kin, the echidna or spiny anteater, are true living fossils, the only two surviving members of the order of monotremes which arrived on earth perhaps 150 million years ago when certain

contracts her abdominal muscles to form a groove or runnel, out of which the young scoop up the thick, cheesy milk. Expert swimmers and divers, duckbills close their eyes underwater, finding food by smell and touch.

lines of reptiles began to evolve into mammals. They have persisted, like the marsupials, thanks to the absence of competition from higher mammals in the isolation of Australia. Though both animals lay eggs, their methods of incubation differ. The female platypus curls up in a ball and clutches her eggs to her breast for a period of nine or ten days. The echidna puts her eggs in her pouch. When they hatch she carries her babies until their spines begin to prickle—then out they go.

A SPINY ANTEATER evades a predator by burrowing into the earth in seconds (top to bottom), leaving its quills exposed for defense. Coiled in its thin beak is a foot-long, sticky tongue to which ants and other insects adhere.

JERBOAS, or jumping mice, living facsimiles of the first tiny pouch-bearing mammals from which all subsequent marsupial lines evolved, dart about in the vegetable debris of the Australian scrublands in quest of insect fare.

Incredibly swift in their movements, they locate their prey by sonar—the sound of whirring wings detected by their acute auditory sense. Though only two inches tall, they can leap six feet in the air to catch a bug on the wing.

THE RABBIT BANDICOOT, a nocturnal, insectivorous marsupial, is distinguished by its long, rabbity ears and its burrowing speed. With its long-clawed forefeet it can dig even faster than a human pursuer with a spade.

THE MARSUPIAL CAT somewhat resembles the house cat of civilization. Though fearless and intelligent, it shares the genetic inefficiency of all marsupials. The female bears up to 24 young, but has only six teats in her pouch.

A PYGMY POSSUM fixes a fervent eye upon a monarch butterfly, as big as itself, upon which it proposes to make a light repast. Smallest of the possum family, the pygmy weighs barely an ounce. Its body, two and one half inches long, is augmented by a two-inch prehensile tail, which it employs with simian skill in its nocturnal travels among the trees. In addition to insects this tiny marsupial also relishes the nectar and pollen of blossoms.

CLUES TO MARSUPIAL

In the arid wastes of central Australia wind-bared fossil bones reveal a primeval

THE curious animal populations of the island continent of Australia were virtually unknown a mere half century before Darwin's arrival in 1836, and their role in evolution came to light but gradually during his lifetime. It is indeed only in the last few years that important fossil finds began to illuminate the place of marsupials and monotremes in the development of animal life from reptiles to the mammals that now dominate the earth.

The earliest descriptions of marsupials were set down by Arab merchants in the South Pacific. In the 11th Century one Ali Abul Hassan Masudi, while trading among the Indonesian islands, noted an odd little animal and recorded in surprise that "it lives for seven months in its mother's belly and always goes back there to feed." What he had seen was undoubtedly the ubiquitous opossum. During subsequent centuries other reports of opossums trickled back to Europe via the journals of various wanderers in both hemispheres. By the middle of the 18th Century the opossum was well enough known to be included by the great Swedish taxonomist, Linnaeus, in his exhaustive catalogue of flora and fauna. The fact that it carried its young in a brood pouch he regarded as an idiosyncrasy of this one animal.

In 1640 a representative of the Dutch East India Company returned from Australia to say he had seen "a creature as large as a man with the head of a deer and a long tail, which stands on its hind legs like a bird, but can hop like a frog." His observations were ascribed to indulgence in spirituous liquors. Incredulity greeted still another Dutch globetrotter, the painter Corneille de Bruyn, in 1717 when he reported a similar apparition seen in New Guinea, adding, "The extraordinary fact is that it has a sacklike opening on the belly into which the young ones enter, even when they are quite large. Their head and neck may often be seen peeping out."

It was not until the return of Captain James Cook from the first of his three voyages of scientific exploration that remote Australia began to interest the western world and that European zoologists began to realize that the implausible beasts reported there were not hallucinations. On June 24, 1770 Captain Cook himself spied his first kangaroo and described it in his journal: "It was of a light Mouse colour and the full size of a grey hound and shaped in every respect like one, with a long tail which it carried like a grey hound . . . but for its walking or running in which it jumped like a hare or a deer." Cook and his associates somehow failed to observe the belly pouch, possibly because his specimen was a male. But he did gather, by listening attentively to the jabber of the local aborigines, that they referred to the animal by a word that sounded like *kangaroo.*

In the closing decades of the century the pioneer settlers of Australia—farmers, squatters, convicts, deportees—began hunting down the singular neighbors with which they shared the huge, unknown wilderness. Some of the more educated in their ranks shipped specimens, skins, skeletons or drawings back home. Bewildered by the strange forms, they wrote of them as local varieties of "mice," "rats," "weasels," "badgers" and other familiar mammalian species. In 1790 a group of zoologists met in London and put their heads together in an attempt to classify their growing collection from the antipodes. To their astonishment they discovered that every one of the specimens on hand had a marsupium, or pouch. As a consequence the new order of marsupials was officially recognized and admitted to the Linnaean register of living things. In addition to the Australian members the order of the pouch included the well-known South American opossum and wolflike, bearlike and shrewlike marsupial predators from Australia and its neighboring island of Tasmania. Swiftly thereafter new forms were found—the cute koala, the clumsy wombat, the agile wallaby and a host of others revealing the diversity of this eccentric category of life.

No sooner had European zoology adjusted its thinking to the marsupials than an even more extraordinary prodigy emerged from down under. The first duck-billed platypus arrived in London posthumously in 1799, and was regarded by many scientists as a hoax, a product of ingenious taxidermy. Careful examination, however, revealed no signs of fraud, and a year or so later two more specimens came to the British Museum, accompanied at about the same time by an obviously related but equally paradoxical creature—the echidna or spiny anteater *(pages 174-175)*. In 1803 they were classified as the charter members of the new order of Monotremata —a word derived from the Greek *mono* (one) and *trema* (hole), signifying that, like reptiles, they possessed but a single, all-purpose posterior orifice. Six years later the French evolutionist, Lamarck, precursor of Darwin, postulated that the platypus and the echidna stood upon a tenuous threshold between reptiles and mammals. He classified them as Prototheria or pre-mammals.

Although Lamarck's view was not generally accepted, it influenced Darwin's thought. The difficulties of studying the platypus either in its remote habitat or in captivity (where it quickly died) enjoined zoologists for many years from establishing the

APPROACHING FOSSIL SITE, Dr. Ruben Stirton *(right)* and R. H. Tedford, paleontologists from the University of California, pause in the sand dunes of central Australia, facing the dry lake bed which contained their epic marsupial find.

fact, beyond doubt, that it did indeed lay eggs and that it did indeed suckle its young. The few eggs (soft-shelled like those of reptiles) turned up by naturalists in nesting burrows were dismissed by European skeptics as products of abortion brought about by sudden fright. The rather thick mammary secretions of the female platypus were identified as mucus or musk. It was not until the final years of the century that the paradox of the oviparous, lactating platypus was finally resolved by incontrovertible evidence, and science accepted it for what it is—a "living fossil," the progeny of a family of pre-mammals, that has survived in the isolation of Australia for 150 million years.

Darwin, his vision unclouded by controversy, saw that Lamarck's view was the correct one and that in the pyramid of evolution the ascending stages proceeded from reptiles to monotremes to marsupials to placental mammals. In 1871 he wrote: "The Marsupials stand in many important characters below the placental mammals. They appeared at an earlier geological period, and their range was formerly much more extensive than at present. Hence the Placentata are generally supposed to have been derived from the [Marsupials]; not, however, from forms closely resembling the existing Marsupials,

LINEAGE

family tree for the modern marsupials

but from their early progenitors. The Monotremata are plainly allied to the Marsupials, forming a third and still lower division in the great mammalian series. They are represented at the present day solely by the platypus and Echidna; and these two forms may be safely considered as relics of a much larger group, representatives of which have been preserved in Australia through some favorable concurrence of circumstances. The Monotremata are eminently interesting, as leading in several important points of structure toward the class of reptiles.

"The Monotremata have the proper milk-secreting glands with orifices, but no nipples; and as these animals stand at the very base of the mammalian series, it is probable that the progenitors of the class also had milk-secreting glands, but no nipples. . . . The Marsupials differ from the Monotremata by possessing nipples; so that probably these organs were first acquired by the Marsupials, after they had diverged from, and risen above, the Monotremata. . . . We have seen that birds and reptiles were once intimately connected together; and the Monotremata now connect mammals with reptiles in a slight degree . . . the steps are not difficult to conceive which led from the ancient Monotremata to the ancient Marsupials; and from these to the early progenitors of the placental mammals."

IN his speculations on the succession of animal life in Australia, Darwin was handicapped by the poverty of the fossil evidence. Whereas in South America, largely owing to his own discoveries, he was convinced of "the wonderful relationship in the same continent between the dead and the living," he could only hope that in the future the endeavors of paleontologists would unearth the relics of ancient Australian marsupials allied to existing forms. In his day the great parched wastelands of the interior had scarcely been scratched. He knew, presumably, that in 1830, just a few years before his own arrival, a fellow countryman named George Ranken had descended into the Wellington caves of New South Wales and there found the bones of the first extinct mammalian animals ever uncovered in Australia. Along with relatively familiar forms, Ranken found embedded in the red clay of the cave floor some enormous bones of an unidentifiable beast. At a time when popular assumption tended to interpret fossil finds as the relics of unlucky creatures drowned in Noah's flood, it was thought that these big bones must once have undergirded the body of a sinful elephant. But subsequent examination proved that it was an animal unlike any now on earth, a giant marsupial vaguely resembling both a gigantic guinea pig and a rhinoceros. It stood six feet high at the shoulder and measured ten feet in length. In its lower jaw it carried two enormous chisel-like incisors. Its leg joints suggested that it could sit back on its hocks and graze in the lower branches of the trees for foliage. Because of its dental features it was named *Diprotodon*, meaning "two front teeth."

From time to time in ensuing years the remains of many diprotodons have been found gleaming white in the salt wastes of central Australia. But for years opinion differed as to whether they became extinct millenniums ago, or whether some might still survive unobserved by men deep in the inhospitable interior of the continent.

In 1939 the stubborn, complex riddle of dates and extinctions was resolved when paleontologists found a prehistoric campsite littered with the soot-charred bones of diprotodons. The evidence was clear that the animals had been cooked and eaten. So in the end, after millions of years of tranquil survival, the giant, slow-witted marsupials had succumbed to a smaller, smarter placental mammal—man.

In 1953 an American, Dr. Ruben A. Stirton of the University of California, began excavating one of the most massive finds in the history of paleontology—the remains of a herd of diprotodons, more than 500 in all, sprawled flank to flank, their feet drawn up as though in slumber, in the dry bed of an ancient salt lake. It was this find that ultimately revealed the likely fate of these creatures.

But many questions still linger unanswered. No one knows precisely how or when the first primitive mammals—the ancestral marsupials and monotremes—reached Australia. No one can define their relationship to the mammal-like reptiles that rose above their sluggish genealogy in the long sunset of the age of dinosaurs. But it is certain that future explorations in the huge, dry, empty heart of Australia will piece together, eventually, the prehistory of the planet's least-known continent.

SORTING HIS FOSSILS, Dr. Stirton arranges the bones of the diprotodon he found in Australia. Its name comes from Latin and Greek—*di* (two), *pro* (front), *odon* (tooth)—after its two prominent front teeth *(lower right)*.

JOSEPH SIBAL

THE
EVOLUTION
OF
COURTSHIP

THE opening rituals of the courtship ceremony, an important element of the evolutionary process, are shown here in the antics of two male birds of paradise. At the left a magnificent bird of paradise has snipped the leaves from a sapling and is doing acrobatics in front of a plainish female. At the right a Pennant's six-wired bird of paradise parades on a patch of ground cleared for the purpose. Such unusual behavior suggests these birds possibly may be evolving from treetop to ground courtship.

THE EVOLUTION OF COURTSHIP

The elaborate rites of bowerbirds demonstrate sexual selection

BEAUTY," Darwin declared, "is sometimes even more important than success in battle." In this memorable epigram Darwin states the essence of his concept of sexual selection as a factor in evolutionary change. Where natural selection fosters the survival of the fittest, sexual selection promotes the proliferation of the most attractive. For throughout the animal kingdom the female is often more than a mere passive prize that falls automatically to the victor in male competition. "In very many cases," Darwin wrote, "the courtship of animals is by no means so simple and short."

It is in the society of birds that the artifices of sexual selection have attained fullest development. "The most pugnacious . . . males rarely . . . depend for success solely on their power to drive away or kill their rivals," Darwin said, "but have special means for charming the female. With some it is the power of song or of giving forth strange cries. Many birds endeavor to charm the females by love-dances or antics." The strutting of pigeons and the spreading of the peacock's train are classic examples of display. Less familiar and far more intricate are the prolonged courtship ceremonies of the bowerbirds of New Guinea and Australia. They build elaborate pleasure domes *(chart below)* adorned with colored shells, flowers and insect wings—not as nests, but as bowers for wooing and winning. No other creature, save man, expends such effort to this end.

A fact that long puzzled ornithologists is that the brilliance of the bowerbirds' plumage fades in inverse ratio to the ornateness of their bowers—the brightest birds build the simplest bowers; the plainest birds embellish their bowers in fantastic and colorful detail. Naturalists have therefore concluded that brilliant plumage is not necessarily a gauge of evolutionary status, as earlier theorists believed. Indeed, since the gaudier birds are more visible to enemies, it is their drab cousins who have survived to become the family's master architects.

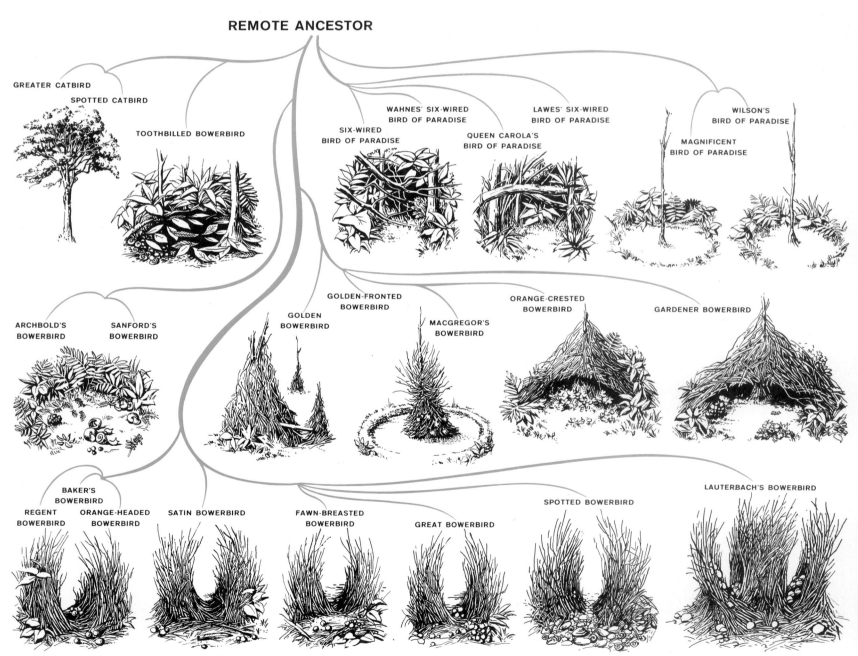

COURTING CHAMBERS of bowerbirds and their near relatives are shown above. At top left is the tree used for courting by the bowerbird catbirds, in the manner of the remote progenitor of all the birds. Below it, at left of the main stem, are the simple bowers of mat builders and to the right *(top row)* those of the birds of paradise. The complex bowers of maypole builders are in the second row *(right)* and those of avenue builders in the bottom row.

ANTICS OF AN ABJECT COURTSHIP

Odd even among the ritualistic bowerbirds is Sanford's golden-crested bowerbird. The male makes a mat of ferns which he curtains off with ferns and bamboo streamers. He decorates it with shells, insect skeletons, bits of resin and berries which he moves about so that streams of sunlight play on his offerings. When the female appears, the male grovels on the ground, convulsively chewing a strand of vine and uttering chirring sounds. This abject behavior apparently excites the female, who thrashes him violently with her wings. The spectacle attracts other birds, like the whistler and warbler *(lower left)*, Loria's bird of paradise *(top left)*, two mocha-breasted birds of paradise and a shield-billed bird of paradise *(top right)*, a honey eater and babbler *(right center)*. After mating, the male bobs about alertly in the bower, rearranging the disheveled piles of ornaments which his courting left completely disorganized.

183

COMMON LORY
FOREST RHIPIDURA
        FLAME-CRESTED BOWERBIRD (MALE)
        FLAME-CRESTED BOWERBIRD (MALE)
     FLAME-CRESTED BOWERBIRD (FEMALE)
                GREEN CATBIRD
                MOUNTAIN SICKLE-BILLED BIRD OF PARADISE
                GIANT FLOWER PECKER

MAYPOLE BUILDERS AND THEIR FESTIVE BOWERS

In the lush New Guinea mountains a convocation of forest birds looks down on the activities of a group of bowerbirds, the maypole builders. One of the most primitive of all the maypole builders is the flame-crested bowerbird *(left)*, whose orange plume still preserves in muted form the ancestral elegance that flowered to produce its gaily colored relative, the bird of paradise. Because of his fine feathers, the flame-crested male can exert his attraction for the female merely by disporting himself before her. But the species enhances this display of plumage with a bower. Each spring the flame-crested birds begin their bowers by clearing a circular space on the forest floor around a small sapling, and then decorating it with special mosses

BLUE BIRD OF PARADISE (MALE)   BLUE BIRD OF PARADISE (FEMALE)   MAGNIFICENT BIRD OF PARADISE (FEMALE)

RIBBON-TAILED BIRD OF PARADISE (MALE)   SHORT-CRESTED BOWERBIRD (FEMALE)   SHORT-CRESTED BOWERBIRD (MALE)   MAGNIFICENT BIRD OF PARADISE (MALE)

CRESTLESS BOWERBIRD (MALE)

gathered high up in the trees. When the lawn is completed, the birds forage about the forest for dead twigs, which they intertwine about the lower part of the sapling to form a column that often reaches three feet in height. Then the male flutters around the pole, showing off his fine feathers and bower to stimulate his chosen mate.

A more highly developed maypole builder is the short-crested bowerbird (center), whose plume is sometimes long and colorful, sometimes as short and drab-colored as the female's head feathers. Because this crest varies so capriciously from one male to another, it can have little actual value in the basic attraction of a mate and will probably vanish as the species continues its evolution. Thus the short-crested male is dependent on his bower and its ornaments to excite his mate and his bower is correspondingly more elaborate than that of his flame-crested relative. In addition to the lawn and maypole, the male adds a small tepee of twigs to the top of the sapling and scatters about, on the lawn beneath, colorful flowers and shells which he gathers in the forest.

Thoroughly settled in drabness is the crestless bowerbird (right), whose plumage has become virtually indistinguishable from that of the female, and whose bower has grown increasingly ornate to take the place of colorful feathers. Besides constructing a tepee and foraging for blossoms, the male gathers up insect skeletons, shells,

FOLD OUT, DO NOT TEAR

COMMON GOSHAWK   **COMMON GOSHAWK**

SATIN BOWERBIRD (MALE)   **SATIN BOWERBIRD (FEMALE)**   **SCRUB TURKEY**

birds spend up to half a year embellishing and refining their bowers. So intricate has the courtship of three species of these birds become that it requires an almost human skill—painting the bowers. The birds mix their pigments by chewing colored berries and charcoal and then apply the mixture with their bills. At the peak of courtship two of the species hunt out porous bark or vegetable matter and use it like a paintbrush to apply pigment to their thickets.

Not only do the avenue builders adorn their walled enclosures with colored objects and colorful paint, but they orient them with a keen instinct for the advantages offered by the sunlight which falls on the grasslands in which they live. Parallel walls run north and south,

with the main displaying area just outside the northern doorway. In the southern hemisphere the sun falls there all day long to illuminate the parade grounds of the male birds.

The most brightly colored and simplest architect among the avenue builders is a species called the regent *(left)*. Perched above it is the colorful Newton's bowerbird, the only representative of the maypole builders found among Australia's avenue builders. The regent makes a pair of parallel walls by forcing sticks and stiff grass into his mat of twigs. The attractiveness of the bower is increased by a few shells and colored pebbles which the male gathers for his avenue.

Of similar construction is the bower of the less colorful satin. Like

SULPHUR-CRESTED COCKATOOS
REGENT BOWERBIRD (MALE)

NEWTON'S BOWERBIRD
REGENT BOWERBIRD (FEMALE)
LOVELY WRENS

AVENUE BUILDERS
AND THEIR
INTRICATE RITUALS

The complicated courtship of the maypole builders, the search for ornaments to decorate the bowers and for twigs to embellish them, is carried to another ornate extreme by a branch of the bowerbird family called the avenue builders. Moving out to the edge of the New Guinea and Australian forests, and into the grasslands beyond, they adopted new materials and new ornaments and evolved a completely different type of bower. Instead of entwining sticks into maypole ornaments, they form long rectangular mats from them. To these they add parallel walls formed by twigs thrust into the mats. These walls give their mating ground the appearance of an avenue. Pounds of attractive ornaments are gathered for decoration, and some

CRESTLESS BOWERBIRD (MALE)

KING OF SAXONY BIRD OF PARADISE

BELFORD'S VARIABLE HONEY EATER

RIBBON-TAILED BIRD OF PARADISE (FEMALE)

CRESTLESS BOWERBIRD (FEMALE)

seeds and charcoal, all of which the crestless bowerbird arranges in neat piles on the lawn. As the flowers fade, he replenishes them with fresh ones, and disports himself in the bower by bobbing and weaving while holding one of his carefully collected, colorful objects in his bill, usually one of the flowers he has picked in the forest.

Because the courtship gestures of all male bowerbirds include not only building but a remarkable display of ventriloquism, in which they tirelessly mimic the songs and calls of many of the forest birds, the singing attracts an excited mob of feathered spectators to the scene of any courtship in the New Guinea forest. The birds of paradise display their plumage in the branches above the bowers, and smaller birds fly agitatedly about the trees. This gathering of small spectators may reveal the location of the bower to any predator, but it also provides the scene with an audience of bird life that is quick to warn of any danger which may threaten the courting pair.

Attracted by the ornateness of the male's bower and the antics of its builder, the female finally enters and the pair mate. Then she promptly flies off to build her nest elsewhere and to raise her young in solitude. The bowerbirds mate only once each season and, after mating, the male continues to tend his bower for weeks on end, still displaying the colorful objects he has so carefully collected throughout the spring, all the while remaining faithful to his chosen mate.

GREATER BIRD OF PARADISE   RACQUET-TAILED KINGFISHER   LESSER BIRD OF PARADISE
                            LAUTERBACH'S BOWERBIRD (FEMALE)   LAUTERBACH'S BOWERBIRD (MALE)

the other males in the bowerbird family, he postures, preens and
parades for weeks on end, marching up and down within his alley.
During these incessant maneuvers the female shows only occasional
interest by perching for a moment on a nearby branch. When she
does, the male picks up one colored object after another which he
flashes in his bill to attract her. Finally the female enters the bower
where, after a courtship fight, shown in this painting, the birds mate.

Lauterbach's bowerbird is the least colorful of the avenue builders,
and his bower is correspondingly more elaborate *(right)*. After com-
pleting one pair of parallel walls he adds a third wall in front of
them and a fourth behind. Frequently over 3,000 sticks are required

to build the bower and the resulting structure is so rigid it can be
lifted up and carried off like an orange crate. Equal attention is paid
to ornamentation. Up to 1,000 stones are gathered to decorate the
bower and the bird piles them neatly against the walls. Further to
lure the female, the male adds colorful berries to the bower each day.

After the avenue builders mate, the females look for a secluded
spot to build their nests and hatch their eggs. The males, meanwhile, continue to disport themselves in the bowers for many hours
each day, keeping them clean and replenishing them with berries.
Ultimately the females return with their fledglings, and the families
join other bowerbirds to fly to better feeding grounds for the winter.

THE VITAL ROLE OF

Scientists are now certain that the motive for varied courtship rituals in nature is

IN the 19th Century garden of opinion within which his theories germinated like unwanted weeds thriving on adversity, Darwin was often regarded as a heartless materialist who found no place in nature for those finer impulses dear to Victorian sensibilities. Yet, by comparison with present-day interpretations of animal behavior, his attribution of esthetic feelings to the lower orders of life often endowed them with almost human emotions. This tendency runs through many of his observations on courtship.

Observing that a sense of beauty and an admiration for it is generally regarded as peculiar to man, Darwin added, "When we behold a male bird elaborately displaying his graceful plumes or splendid colours before the female, whilst other birds, not thus decorated make no such display, it is impossible to doubt that she admires the beauty of her male partner. As women everywhere deck themselves with these plumes, the beauty of such ornaments cannot be disputed. . . . The nests of hummingbirds, and the playing passages of bower-birds are tastefully ornamented with gaily-coloured objects; and this shews that they must receive some kind of pleasure from the sight of such things. . . . The sweet strains poured forth by many male birds during the season of love are certainly admired by the females. . . . If female birds had been incapable of appreciating the beautiful colours, the ornaments, and the voices of their male partners, all the labour and anxiety exhibited by the latter in displaying their charms before the females would have been thrown away; and this is impossible to admit."

Although naturalists now are in agreement that animal intelligence encompasses little artistic discrimination or choice, they do not, however, dispute Darwin's evaluation of the biological role of courtship as a strong force in sexual selection. The astonishingly varied displays of male animals and birds in the mating season may not themselves induce a conscious choice by the female in the same sense that a woman may select one of several gentlemen suitors in accord with her reaction to the variety and splendor of his personality and habiliments, but they undoubtedly hasten receptivity in the object of attention, stimulate her responses, and drive off rival birds—all of which involve both physiological and nervous reactions.

Subtleties and complexities of courtship do not invariably imply an elevated rung on the evolutionary ladder. Many insects, fish and amphibians exhibit greater variety and ritual in courtship than superior orders of animal life. Jewel fish, for example, stage elaborate performances, quivering, changing color, digging sand and standing on their heads. Salamanders dash about, poking, nudging, butting and releasing stimulating odors. Frogs and toads execute stately ritualistic dances prior to fertilization. In these categories of life the initiative rests almost entirely with the male.

Among mammals, however, spectacular displays are rare. The female plays a more important role and often, as in the case of *Homo sapiens,* the role of aggressor. She knows how to tease and entice. The doe pretends to run away so that the buck will pursue her. The female giraffe also invites the male to chase her, cantering

with a special swaying gait that proves irresistible. The female gnu drops to her knees and nudges the male as he wanders past. The tigress parades before her potential mate provocatively, flicking her tail and drawing it across his muzzle. But in the polygamous society of gorillas, highest of the primates below man, the female simply presents herself.

Of all classes of vertebrates, the birds have evolved the most striking techniques of courtship display. It is significant that many monogamous species with fixed territorial habits dispense with ceremony altogether. The constant presence of the male, his assistance in building a nest and providing food, his song (which warns rivals not to trespass on his local domain) provide sufficient stimulus to his mate. Displays attain the greatest flamboyance where the union of the two sexes is transient. In the case of such lighthearted birds, the males are frequently highly decorative and expend great energy in the exhibition of their charms, since their impact on females, being of short duration, must be very intense to succeed in the face of intense competition from numerous rivals. The specific ornaments of the bird dictate his attitudes of display. The blue-footed booby goose-steps to show off the color of his feet. The fulmar or sea mew suddenly opens his beak to reveal the startlingly unexpected purple lining of his mouth.

Apart from the peacock, the most exotically decorated creation of the avian world is the classic bird of paradise. In its courtship ceremony the male opens the show by uttering loud, raucous cries. Next it goes into its dance routine, typically along the limb of the tree which it has chosen as its theater of operations. The dance begins with head lowered, swinging gently from right to left. Gradually, as the movement increases, the wings open, the long plumes of the flank are lifted. Then suddenly the bird bends forward, lowers its wings, and raises the sprays of plumes that circle its head like a glittering coronet. Of forty-one species of birds of paradise, thirty-five conduct their elaborate courtship in the trees. But six species have now descended to the ground and it is these which, by their cropping of leaves and preparation of cleared areas of performance for their courtship rites, forecast the more elaborate constructions of their evolutionary legatees—the maypole-building and avenue-building bowerbirds.

It is only in recent years that the link between birds of paradise and bowerbirds was disclosed in its true relationship. Darwin, for all his fascination with the architectural skills of bowerbirds—which he accurately recognized as being partially motivated by sex—postulated that they were "no doubt the co-descendants of some ancient species which first acquired the strange instinct of constructing bowers for performing their love antics." After Darwin's death other naturalists adduced various theories to explain their "highly decorated halls of assembly." Some interpreted their bower building as a kind of hobby, undertaken for fun and relaxation; others acclaimed them as Michelangelos of the bird world, endowed with esthetic taste and intelligence far above all known capacities of the normal bird brain. It was generally believed that the rather plainly attired

SEEKING RARE SPECIES, Dr. E. Thomas Gilliard of the American Museum of Natural History and his wife, Margaret, lead a 60-man safari through New Guinea in their 1959 search for Baker's bowerbird, unseen since it was discovered in 1928.

WOOING

fundamentally biological, never esthetic

bowerbirds represented a family quite distinct from the flashily dressed birds of paradise who dwelt with them in the same South Pacific habitats. And in accordance with accepted Linnaean doctrine the resplendent plumage of the birds of paradise was regarded as the insignia of a higher evolutionary stage.

In 1958, however, Dr. E. Thomas Gilliard, ornithologist of the American Museum of Natural History in New York, recognized the kinship between bowerbirds and birds of paradise, and enunciated the radical theory that the plainest and drabbest of the bowerbirds were actually the most advanced of the entire evolutionary line. In the course of six expeditions to the jungles of New Guinea, Dr. Gilliard noted that the birds with the most elaborate and ornate bowers lacked all the furbelows of gaudy sexual plumage and, conversely, that the species costumed in bright colors and adorned with flashy upswept hairdos invariably produced relatively simple courting areas. Dr. Gilliard therefore decided that through natural selection the function of "the structural characters of the bird itself," that is, the plumage, had been transferred to "external objects, namely, the bower." Psychologically but no longer physically linked to the male, the inanimate stimuli—such objects as flowers, berries, seeds, shells, etc.—afford a much greater range of expression than mere feathers alone.

Following the transfer of the sex stimuli from the body to the bower, the vivid sexual plumage of the male became not merely useless but a serious disadvantage in a world of predators. In accordance with the Darwinian concept of natural selection, the least conspicuous, shortest-crested and most protectively camouflaged birds in each generation enjoyed the longest reproductive life. Thus eventually flashy sexual plumage was lost and the male became as demurely attired as his more somber mate.

THE initial stage in the evolution of the bower, according to Dr. Gilliard's theory, was the gradual lowering of the exhibition stage from the crown of the forest to the forest floor. When the focal point of the stage descended to saplings and vines close to the earth, the clearing of ground was incorporated into the ritual. Through this step the birds achieved protection against enemies with protective coloration—snakes, lizards and other foes endowed with camouflage effective against a background of fallen leaves, twigs, and variegated jungle litter. It is possible that in this act of clearing the birds piled up the debris of the forest floor into a rudimentary bower which then developed into more fixed and stylized patterns. Today it is recognized by ornithologists that both the drab coloring of the bowerbirds and their elaborately constructed bowers are clear marks of an evolutionary development that places them later rather than earlier in the evolutionary scale than their resplendent cousins, the birds of paradise.

Another student of bowerbirds, Dr. A. J. Marshall, zoologist of the University of London, has ascertained that the periodic and recurrent building and tending activities of the male bowerbird are governed by seasonal sexual rhythms. A castrated bird does not build a bower. Dr. Marshall further discovered that the selection of decorations in the bower of any species is uniform. Noting, for example, that the blue satin bowerbird invariably chooses blue and yellow objects to adorn his bower, Dr. Marshall surmised that the color scheme reflected not an instinct for those particular colors but a displaced expression of aggression against their male rivals. "Experiments have shown," he observed, "that the male satin bower bird chooses decorations in the image of competitors of its own species; the blue flowers and feathers that it tosses about so ferociously match the eye color of its rivals, while the lemon-yellow objects it selects match the color of the adult male's beak tip. The savage intensity with which the bower owner displays these objects effectively keeps marauding rivals away from his bower and his female as long as he remains strong and healthy."

Today, as modern civilization encroaches everywhere on habitats that once were wild, the bowerbirds of Australia and New Guinea are finding new and more civilized baubles with which to decorate their jungle bowers. Recent observations have disclosed bowers being tastefully adorned with bits of broken glass, with bottle tops, car keys, coins, teaspoons, nails, brass cartridge cases, thimbles—and on at least one occasion, a glass eye.

COMPARING BIRDS, Gilliard matches a Baker's bowerbird with a painting of one seen in 1928 by Rollo Beck, discoverer of the species. A Sepik hunter, whose tribe had never seen the bird living in its midst, looks on.

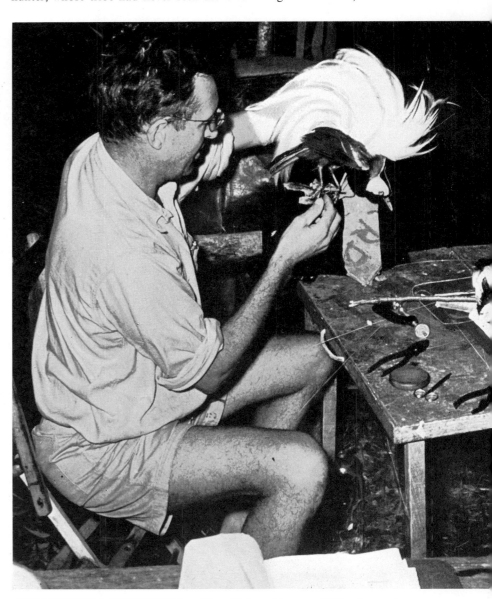

ARRANGING A SPECIMEN in a New Guinea bivouac, Gilliard mounts a lesser bird of paradise in a courtship pose. This polygamous bird, a cousin of Baker's bowerbird, meets each of its mates only a few minutes each year.

THE ENIGMA OF CORAL ISLES

THIS shamelessly adorned fish, called a wrasse, is a resident of one of the world's most profuse domains of life: the coral reef. The nature of coral reefs and the manner of their creation were virtual mysteries until Darwin reached the Cocos Isles in 1836 and found most of the answers. Of the manifold creatures that inhabit the caverns and grottoes of coral reefs, many wear brilliant colors. This wrasse boasts not only gaudy fins and scales, but blue teeth with which it crushes the shellfish on which it feeds.

NORTH KEELING ISLAND, a member of the Cocos group where Darwin hit upon his classic solution to the ancient enigma of the origin of coral reefs, is a typical ring-shaped atoll. Riding in the Indian Ocean about 2,000 miles northwest of Australia, its coral rim encircles a sandy-bottomed lagoon nearly one and a quarter miles long and one half mile wide. At its thickest point the rim measures 400 yards across. Its vegetation consists of palms and tea shrub.

THE ENIGMA OF CORAL ISLES

On a far-away atoll, Darwin resolved a mystery of oceanic life

IN the autumn of 1835, H.M.S. *Beagle* completed its survey of South American shores and headed across the Pacific. Midway in this voyage, Darwin wrote, "We saw several of those most curious rings of coral land just rising above the water's edge, which have been called Lagoon Islands. These low coral islands bear no proportion to the vast ocean out of which they abruptly rise; and it seems wonderful that such weak invaders are not overwhelmed by the all-powerful, never-tiring waves of that great sea, miscalled the Pacific."

Everywhere Darwin's insatiably inquiring eye flashed questions to his mind. And the same genius for synthesizing apparently unrelated details that engendered *The Origin of Species* inspired a number of minor classics. One of these emerged from his brief visit to the Cocos Islands in the early spring of 1836. Here in a group of tiny atolls in the Indian Ocean he found the answer to a mystery that had baffled observant mariners for centuries—the enigma of the creation of coral isles, rising unexpectedly from the abyss of the unbroken sea.

Darwin was perfectly aware that coral formations consisted of the calcareous remains of countless generations of small, static, colonial animals. But his observations revealed a paradox. The outer walls of coral reefs and atolls plunge precipitously to enormous depths. Yet it is only in the lighted upper levels of the sea, extending no more than 180 feet below the surface, that living corals can exist. The crucial question, therefore, as Darwin phrased it, was, "On what have the reef-building corals, which cannot live at great depth, based their massive structures?" His resolution of the coral riddle, described on pages 198-199, with very few revisions is still valid today.

CORALS AND FISH abound in the calm and shallow reef waters of the Cocos Islands. Here dainty damselfish flash their turquoise scales amid clusters of stony branches. These tiny fish usually swarm in large schools and stay close to their protective coral home. At top and left, colonies of staghorn corals extend their graceful interlocking antlers. The rounded or cylindrical corals in the center are Porites, which Darwin both studied and admired.

A CORAL BARRIER (*foreground*) protects West Island, the largest of the Cocos group, from the sweeping surge of the sapphire sea. In the background is the atoll's quiet lagoon, seven miles wide and rimmed with scattered islets.

GIANT BREAKERS (*below*) crash endlessly on the reef. "It is impossible to behold these waves," Darwin observed, "without feeling that an island would ultimately yield and be demolished by such an irresistible power."

REEF, SURF AND ISLETS

"The shallow, clear water of the lagoon is of the most vivid green," Darwin wrote, in describing the scene above. "This brilliant expanse is divided by a line of snow white breakers from the dark heaving waters of the ocean. As a white cloud here and there affords a pleasing contrast with the azure sky, so in the lagoon bands of living coral darken the emerald green water."

Along with the beauty of the atolls, Darwin was also impressed by their resistance to the violent pounding of the surf engendered by the incessant trade wind. "The ocean and the land seem here struggling for mastery," he explained, ". . . yet these low, insignificant coral islets stand and are victorious. . . . Let the hurricane tear up its thousand huge fragments; yet what will that tell against the accumulated labor of myriads of architects at work, month after month? Thus do we see the soft and gelatinous body of a polyp, conquering the great mechanical power of the waves of an ocean."

A REEF FLAT, built over untold centuries of diverse corals, lies just below the surface of the sunlit water. Darwin made several excursions to these wide flats, wading out at low tide and marveling at their complex submarine structures of coral and the infinite variety of multicolored life.

THE FIRST STAGE in the evolution of a coral atoll begins with the formation of a fringing reef around the shores of a volcanic island. Here the volcano, rising from the ocean floor, one mile high and still active, is depicted in a cutaway section—*i.e.,* a pie-like wedge has been cut from land and water. The white line denotes sea level. Black lines trace the lava flow. Coral islets of the new reef rising from the shallows are separated from shore by a lagoon.

THE THIRD STAGE is characterized by a continuing expansion of the lagoon as the volcano settles ever lower in the sea and the corals of the barrier reef spread outward, thriving in turbulence and crashing surf. While the shrinking slopes of the volcano leave less and less room for vegetation on the central island, the sandy surfaces of the reef develop a rich mantle of palms and varied plants. By now the lagoon is three miles in diameter.

THE EVOLUTION
OF A CORAL ISLE

In his study of coral formations Darwin noted three varieties: atolls, barrier reefs, fringing reefs. The atoll, he saw, comprises a ring of coral islets enclosing a shallow lagoon. The barrier reef is a rampart of coral surrounding a volcanic island and separated from it by a channel of water. The fringing reef is concentrically smaller than a barrier reef, closer to the shore or contiguous with it. In these three types he discerned an evolutionary sequence. His visit to the Andes had provided

THE SECOND STAGE involves the gradual transmutation of the fringing reef into a barrier reef. Here the volcano, cold and extinct, has begun to sink into the sea. Meanwhile the corals continue to build on their old foundations.

With the island reduced, the lagoon is correspondingly wider. Reef debris, shells and coral boulders accumulate on the slopes of the reef and finer sediments settle in the lagoon. Vegetation appears on the sand-covered reef flats.

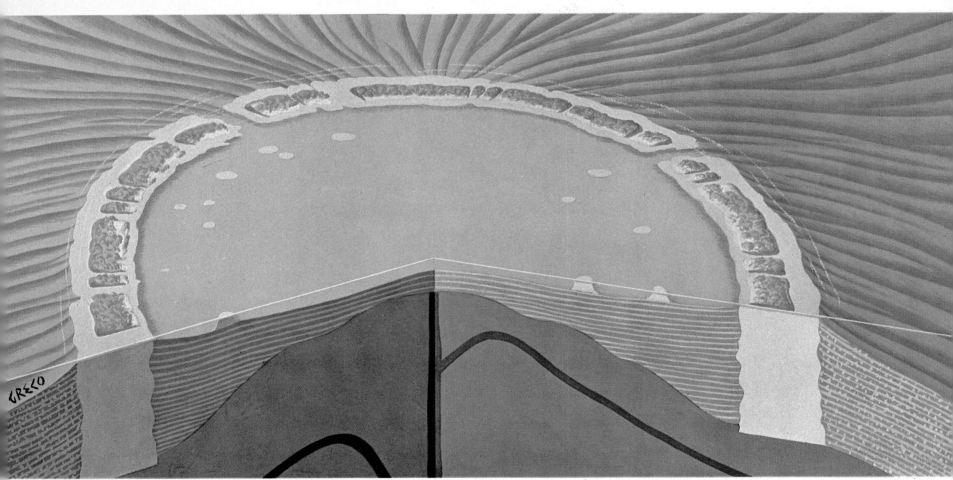

THE FOURTH STAGE completes the growth cycle of the atoll. Here the volcano has disappeared entirely, leaving only a necklace of coral isles encircling a turquoise lagoon. From the shallow central waters clumps of coral rise like frozen flowers above the surface. The exterior walls of the atoll fall away as dizzily as mountain precipices, for now, after one million years of growth, the living corals stand nearly a mile above the original base.

firsthand experience of the forces within the earth that recurrently cause mountains to rise in one region while elsewhere the crust subsides. He concluded, therefore, that coral formations were end products of eons of slow, reciprocal processes: the uplifting of an island by submarine volcanic action; the colonizing of its slopes by myriad coral polyps; the gradual subsiding of the island into the sea. In his view the fringing reef came first, reared by corals in the sunlit shallows of the new island's shelving shore. Then, as the island subsided, the corals, ever building on the foundations laid down by the skeletons of incomputable former generations, were separated from the shrinking shore and their edifice evolved into a barrier reef. In the end the island disappeared completely, leaving only the circular atoll standing like a monument to mark the watery burial place of a vanished volcano. The birth of an atoll, shown above, requires not less than a million years.

ROOSTING IN A TREE *(left)*, the red-footed booby rests between flights out to sea. It sights fish from 50 feet or more and dives after them. The booby cannot take flight from the ground; it must first climb onto a bush.

IN HOVERING FLIGHT the white fairy tern, shown in the two photographs above, seems the most ethereal of sea birds. When it soars against the sky its skeletal structure is clearly silhouetted within translucent wings.

AN ATOLL'S SEA BIRDS

In describing the vastly varied bird population of the Cocos, Darwin remarked that the islands' wooded areas, covered with shrubs and palms, might, "from the many nests and from the smell of the atmosphere, be called a sea rookery." Insatiably delighted with all bird life, Darwin expressed his special enchantment with the white tern—"a charming bird, which smoothly hovers at a distance of a few feet above one's head, its large black eye scanning with quiet curiosity your expression. Little imagination is required to fancy that so light a body must be tenanted by some wandering fairy spirit."

THE GHOST CRAB is one of the liveliest but most timorous members of its family. Creeping forth at night to feed, it dashes for safety at the slightest hint of alarm. It burrows with amazing speed, hurling sand three feet away.

THE ROBBER CRAB intrigued Darwin by its unusual characteristics—a fondness for coconuts and the great strength of its claws. Darwin described how one escaped from a strong tin box by bending and piercing the metal.

THE HERMIT CRAB, which is not a true crab but a soft-bodied crustacean, armors itself in the old shells of other reef dwellers. Wedging its vulnerable posterior into a borrowed home, like the turbo shell shown here, it anchors

COLORFUL CRABS

Amid the coral gardens of the Cocos, Darwin found much evidence for his evolving vision of the natural world. He saw how crabs and clams had adapted in various ways to their abode. Of the 100-odd species of crabs on the Cocos isles, each has its niche in the life of the atoll. One crab is so static that in time the growing corals enclose it forever in a calcareous prison. Several species camouflage themselves with sponges and algae, while the hermit crab resides in borrowed shells. Darwin's interest was most taken by the robber

THE MANGROVE CRAB, a good swimmer, prefers the water to the shore. Most are characterized by brown or green coloration. This blue specimen, searching the shallow flats for worms and crustaceans, is a beautiful variant.

itself within by means of short rear legs. Then it faces the marine world defiantly in ferocious crablike fashion, brandishing its large anterior claws. When danger appears it withdraws into its fortress, using its claws as folding doors.

AND HUGE CLAMS

crab *(left)* which eats coconuts. "It would at first be thought quite impossible for a crab to open a strong coconut," he wrote. "The crab begins by tearing the husk, fiber by fiber . . . till an opening is made. Then turning round its body, by the aid of its posterior pincers, it extracts the white albuminous substance. I think this is as curious a case of instinct as ever I heard of, and likewise of adaptation in structure between two objects apparently so remote from each other in the scheme of nature as a crab and a coconut tree."

THE GIANT CLAM above is a foot across. Others may attain four times this size, weighing 600 pounds. Darwin noted if such a clam seized a man's hand, "he would not, as long as the animal lived, be able to withdraw it."

REEF'S ODD CREATURES

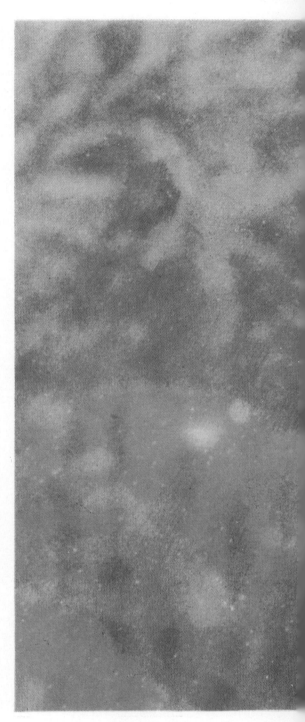

A FEATHER STAR, relative of the sea lily, starfish and sea urchin, flutters gracefully through the waters like some strangely indolent bird. When

A CHINESE FISH hovers over a golden, flower-like cluster of deep-sea coral. A rare and beautiful denizen of the New Caledonia reef, it was only recently discovered. Scientists as yet can provide no explanation for its tendency to swim in an almost vertical posture, as shown here.

In the light of modern marine biology, Darwin's comprehension of the teeming underwater world of coral remains a miracle of insight. Today scientists can descend into the submarine forests of the tropical seas and examine their inhabitants at leisure. But Darwin could peer down at them only from man's ancient landlocked point of view. "I waded over the outer flat of dead rock as far as the living mounds of coral," he wrote on April 3, 1836. "In some of the gullies and hollows there were beautiful coloured fishes and the forms and tints were admirable. It is excusable to grow enthusiastic over the infinite numbers of organic beings with which the sea of the tropics . . . teems." It is not difficult to envisage the even greater enthusiasm Darwin might have articulated had he been able to discern some of the brilliant creatures, shown here and on the following pages, that populate the coral reef.

feeding, a feather star attaches itself to a rock or shell by means of its claws. It eats plankton, marine microorganisms and dead organic material.

A CLING FISH (*below*) poises on a rock, hanging on by means of a sucker pad on its pectoral fin. Fragile, scaleless, small finned and a weak swimmer, a cling fish finds itself virtually helpless in strong currents or heavy seas. To survive, it developed the adaptation for which it is named.

A DAMSELFISH snuggles among tender young polyps of the spiny, porous coral *Alveopora* found in the ocean floor off the warm, sandy shores of New Caledonia. This brilliant carmine fish normally lives in friendly relationship with the tentacled sea anemones dwelling on the New Caledonia reefs. But here it has been able to find solace among the *Alveopora*, which usually rejects such rash intruders by seizing them with its extended, writhing tentacles.

A YELLOW CHAETODON, in its death throes, struggles to escape from the tentacles of a colonial reef coral. Virtually invisible in intense light, the chaetodon's colors brighten with darkness. At night it is brilliantly luminous.

A STRIPED GOBY, nuzzling into the sea bottom, bulldozes sand into its jaws to carry elsewhere for the construction of a nest. A timid fish, it makes certain it is unobserved before it dives into its sandy home each evening.

A SLATE-PENCIL SEA URCHIN scuttles silently across the sea bottom in search of prey. Like all sea urchins it is a hard-shelled vegetarian, which laboriously transports itself on movable spines protruding from the hard plates which surround its soft body. In its centrally located mouth are five sets of teeth. Unlike the light, sharp-spined sea urchin, which is relatively common, the lumbering, heavily armed slate-pencil urchin is rarely seen.

TWO SLENDER PIPEFISH glide past each other. Slow swimmers, they depend on bony armor for protection. In a brief meeting, the female lays eggs in a bag below the male's body, whence the young emerge in a week or two.

AN ANEMONE SHRIMP sways by a rock, occasionally flicking its luminous tail at the end of a roll. Nearly transparent, its internal organs can be clearly seen in nature. From its markings, this one is probably a female.

MYSTIC LIGHT OF

For centuries travelers to the tropic seas have marveled at the brilliance of the underwater world of coral, a domain more colorful than any realm of land or air. Here below the shimmering surface coral trees and shrubs grow in coral gardens; coral fans and whips wave in the wash of the tides; coral spires and boulders loom among the crags, brightening the waters with iridescent colors. Through the ages specimens of coral—polished fragments of the skeletons of innumerable architects of the reef—have been prized by collectors in all lands.

It is only in recent times that the techniques of modern scientific research have enabled man to penetrate far beneath the sunlit upper layers. In 1958 divers off the New Caledonia coast descended into depths where the water filters out all rays of the solar spectrum save the short ultraviolet wave lengths. And there they made a momentous discovery. At a level of 120 feet they noticed certain unfamiliar corals aglow with lovely inner light. With infinite care, each cradled in an individual basket, the fragile corals were brought slowly to the surface and transferred to tanks. At once their colors faded; they

A SOLITARY REEF CORAL, a soft-bodied animal equipped with a single mouth, lies inconspicuously tan in sunlit waters *(above)*. In darkness, stimulated by ultraviolet rays, it emits fluorescent red and violet hues *(below)*.

DEEP SEA CORALS

turned brown and drab *(left and right)*, looking like sea Cinderellas compared to their gaudy shallow-water sisters. But when exposed to an ultraviolet lamp, as shown below, they again glowed to life in myriad jewel-like shades. The eyes of man thus looked on a baffling phenomenon of nature: the fluorescence of corals.

Marine biologists cannot now explain why these hitherto unknown corals are endowed with the ability to fluoresce—to glow with unearthly color when stimulated or irritated by radiation of a certain limited wave length. Darwin pondered the question of luminescence in certain nocturnal insects—fireflies, glowworms, elater beetles and others—and considered the possibility that its purpose might be to frighten off enemies or guide the female to the male. He concluded that for some unpalatable insects and their mimics it represented a bright warning of distastefulness. Certain deep-sea fish, perhaps for similar reasons, emit light in their dark domain. But the mystery of luminous coral remains. Why the writhing corals should fluoresce is a question as obscure as the depths where they make their home.

A COLONIAL REEF CORAL, composed of many fingerlike tentacles surrounding three central mouths, appears a pale mottled shade under natural light *(above)*. When fluorescing *(below)*, it is transmuted into an emerald green.

FLUORESCENT CORALS, excited by ultraviolet radiation, form a magic garden in this remarkable picture taken by their own unearthly light. These living specimens, many of them rare, are found in New Caledonia waters.

NEW WONDERS OF THE

Probing coral structures and their foundations, scientists have won deeper insights

WHEN Darwin's work *On the Structure and Distribution of Coral Reefs* appeared in 1842, it was acclaimed by naturalists and geologists the world around. Yet, like other Darwin writings, it precipitated controversies that have not abated since. For the most part its conceptions received assent from men of science, as well as interested attention from Victorians who liked to decorate their parlors with coral curios and shells. With characteristic modesty Darwin seemed unaware of the importance of his achievement.

"No other work of mine," he wrote rather apologetically in his autobiography, "was begun in so deductive a spirit as this, for the whole theory was thought out on the west coast of South America before I had seen a true coral reef. I had therefore only to verify and extend my views by a careful examination of living reefs.

"But it should be observed," continued Darwin, "that I had, during the two previous years, been incessantly attending to the effects on the shores of South America of the intermittent elevation of the land, together with the denudation and the deposition of sediment. This necessarily led me to reflect much on the effects of subsidence, and it was easy to replace in imagination the continued deposition of sediment by the upward growth of corals. To do this was to form my theory of the formation of barrier-reefs and atolls."

Pre-Darwinian conjecture on the creation of coral reefs had clouded rather than resolved the mystery of their existence. The voyagers and explorers during the 17th and 18th Centuries fancied that the coral animals built their circular parapets for reasons of self-defense, and they also compared them with beehives and the geometrical nests of wasps. One early naturalist deduced that the reefs were "built by fishes by means of their teeth." In both prose and poetry, nature writers eulogized the "skill" and "industry" of the "coral insect" in fabricating its "home."

Darwin knew that the giant edifices of reef-building corals were no more the products of skill and industry than the shells of lobsters or crabs. The fanciful picture of atolls as circular fortresses reared by the corals for reasons of defense he dismissed with the simple observation that the active reef builders flourished only on the seaward side of atolls and could not live within the lagoons, and that therefore the reef was no protection for them.

The problem of foundation, however, was the troublesome one. In Darwin's day studies of coral formations were relatively few, but a prevailing theory held that the ring shape of atolls indicated they rested on the rims of submerged volcanic craters. "But when we consider the form and size of some [atolls]," Darwin reasoned, "this idea loses its plausible character." He then proceeded to cite examples of atolls which were five times as long as they were wide, which had varying looplike or undulating shapes, and one in the Indian Ocean which measured 88 miles in length. "It is, also, not a little improbable," he added, "that there should have existed as many craters of immense size crowded together beneath the sea, as there are now in some parts atolls."

Darwin's concept of the creation of coral reefs by the joint, reciprocal, constructive and destructive processes of organic growth and slow subsiding of the foundations (as described on pages 198-199) is still the classic theory today. But as he himself acknowledged, it is oversimplified and incomplete. Modern oceanographers agree that most atolls stand on volcanic foundations which have slowly sunk into the sea. During World War II the U.S. Navy discovered the

EXPLORING THE REEF off New Caledonia, Dr. René Catala looks forward through the viewing box of his pontooned craft. To peer beneath the surface, he swings the glass box down, creating a clear window into the reef world below.

existence of submerged flat-topped volcanic mountains, called guyots, scattered throughout the depths of the Pacific Ocean. Dredging operations brought up pebbles that had obviously been sculptured by wave action, indicating that in the past these drowned plateaus had been islands protruding above the surface of the sea and planed smooth by the everlasting surf. Hence the fact of subsidence, as postulated by Darwin, was sustained.

But subsidence is relative—*i.e.,* it may result either from sinking of the island foundations or from a rise in sea level. Fluctuations in the ocean level have occurred repeatedly in earth history as the result of alternate freezing and melting of the polar icecaps. In glacial eras much of the planet's water vapor was locked up in ice and snow, and the sea level accordingly fell. When a succeeding epoch of warm climate arrived, the icecaps melted and the oceans of the earth rose. Recent studies of fossils and rock samples obtained from drill holes in Pacific reefs have revealed that the evolution of coral formations is more complex than Darwin conceived in his vision of a straightforward sequence from fringing reef to barrier reef to atoll.

In a letter written in 1881, one year prior to his death, Darwin exclaimed, "I wish some doubly rich millionaire would take it into his head to have borings made in some of those Pacific and Indian atolls, and bring home cores for slicing from a depth of 500 to 600 feet." His wish has been realized far beyond his conception. Deep borings have recently been made at three sites in the Pacific—in the Ellice Islands, the North Borodino Islands and in the Marshall Islands—and have provided important confirmations and revisions of Darwin's ideas. The deepest hole was bored in the Marshall group at Eniwetok in 1952, penetrating to 4,600 feet and reaching the foundation on which the earliest substructure of the reef was laid down. It showed that the foundation of the Eniwetok atoll was indeed a submarine volcano, rising two miles from the ocean floor. The volcano at one time projected above sea level. Then, when volcanic action ceased, it slowly sank, and as it returned to the depths, corals and their associated forms of life began building on the submerging slopes. The fossils of these organisms—corals, algae, foraminifera and mollusks—found in the layers of sediment capping the volcanic foundation date as far back as the Eocene period, 60 million years ago. Oceanographers estimate that the Eniwetok atoll has been subsiding at the rate of .08 inch per century since that time.

Hence the most recent discoveries of modern science confirm the heart of Darwin's theory of atoll formation—*i.e.,* subsidence. The major revision or emendation of his hypothesis lies simply in the realm of sequence. Darwin himself realized that an atoll could, under certain conditions, form on a submerged bank, without passing through the fringing or barrier stages. And today scientists are inclined to believe that coral formations can occur as the result of uplifts of islands or drops in sea level, as well as by subsidence and rising sea levels. For example, the fossiliferous rocks discovered at Eniwetok almost a mile below sea level have precise geological counterparts in identical strata in the highlands of the Marianas and Fiji, a mile *above* sea level.

Since the growth of coral reefs is too slow to be observed, all of our knowledge of them is the result of inference and deductive reasoning, based on the classic precept of geology—"The present is the key to the past." Current research can add little more to Darwin's

REEFS
into the atoll and its varied inhabitants

theory of coral evolution. There are other aspects of coral, however, which have engaged the interest of scientists in many parts of the world. One is the elementary problem of geography—of locating and describing all the reefs in all the seas of the earth. Today it is known that the oceans are studded with many reefs that have never been adequately mapped, and many more that have been studied only briefly, if at all. These include the Cook Islands, Pitcairn Island, Easter Island and other coral structures of the South Pacific. In the Western Hemisphere the Panama area has hardly been touched. An attempt to synthesize existing knowledge in this field has been undertaken by Dr. Donald F. Squires of the American Museum of Natural History, who has devoted himself to locating and charting new reefs, classifying the types of coral found on each one and describing varieties of plant and animal life they shelter.

Another approach to the understanding of coral is through the methods of ecology—the branch of science dealing with the interrelationships of varied forms of life. To the ecologist a coral reef provides a perfect theater of observation: it is the most populous, most prolific domain of life on earth, harboring in its submarine grottoes innumerable vertebrate and invertebrate guests. Dr. William Stephenson of the University of Queensland has been examining the Great Barrier Reef of Australia as a sort of jungle or apartment house where all manner of creatures live in close juxtaposition. It has long been known that coral attracts fish—some of them transients, some permanent residents—but only recently did Dr. Stephenson and Dr. Richard Searles of the University of California discover that many fish are tremendously important to coral and, indeed, that the health of coral depends on an abundance of fish. For a major enemy of coral is seaweed, which many species of fish eat avidly as soon as it begins to form in a thin film along the ledges of the reef.

I N the realm of physiology, scientists in many parts of the world are continuing to study the problems of nutrition, growth, calcification, disease and death in corals. Undoubtedly the most fascinating new phenomenon revealed by modern research is the ability of deep-sea corals to fluoresce, as shown on pages 208-211. The discovery was made by Dr. René Catala, director of the aquarium at Nouméa, New Caledonia, a unique institute situated directly upon a coral reef. Opened in 1956, it contains many rare specimens of corals, related invertebrates and fish found nowhere else on earth. (The gaudy wrasse shown in the frontispiece of this chapter is a prize exhibit.) It was in the course of routine dives to collect additional specimens for the Nouméa Aquarium that Dr. Catala's assistants noticed the deep-sea corals glowing softly in the darkness at depths of 120 to 130 feet. Suspecting that they might react to short-wave ultraviolet radiation, Dr. Catala arranged for their transportation to the surface. Despite the extreme fragility of the corals the move was successfully accomplished, and when Dr. Catala exposed them to ultraviolet rays in his laboratory he looked for the first time on the amazing beauty of their fluorescent hues.

Following his discovery Dr. Catala continued to apply himself to the mystery of coral fluorescence. He ascertained additional facts: the same species of coral generally emits the same color; only the fleshy parts of the polyp fluoresce, the skeletal elements do not; the phenomenon ceases as soon as the stimulation ceases, there is no residual photoluminescence. Prolonged exposure harms the corals and eventually kills them. But many puzzles remain. Why do the corals fluoresce only on exposure to short wave lengths? Why do only these corals possess this quality? What is the essential mechanism of fluorescence and its purpose in nature?

Wherever scientists are at work on the still-unsolved mysteries of coral, their motivation is the same as that which stirred Darwin when he peered down into the clear waters and discerned beneath him a brilliant and fabulous new dominion of life. "Such formations surely rank high amongst the wonderful objects of this world," he wrote on leaving the Cocos isles on April 12, 1836. "We feel surprise when travellers tell us of the vast dimensions of the Pyramids and other great ruins, but how utterly insignificant are the greatest of these, when compared to these mountains of stone accumulated by the agency of various minute and tender animals! This is a wonder which does not at first strike the eye of the body, but after reflection, the eye of reason."

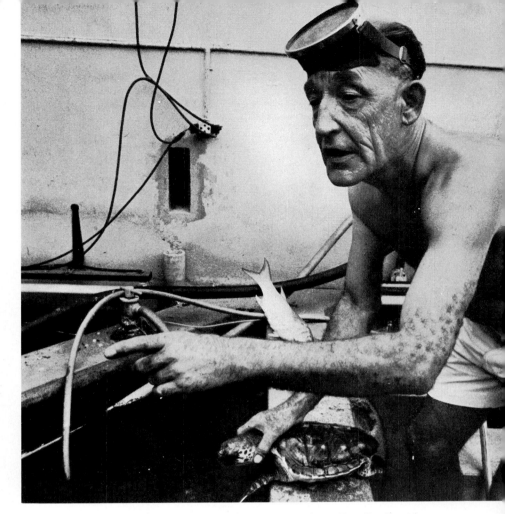

CLEANING A TURTLE at his New Caledonia aquarium, Dr. Catala—his body seamed by exposure—works with one of his specimens. Once a coffee grower, Catala turned his hobby of ichthyology into a renowned career.

DIVING FOR CORAL on a reef off the Bahamas, Dr. Donald F. Squires of the American Museum of Natural History hunts for specimens to send to New York—a delicate undertaking since corals rarely survive when transplanted.

MOST
PRIMITIVE
OF
PRIMATES

A languid lemur, reclining on a comfortable branch, gazes upon the world of man, whom he antedates on earth by nearly 75 million years. For lemurs are the most primitive of all the living primates. They evolved long before their more intelligent cousins, the monkeys and apes, whose aggressive competition subsequently drove them into isolated niches of the earth. Today they thrive mostly on the island of Madagascar. This creature, known as the red-ruffed lemur, is four feet long, including much tail.

THE MACACO LEMUR is a treetop dweller, inhabiting the deeper forests of Madagascar. Though this creature is sometimes referred to as the black lemur, the name is applicable only to the darker male; the female *(right),* as Darwin noted, usually wears some shade of russet or brown, with lighter bodice and ear ruffs. Gregarious, polygamous, they travel the arboreal highways in noisy bands of 12 to 15, eating, sleeping and vocalizing *en masse.*

MOST PRIMITIVE OF PRIMATES

The ancient order of lemurs still clings to life in Madagascar

AT some moment in the evening of the long reign of the dinosaurs, perhaps 75 million years ago, most of the small, furtive mammals which had dwelt in the trees descended to the ground to adopt a new way of life. But a few still clung to their arboreal abode, and it was these keen-eyed, agile creatures that eventually engendered the great order of primates, including the top primate, man. The order also includes a family of poor relations, the shy and gentle lemurs, which still live on the remote island of Madagascar, off the southeast coast of Africa. Their name, probably inspired by their staring, somnambulist eyes and silent, secretive habits, is derived from the Latin *lemures,* meaning "ghosts of the dead."

Most primitive primates, the lemurs once ranged throughout the world. But their more intelligent cousins gradually crowded them from most of the continents. In Madagascar the lemurs—and various other creatures native to the island *(pages 222-223)*—have prospered unmolested in their isolated domain. On the evolutionary scale, from reptiles to monotremes to marsupials to placental mammals, Darwin declared, "we may thus ascend to the Lemuridae, and the interval is not very wide from these to the Simiadiae. The Simiadiae then branched off into two great stems, the New World and the Old World monkeys; and from the latter, at a remote period, Man, the wonder and glory of the Universe, proceeded."

THE WOOLLY AVAHI is a wistful, wide-eyed lemur, barely one foot tall, which grazes at night amid the foliage and sleeps through the day curled up with one or more companions in the fork of a tree. Its unique hands have fingers of unequal length and huge, opposing thumbs. In the dark branches avahis perform prodigious leaps, soaring through the forest canopy like trapeze artists. On the ground they hop in ungainly fashion with hands held high.

THE RING-TAILED LEMUR *(left)* is the most prevalent member of his family. Diurnal and mainly terrestrial, ringtails are more often seen

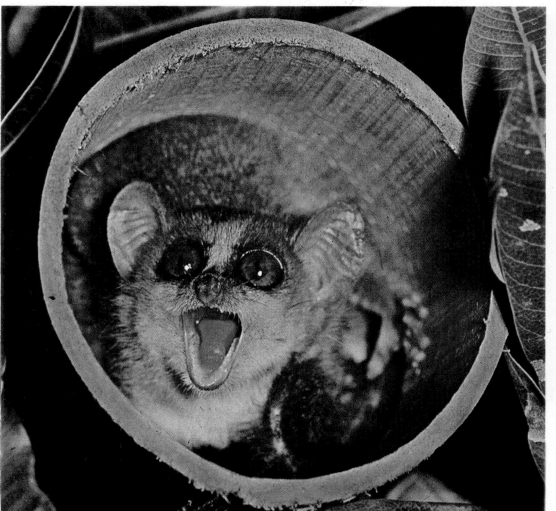

THE LESSER MOUSE LEMUR *(left)* is the smallest of all primates. Barely five inches long, but with a six-inch tail, it nests by day in hollow

among rocks, where they nest, than in the trees. Like all lemurs, however, they are excellent acrobats, capable of executing spectacular leaps like the one shown above. In flight they employ their bushy, two-foot-long tails as stabilizers; at night they wrap them around their necks for warmth. Tame, and extremely neat and clean, they make engaging pets. They can be house-broken and respond to human affection with a sound like a cat's purr.

stems or in the holes of trees and expresses shrill exasperation when disturbed. At night it hunts insects and fruit in the trees, leaping unerringly through the darkness among the slender branches as shown above. Difficult to observe and capture, these creatures do not adjust well to confinement. Unlike their larger, amiable cousins, lesser mouse lemurs have mean dispositions. Although they do not hesitate to bite, they can inflict little damage.

THE SIFAKA LEMUR is sometimes called the monkey lemur because of the white cowl that frames its dark face, suggesting the tonsure of the familiar capuchin monkey of the organ grinder. Essentially arboreal and highly acrobatic, these lemurs sometimes descend to the ground to play, leaping about on long, springy hind legs with amazing agility *(left)*. Baby sifakas attach themselves to their active mothers by curling around their waists or

clinging to the silken fur of their chests or bellies. The golden-eyed baby shown at right is three months old. When it grows a little more it will ride piggyback. Distributed over most of Madagascar, sifaka lemurs move about in family groups, feeding on fruit, flowers, leaves and some bark. They call one another by a series of hiccups. When alarmed they emit a little admonitory growl which sounds like "shi-fak," and from this derives their name.

ODD ISLAND NEIGHBORS

In addition to its remarkable first family, the lemurs, Madagascar shelters in its well-stocked forests and warm coastal plains a variety of other rare and original fauna. For the geological circumstance that provided the lemurs with a sanctuary, isolated from the mainland, enabled other small creatures to diversify free from the threat of larger competitors. Madagascar lacks lions, tigers, leopards, and other great beasts of prey; it has no elephants, rhinoceroses, giraffes, antelopes, nor any of the hoofed herbivores that graze the plains of neighboring Africa; it has no monkeys, gorillas, chimpanzees, nor any primates save the lemurs and man.

As a consequence its animal population consists almost entirely of shy, nonaggressive species, quite different from those of Africa. So many are archaic in character that the entire island conveys a sense of having only recently emerged from the mists of the prehistoric past. Typical of its subfossil curiosities are the catlike fossa *(left)*, unpopular with man for its occasional raids on domestic fowl, and a number of odd insectivores like the primitive tenrec *(below)*.

Other realms of life are more varied. The air flickers with the wings of 300 species of birds, half of them found nowhere else on earth, and hums with multitudinous insects, including 800 species of butterflies. In the island's many rivers and lakes, fresh-water fish of brilliant and bizarre coloration flash their glistening scales. Madagascar is completely free from poisonous snakes, but the island does have a few boa constrictors as well as many crocodiles, lizards, tree frogs, and varicolored, swivel-eyed chameleons like the specimen pictured on the opposite page.

THE FOSSA, a predatory mammal, is unique to Madagascar. Somewhat resembling the wild-cat, it is short-legged and plantigrade—*i.e.,* it puts its heels down first in walking, like bears and men. Equally at home in the trees and on the ground, the fossa preys on both lemurs and birds.

THE TENREC, a spiny insectivore, ranges over most regions of Madagascar from sea level to the medium uplands. Its diet consists of caterpillars, beetles and selected worms. When disturbed or frightened it curls up like

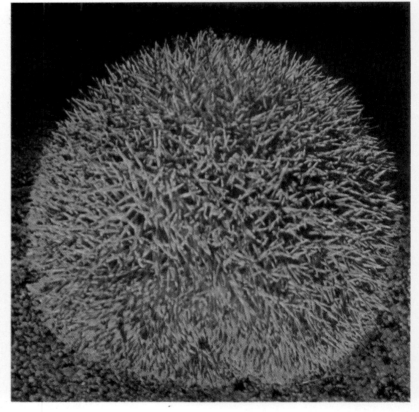

a hedgehog *(right)* and maintains a catatonic state with a sharp drop in body temperature and no perceptible respiration. Despite a powerful odor, tenrecs are prized by the natives as food and sometimes as household pets.

THE CHAMELEON, like all lizards, is a sluggish and slow-moving creature. Camouflaged by its well-known changeable coloration, it lies amid the dappled foliage of the Madagascar forests during daylight hours, waiting for unwary insects to buzz within range of its long, sticky tongue. The chameleon is further endowed with exophthalmic eyes which can revolve either fore *(above)* or aft *(below)*, each eye focusing independently of the other.

THE DISAPPEARING

Beset by man's fires and man's hunger for land and food, the last survivors of a

IN his endeavor to find order among the seemingly chaotic populations of the earth, Darwin never lost sight of the opposing forces of competition and isolation as factors in the creation and shaping of species. He had seen how they had operated to produce unique forms of life in the lonely Galápagos archipelago and in the solitary, sea-girt wastelands of Australia. Thus, in speculating on the peculiar distribution of the lemurs and their separation from the higher primates, he decided that they represented a vestigial group, fragments of a once far-flung population that had been reduced in numbers and restricted by circumstance to their present insular habitation.

"The Lemuridae," Darwin reasoned, "constitute a very distinct family of the Primates. . . . This group is diversified and broken to an extraordinary degree, and includes many aberrant forms. It has, therefore, probably suffered much extinction. Most of the remnants survive on islands such as Madagascar and the Malayan archipelago where they have not been exposed to so severe a competition as they would have on well-stocked continents."

Rising up from the Indian Ocean off the eastern shore of Africa, Madagascar is sundered from the mainland by the deep Mozambique Channel, which varies from 250 to 500 miles in width with the undulating contours of the coast. The fourth largest island in the world (after Greenland, New Guinea and Borneo), Madagascar encompasses an area equal to that of France, Belgium and Holland combined. An immense rocky and semiarid plateau ribs the 995-mile length of the island, with an occasional mountain peak thrusting up nearly 10,000 feet above the ocean. Elsewhere in the island's lower elevations the landscape varies from savanna country to coastal plains, and from desert to dense forest. It is in the depths of these forests, now rapidly falling before the destructive hand of man, that the lemurs have found their last stronghold.

Though they were observed by Arab traders, and even earlier by seafaring Romans, information about the lemurs was misty and apocryphal until Darwin's day. Perhaps the first authentic description of a lemur by a reliable witness was that of a French ship's doctor and naturalist who, while exploring the island with some companions on an expedition in 1768, spied a strange creature sitting upright on a branch like a miniature human, eating fruit with its hand. The physical details as reported by the doctor tallied with later classifications of the largest member of the lemur family, the *Indri Indri*.

Some years later the rarest and most primitive of the lemurs, the eerie aye-aye, which the natives regard as a portent of evil and a harbinger of death, was sighted for the first time. In the middle of the 19th Century several aye-ayes were captured; two specimens preserved in spirits found their way to Paris and Berlin, while a living individual was delivered to the London zoo. The aye-aye aroused considerable discussion among European zoologists, some of whom contended it must belong to a new and distinct order of mammals. It was not until

1863 that a serious attempt to study the lemurs was made. In that year a young Dutch naturalist, François Pollen, journeyed to Madagascar with the aim of conducting an exhaustive investigation. He remained there for three years, and on his return assembled his findings in a book containing the first truly detailed information about the lowest primate family. His discoveries and interpretations were known to Darwin, who referred to them in his own great works.

Such was the start of present-day scientific interest in lemurs. Today, despite their elusiveness, some 21 distinct species of lemurs have been identified, revealing great diversity in form and habit. In the same way that the marsupials of Australia flourished in isolation and radiated into every niche of their environment, so the lemurs of Madagascar, sunk in the protection of their forest hideaways, freed from the competition of more aggressive primates, have mutated into various physical forms and meandered into many diverging byways of behavior. Some have shrunk to the proportions of a wee mouse, others have attained the stature of a sturdy setter. Some are nocturnal and solitary, others are diurnal and sociable. Some are monogamous, others polygamous. Some can leap audaciously through the trees, and others stride surely along the ground. Some carry long bushy tails wrapped around their necks and others bear only stumps. Their dietary preferences include bark, buds, fruit, flowers, insects, nuts, roots and, in rare instances, young birds. Despite their differences all lemurs are temperamentally shy, gentle and charming, and in some instances can be tamed and taught to live with man.

Since Darwin's death, new discoveries have uncovered a great deal of additional evidence confirming his conjecture that lemurs had in past ages "probably suffered much extinction" and that the species we see today are "remnants of a once great family." Their fossil ancestors, dating back to the Paleocene period,

TINY LEMURS, exhibited here by French Zoologist Jean-Jacques Petter, are *Cheirogaleus Medius (left)* and the lesser mouse lemur, the smallest of the primates. Extremely sensitive to climate, these lemurs are hard to keep in captivity.

75 million years ago, have been found in abundance throughout the world, and especially in the bone beds of Europe, North America, Indonesia and Ceylon. Their primordial progenitor, regarded by many paleontologists as the progenitor of all primates, was an insignificant, arboreal, probably insectivorous creature, about the size of a rat, named *Plesiadapidés*, which flourished, among other places, in the western plains of the U.S. The aye-aye of Madagascar is perhaps its closest lineal descendant. By the end of the Eocene epoch, 45 million years ago, all lemurs had disappeared from both Europe and America, doubtless due to pressures from more advanced primate lines.

Precisely when they took refuge in Madagascar and how they were transported there are questions no one can now answer with certainty. Nor is it known whether numerous established species arrived at intervals in the prehistoric past, or whether only a single ancestral form settled there and gave rise to all the others.

Outside Madagascar the only existing lemur species are the large-eyed loris of Malaya and Ceylon, and the agile galago, potto and

LEMUR

great island population face extinction

angwantibo of Africa—all small and nocturnal. The spatial relationship between these lemur outposts and the main population center in Madagascar, and the temporal relationship between contemporary species and their fossil forebears, constitute two of the problems investigated in recent years by the world's outstanding authorities on lemurs, the French zoologists Jean-Jacques Petter and his wife, Arlette.

In 1956, alarmed by the steady erosion of Madagascar's lemur population induced by the destruction of their forest preserves, the Paris Natural History Museum and the International Union for the Conservation of Nature (an organization dedicated to preventing the extinction of rare and vanishing fauna) asked the Petters to undertake an intensive study both to develop new information about the lemurs, and to conceive measures for their protection. For a year Dr. and Mme. Petter roamed the Madagascar forests, studying lemurs in their natural haunts. They also collected about 30 live specimens, which they brought back with them to the Faculté de Médecine in Paris. There several of the lemur families proceeded to bear offspring, among them the tiny lesser mouse lemur, which had never before been known to reproduce in captivity, owing to its finicky requirements with respect to temperature, humidity and insect fare. As a consequence of this happy event the Petters were able to observe for the first time certain interesting procedures involved in the breeding and raising of the young of this smallest of all primates.

In preparation for her confinement, the mother made a nest of leaves and grass in the hole of a tree, and there the babies were born. To feed them she lay prone across their minuscule bodies, while they suckled from underneath. She carried them catlike in her mouth from place to place, and in catlike fashion washed them carefully with her tongue. Another idiosyncrasy was that in periods corresponding to the cool, dry season in Madagascar, the lesser mouse lemur went into hibernation. Every 15 to 20 days it awakened briefly to eat, then slept again until the seasonal cycle was over. Since hibernation is a trait unknown in any of the higher primates, the Petters felt that this discovery gave added confirmation to the Darwinian precept that the lemurs stand on the lowest stage of the primate pyramid, not far above the quadrupedal mammals from which they arose.

OVER and above their scientific studies Dr. and Mme. Petter concerned themselves with the grave problem of conservation. Although the forests where the lemurs live were zoned into reservations which no one may enter without authorization, enforcement of the rules had been notoriously lax. In October 1958, Madagascar became a republic—the Malagasy Republic—within the French community, and the difficulties of establishing a stable system of self-government cast into the background peripheral problems of forest conservation and the protection of wild life. Confronted with multitudinous calls on the public treasury, the new government was disinclined to allocate funds for additional game wardens, forest rangers and guards.

The greatest single threat to the lemur population is the heedless destruction of their habitat by fire. Each year the improvident natives burn large areas of scrubland to encourage the growth of new grass for their cattle; and from these annual conflagrations the flames often spread into the lemurs' preserves. Hence, year by year, the magnificent Madagascar forests, once among the grandest in the world, have gradually been converted into open land. Current estimates indicate that of the original primeval trees only about one tenth now remain. In addition, many of the natives also hunt the lemurs for food. The conservation problem on Madagascar bears many analogies with that affecting the Galápagos Islands prior to the creation of the Charles Darwin Memorial Foundation. Dr. Petter suggested in his report that a similar international foundation, empowered by the Malagasy government to raise funds for strict enforcement of the conservation laws, was the only solution if the lemurs were to be preserved.

Should they become extinct, man will have needlessly destroyed a collateral link in his own genealogical tree—a most important link, for it was from the ancestral line of the little lemurs that he drew certain priceless bequests. From the flat face and close-set eyes of some common progenitor of all the primates man derived his stereoscopic vision, enabling him to see the world in three dimensions, to gauge distances, and to move swiftly and surely in a single optical field. Thence too he inherited his marvelous manipulative hands. In the end, given such sight and hands, he evolved a brain to direct them.

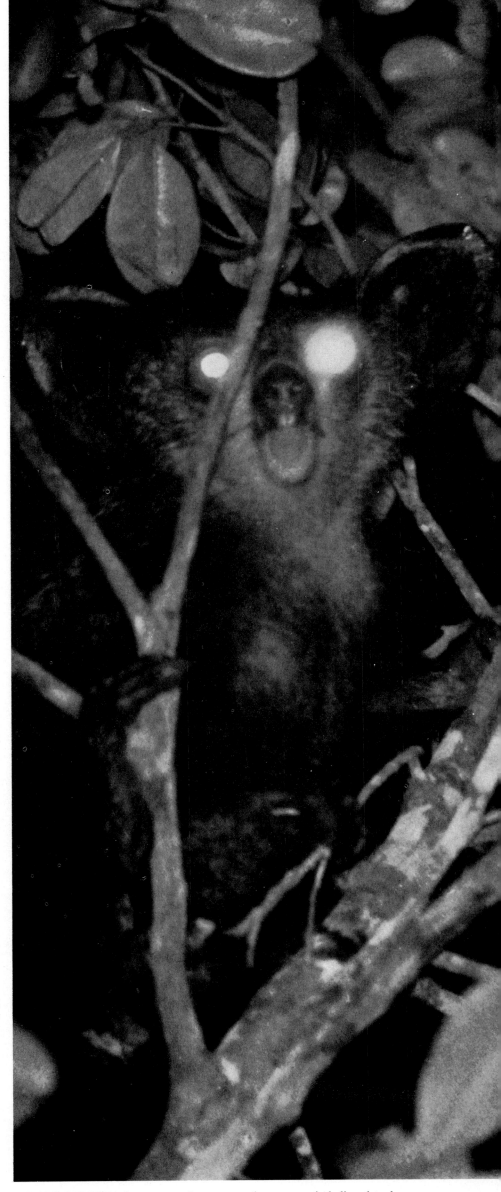

A RARE LEMUR, the nocturnal aye-aye, whose name is believed to have come from the strange cry it utters, is seldom seen and even less frequently photographed. This picture was taken in the forests of Madagascar by Petter.

ODD PARTNERSHIPS FOR SURVIVAL

THE lazy three-toed sloth of South America is a partner in what biologists call "symbiosis"—an association between dissimilar forms of life. In its hair grow tiny plants known as algae. In the dry season the algae are brown; in the wet season they turn green, camouflaging the sloth. It is a profitable association for both, which is not always true of symbiotic relationships. The sloth moth in the foreground feeds on secretions in the sloth's fur and on some of the algae—with no apparent benefit to its hosts.

14

SHARK'S COMPANIONS ARE REMORAS, ATTACHED TO ITS BELLY, AND STRIPED PILOT FISH

ODD PARTNERSHIPS FOR SURVIVAL

The endless struggle to exist produces strange associations

IN his great works Darwin noted repeatedly the exquisite interdependence of all living things and the astonishing ways in which "plants and animals remote in the scale of nature are bound together by a web of complex relations." The pollination of flowers by bees, the seeding of trees by birds, the husbandry of aphids by ants —all indicated to Darwin the community of life on earth and the importance of partnership in the effort to survive. The most extraordinary of these partnerships is the kind existing between utterly dissimilar creatures. This is called "symbiosis"—a Greek word meaning literally "a living together." Sometimes the association benefits both partners. In the case of the African rhino and the tickbird (below), the bird subsists on ticks embedded in folds of skin on the animal's back. It also serves as a sentinel for its myopic host by chirping excitedly at the approach of other animals. Such a partnership, profitable to both members, is known as mutualism or commensalism.

But sometimes the association benefits only one partner, without harming the other; this is known as synoecy. The cattle egret walks in the wake of the rhino, feeding on insects stirred up by its massive tread—but renders no service in return. A similar relationship exists between the shark and its convoy of remoras and pilot fish (above). The remoras attach themselves to the shark by sucker discs on their heads; the pilot fish swim just ahead. Protected from other predators by the presence of their tolerant host, they feast on the leavings of its kills. Why the shark never eats them is not known.

In some situations one symbiotic partner becomes increasingly dependent and sinks into the role of a parasite living at the expense of the other. Man himself is prey to hundreds of parasitic invaders— from bacteria, viruses and fungi to arthropods (ticks and lice), sucking insects and worms. But ideally in nature, symbiosis is a reciprocal association, mutually advantageous to the species involved.

TICKBIRDS AND LONG-LEGGED CATTLE EGRETS LIVE IN COMPANIONSHIP WITH AFRICAN RHINOS

THE KORI BUSTARD AND THE BEE-EATER

The small carmine bee-eater of southern Africa hops on the back of the kori bustard and rides along till the three-foot-tall bird flushes an insect, such as the mantis *(lower left)*. The bee-eater flies off, snaps up its prey and then resumes its perch. The bustard gains nothing from its companion but tolerates it. The crocodile and the Egyptian plover *(right)* present an example of more mutual benefit—noted 2,500 years ago by Herodotus. The crocodile permits the plover to go inside its jaws and pick leeches from its gums, although it would snap up venturesome birds of other species. Its forbearance may be partially explained by the unpalatability of the plover. In the background of the painting are ostriches and zebras, which sometimes herd together for protection. The ostriches have farseeing vision, the zebras acute hearing and smell. Thus they supplement each other in warning of danger.

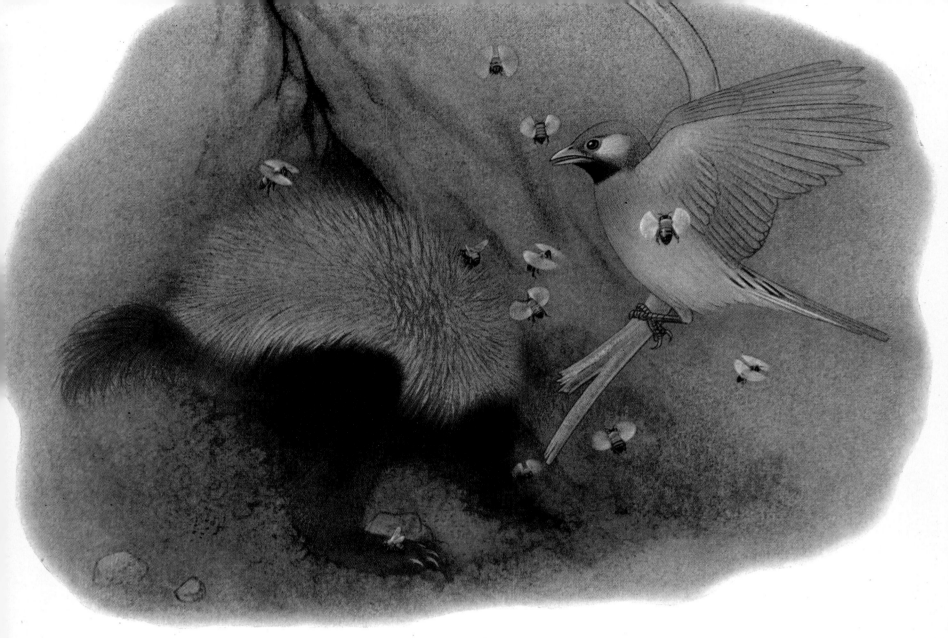

THE HORNBILL
AND THE GUENONS

In the upper Congo forest a single pompadoured hornbill *(left)* often follows chattering guenon monkeys as they move slowly through the high trees, feeding on fruits. The bird, which stays at least six feet below the monkeys' level, uses the animals as beaters to stir up beetles, moths and other insects on which it feeds. Here, fluttering its tail feathers, it is just about to close its serrated beak on a big moth. The natives, who call the hornbill the monkey bird because it is usually around monkeys, say it acts as a sentinel for the guenons. But in all probability the relationship is beneficial only to the bird.

THE HONEY-GUIDE BIRD
AND THE RATEL

In central Africa, the honey-guide bird supplements its insect diet with beeswax. But to get the wax the bird must find a partner who likes honey to help rob the hive. Sometimes the partner is a baboon, sometimes man, but usually it is the badgerlike ratel. The bird leads its companion to the hive by giving out calls, a sort of churring sound that it repeats again and again as it flies ahead of the animal. Once at the hive, the bird waits while the ratel rips it open *(above)* and noses out the honey. After the animal is through eating *(below)*, the bird settles down to feed on the wax combs that are scattered about.

BLUE BUTTERFLY
AND THE ANTS

The life cycle of the large blue English butterfly is shown in these paintings. In June the larva hatches on the wild thyme bushes and for about 20 days feeds on the flowers and other larvae. After moulting the larva stops eating and wanders about aimlessly. At this point, ants gather about the larva (1), stroking its honey gland with their antennae and drinking the sweet droplets it gives off. Finally one ant picks the larva up in its jaws and carries it underground to the nest (2). Here the larva feeds on ant grubs and continues to yield honey whenever the ants stroke it. By winter the larva has become four times its original size and has gone into hibernation. The following spring it becomes active again and soon encases itself in a cocoon (3). In May a butterfly emerges and makes its way above ground where it spreads its wings (4) and flies off to lay eggs.

Several lichens appear on the rocks. A lichen is actually a combination of two symbiotic plants, a fungus and an alga. The alga contains chlorophyll, with which it produces food for the fungus and itself. The fungus encloses the alga, absorbing water and minerals which they both need.

HONEYSUCKLE
AND SPHINX MOTH

The sphinx moth has a long proboscis especially adapted for feeding from long-tubed honeysuckle. The honeysuckle gives off its strongest scent in the evening, attracting the moth, which is nocturnal. In getting its food, the moth pollinates the honeysuckle as it flies from flower to flower.

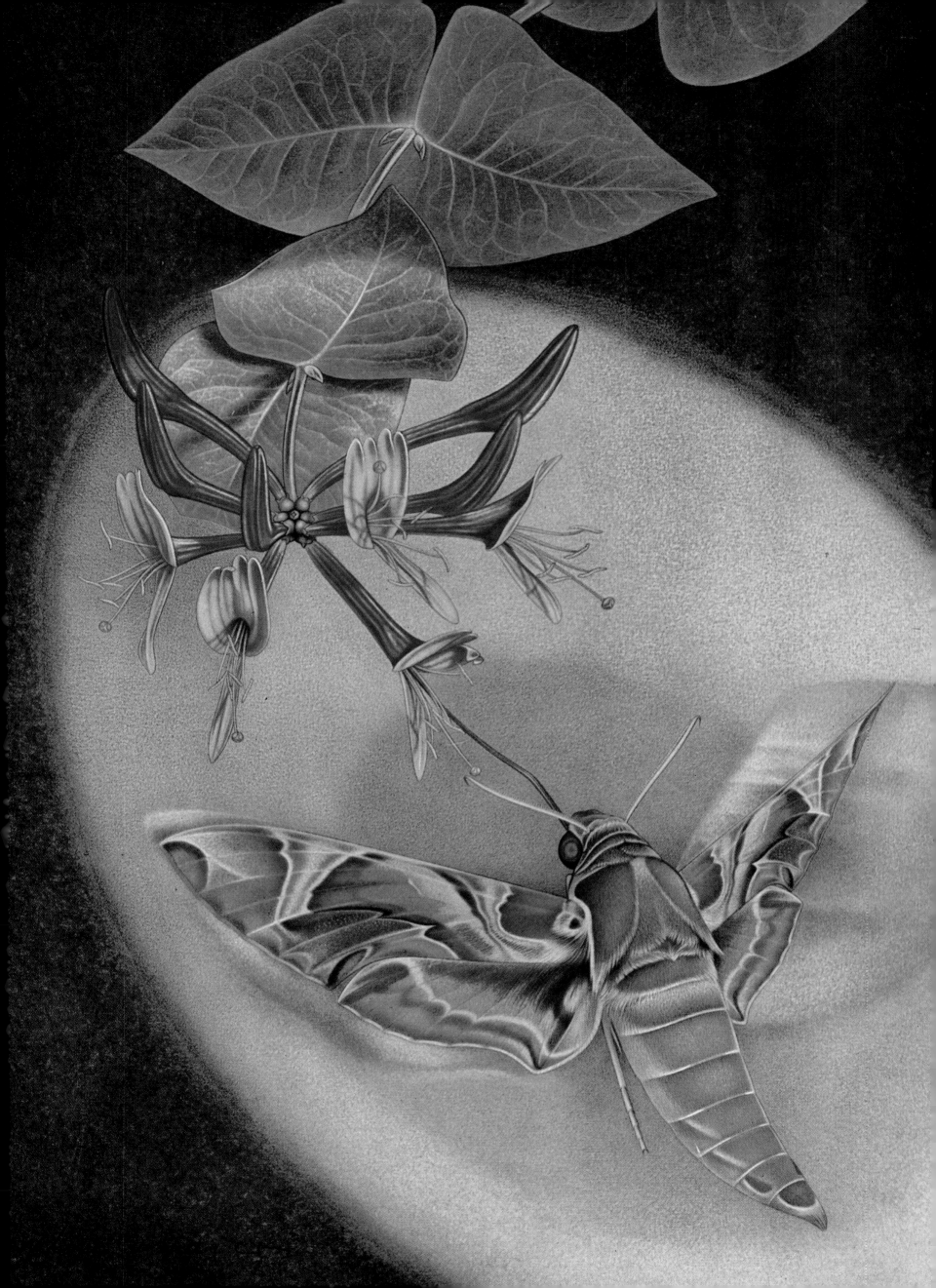

FISH AND JELLYFISH, ANEMONES,

The oceans house many curious relationships. The long-snouted trumpet fish *(upper left)* will swim closely above the back of a bulky parrot fish, concealed from prey below. From its hiding place, the trumpet fish can quickly dart down and seize small prey. Both the anomalops *(far left)* and the squidlike sepiola *(lower left)* have distinctive organs on their bodies which provide luminous bacteria with homes. The anomalops uses the light for defense or to blind its prey; the sepiola sprays out the bacteria in a luminous mass. The big Portuguese man-of-war jellyfish *(center)* in its trailing tentacles and the flowerlike discosoma anemone *(lower right)* in its fleshy tentacles have stinging cells which paralyze the small fish that are their food. But in each case

CRABS AND LUMINOUS BACTERIA

distinctively patterned or colored fish live among the deadly tentacles for protection. They feed on scraps left by their hosts, and sometimes dart out and bring back smaller prey which is shared with their hosts. The *Melia tesselata* crab *(lower center)* carries in its front claws two small anemones which have stinging cells to ward off predators and help capture food. The hermit crab

(right center) attaches another species of anemone to its shell for the same reasons, although the anemone cannot survive long unless the crab supplies it with food. Anemones are immobile, and the crabs, by moving them about, enable them to catch more food. The big carnivorous grouper *(upper right)* allows its mouth and gills to be cleaned of parasites by certain small fish.

235

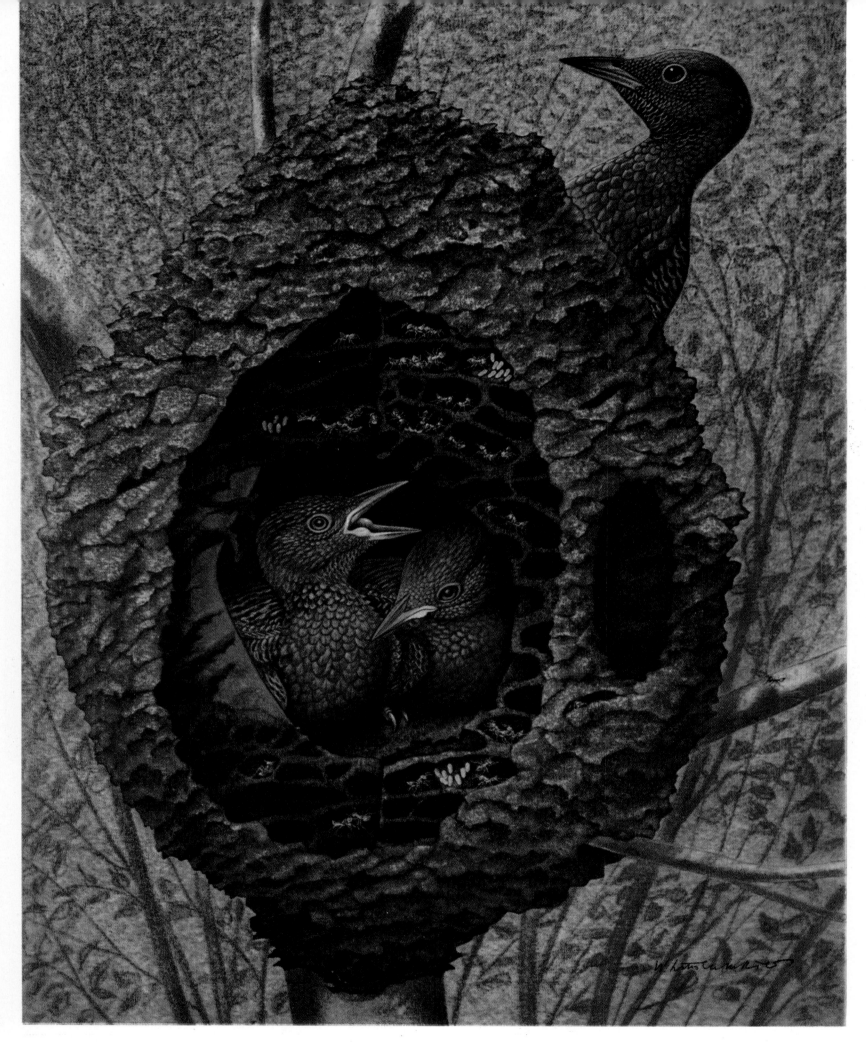

BLACK-CROWNED NIGHT HERON AND THE FISH HAWK

The fish hawk, or osprey *(opposite)*, builds a ramshackle, platform-sized nest on rocky cliffs and old treetops, adding to it year after year. A foot or two under the main section of the nest, the black-crowned night heron sometimes builds its own fragile home. The big nest affords a good shelter from the elements and the fierce, sharp-eyed osprey by its very presence gives the heron protection from other predator birds. The heron is not the only one to move in. Numerous pairs of purple grackles *(left)*, wrens *(center)* and sparrows *(right)* burrow into the side of the nest right under the beak of the osprey, which pays no attention to its guests. Some of these smaller birds also forage for food in the osprey's nest whenever it leaves.

THE RUFOUS WOODPECKER AND THE BLACK TREE ANTS

Normally the southern rufous woodpecker of India and Ceylon *(above)* eats black tree ants. Normally the ants attack and sting any invaders of their home. Yet, under some circumstances, the woodpecker lives amiably in the ants' nest. In the spring nesting season, when the bird is ready to lay its eggs, it makes an opening in the side of the tough, football-shaped nest of the ants and then excavates a six-inch-wide chamber. In the building process some of the ant larvae are killed. But the ants do not attack the bird, and although they eat other birds' eggs, they do not touch the woodpecker's eggs or molest the fledgling birds. And the woodpecker does not eat any of the ants of the particular colony with which it lives.

237

THE NEW ZEALAND TUATARA
AND THE SOOTY SHEARWATER

The lethargic, primitive tuatara *(above)*, a New Zealand reptile and one of the most ancient creatures still in existence, usually lodges in a burrow made by its industrious neighbor, the sooty shearwater, an oceanic bird related to the petrel and the albatross. Since the adult shearwater goes out all day hunting for its food and the slow-moving tuatara goes out to do its hunting at night, the two rarely are in the burrow at the same time. It is thought by many scientists that the tuatara may provide a service for the shearwater by cleaning out the nest of beetles, centipedes and flies. During the winter season, when the bird is away from the nesting site, the tuatara has the underground home to itself and hibernates there till spring.

THE LONG-HORNED BEETLE
AND THE PSEUDOSCORPION

The four-inch, four-winged long-horned beetle *(opposite)* lives in the dank South American rain forest around the buttressed roots of the big trees, where it feeds sparingly but sufficiently on the foliage and damp wood. It is often infested with small parasitic mites that make their way under the wings and into body cracks to feed upon the moisture the beetle's body exudes. A tiny, sharp-beaked member of the scorpion family, called the pseudoscorpion, diligently devours these red mites and thus finds the beetle's back a bountiful and handy hunting ground. It stays with the colorful beetle as long as the supply of mites lasts, ridding its long-legged host of these minute parasites and doing it no harm while living there.

SYMBIOTIC CLEANING

A type of symbiosis, recently revealed, lies in the removal of damaged tissue and

INTRIGUED by the symbiotic association of ants and the sluggish plant lice known as aphids, Darwin performed an experiment one day to test the strength of the relationship. "One of the strongest instances of an animal apparently performing an action for the sole good of another, with which I am acquainted," he related in *The Origin of Species,* "is that of aphids voluntarily yielding their sweet excretion to ants. . . .

"I removed all the ants from a group of about a dozen aphids and prevented their attendance during several hours. After this interval, I felt sure that the aphids would want to excrete. I watched them for some time through a lens, but not one excreted; I then tickled and stroked them with a hair in the same manner, as well as I could, as the ants do with their antennae; but not one excreted.

"Afterwards I allowed an ant to visit them, and it immediately seemed, by its eager way of running about, to be well aware what a rich flock it had discovered; it then began to play with its antennae [upon] the abdomen first of one aphis and then of another; and each, as soon as it felt the antennae, immediately lifted up its abdomen and excreted a limpid drop of sweet juice, which was eagerly devoured by the ant. Even the quite young aphids behaved in this manner, showing that the action was instinctive, and not the result of experience. It is certain that the aphids show no dislike to the ants: if the latter be not present they are at last compelled to eject their excretion. But as the excretion is . . . viscid, it is no doubt a convenience to the aphids to have it removed; therefore probably they do not excrete solely for the good of the ants."

Darwin summarized with this percipient sentence: "Although there is no evidence that any animal performs an action for the exclusive good of another . . . yet each tries to take advantage of the instincts of others." This observation holds true for all types of symbiotic relationships. A newly discovered association that exemplifies Darwin's thought even more vividly than the aphid-ant partnership is found in the symbiotic cleaning of fish in the sea. The term *symbiotic cleaning* refers to the service rendered by one organism when it removes (and eats) various harmful bacteria, parasites, undesirable food particles or damaged tissue from another. Although this phenomenon had been noted among terrestrial animals for many years, it attracted little scientific attention save as a curiosity of nature until the last decade. Today naturalists recognize its prevalence everywhere, and its especial importance to fish.

One of the earliest reported instances of cleaning symbiosis dates back to 1892, just ten years after Darwin's death, when an English entomologist observed that pseudoscorpions apparently cleaned parasites from large insects *(page 239).* In 1924 the famed American

naturalist, William Beebe, reported that he had seen red crabs foraging for red ticks on the leathern hides of marine iguanas sunbathing on the lava ledges of the Galápagos Islands *(page 29).* Four years later Beebe, noting small wrasses at work cleaning fish in the waters off Haiti, compared the relationship to that of the crocodile and plover *(page 229),* and the rhinoceros and tickbird *(page 228).* In 1949 the late Dr. Conrad Limbaugh, marine biologist at the Scripps Institution at La Jolla, California, observed cleaning fish off the American coast and began to investigate the significance of their activities. Five years later Dr. Irenäus Eibl-Eibesfeldt of the Max Planck Institute in Bavaria *(page 39)* published the results of extensive studies of cleaning symbiosis among fishes in both Atlantic and Indo-Pacific waters. He noted that it involved, either as cleaners or cleaned, virtually all free-swimming fish, including reef and open sea forms, and all sizes up to sharks and rays. Known cleaners today include 21 species of highly specialized fish, at least six species of shrimps, one bird (a gull), a crab and a worm.

The cleaning operation differs in minor details, but essentially the procedure is the same whether it takes place in the Caribbean, the Mediterranean or the South Seas. The cleaner—whether a fish or shrimp—offers its services through various attitudes and maneuvers; the client fish accepts the offer and invites the cleaner to go to work with responsive signals. In some instances the encounter is so casual as to appear almost accidental. A tiny wrasse or goby may swim up to a larger fish and forage along the crevices of its body. The ceremony tends to be simple in northern waters. But in tropical seas the bright-colored cleaner fish may put on displays as elaborate as those used in courtship rites. They dart forward, turn sideways, dance around the client fish, nibbling, extending their fins, beating their tails up and down, then retreating and re-

CHECKING HIS DIVING CAGE, Dr. Conrad Limbaugh *(left)* of the Scripps Institution of La Jolla, California, prepares the protective equipment in which he submerges in shark-infested waters to study symbiosis among marine creatures.

peating the process until the object of their attentions slows down. Certain cleaner shrimps have white antennae of exaggerated length which they wave like signal flags to halt the fish they wish to serve.

The client fish react by approaching the cleaner, pausing and assuming awkward positions as though in a hypnotic state. Certain species signal their willingness to be cleaned by floating at odd angles: some stand on their heads, others roll over on their sides. On occasions when the customers outnumber the cleaners they jostle each other and even become unruly, starting vicious fights, snapping and thrashing in a rush to be first in line.

When the cleaning process begins, the client often slumps into an apparent coma. The cleaner carefully forages along its body from head to tail, nibbling with small pointed teeth at the various parasites that trouble fish—copepods and isopods, both minute crustaceans with sharp mandibles—and at bacteria, fungus growths, food

IN THE SEA

parasites from one species by another

particles and segments of sore or damaged tissue. If the client fish holds a fin too close to its side, the cleaner inserts its pointed snout and nudges until the fin is obligingly raised. In the same way it gently encourages the client to spread its gill coverings and open its mouth. The cleaner often enters a larger fish's mouth and disappears completely, working its way along the inside of jaws and palate and down into its throat. Even such predatory and fearsome fish as moray eels, barracudas and sharks submit to this therapy without harming their cleaners.

Some client fish change color during the process. One species, common on the reefs of the Maldive archipelago in the Indian Ocean, turns from near black to light blue while being cleaned. Another genus turns pale. A type of discus fish which is especially troubled by fungus turns almost black, thus bringing the fungus blotches into light relief.

Marine biologists discovered recently that certain fixed locations on reefs, coral heads and other formations mark the sites of cleaning stations to which fish come for servicing at regular intervals. At one such station in the Maldives, Dr. Eibl-Eibesfeldt noted that a large school of one species of fish showed up at the same time every day. All the species that patronized this station summoned the attendants in the same way: they opened their mouths, spread their gill covers and turned their lips inside out. When the job was completed to their satisfaction they closed their mouths, flipped their tails and swam off. At another such station, in the Bahamas, Dr. Limbaugh found that in a six-hour daylight period 300 fish were processed by a single cleaner. Some fish—especially sick or injured individuals—returned many times during the day.

In an experiment designed to ascertain the effects of cleaning—or of the lack of it—Dr. Limbaugh removed all the known cleaners from two small, isolated reefs in the Bahamas where fish were particularly abundant. Within a few days the population was drastically reduced, and in two weeks virtually all but the permanent reef residents had disappeared. Of those that remained, many developed fuzzy blotches, swellings, ulcerated sores and ravaged fins. In Dr. Limbaugh's opinion, many of the places where fish foregather in enormous multitudes—such as the famous fishing grounds off certain islands and shoals of the Atlantic and Pacific oceans—may actually be cleaning stations, which attract their silver hordes by virtue of the services they render.

BOTH Dr. Limbaugh and Dr. Eibl-Eibesfeldt observed that cleaning fish wear a characteristic uniform, whose colors and patterns contrast strikingly with their environment. In general the cleaners are barred or striped. In accordance with the Darwinian theory of natural selection it is not surprising that the cleaners, whose role in life depends on being seen rather than concealed, should evolve toward conspicuous patterns. The cleaning fish of the Indian and Pacific oceans emphasize blue with a black side band. Caribbean cleaners, on the other hand, tend to be yellow, but also with a black side band, running the entire length of their bodies. This lateral bar, therefore, appears to be the guild insignia of cleaning fish around the world, whatever the background colors. It is not without significance that mimics have evolved in the realm of symbiotic cleaning fish as in other domains of life. In the Indian Ocean, for example, a vicious predator named *Aspindontus taeniatus* has evolved the sartorial colors and patterns of the principal cleaner of the area, *Labroides dimidiatus.* Clad in blue, wearing a side bar, the mimic fish approaches prospective clients with the same seesaw flipping motion of the labroid cleaning fish offering its services. But when the unsuspecting client presents itself for cleaning, *Aspindontus taeniatus,* whose underslung jaw is equipped with long saberlike teeth, goes into swift and furious action, tearing large chunks of flesh from its duped victim's body.

Summarizing present-day knowledge of symbiotic cleaning, Dr. Limbaugh observed, shortly before his death, that the phenomenon held important implications for many areas of research—evolutionary adaptation, species composition, behavior interpretation and parasitology. But above all, Dr. Limbaugh concluded, "From the standpoint of the philosophy of biology, the extent of cleaning behavior emphasizes the role of cooperation in nature as opposed to the tooth-and-nail struggle for existence."

CLEANING SCALES, a wrasse removes harmful copepods from a dreamy damselfish. Conspicuous like all cleaners, the white-striped wrasse is equipped with a pointed mouth ideally adapted for snaring these minute parasites.

CLEANING MOUTH, a labroid fish slips inside the lips of a red-and-white-striped barberpole. Nosing its way deep within, it will back out when the barberpole signals that the job is done by shaking or closing its mouth.

HUNTING LUNCH among the stinging arms of a sea anemone, a bulbous skunk clown prepares to search for prey both will share. Poisonous to fish, the anemone tolerates the skunk clown for inexplicable symbiotic reasons.

241

MAN'S INFLUENCE ON EVOLUTION

THIS handsome French cock, glowering from beneath its huge red comb, is a descendant of the jungle fowl of Southeast Asia to which Darwin traced all modern breeds of poultry. In his studies of domestic animals Darwin noted that selective breeding by man had produced numberless variations of ancestral forms. He concluded that species could also be transformed by the slower process of natural selection. This particular specimen belongs to the breed "La Flèche," famed for its regal aspect and white meat.

15

SILKWORM COCOONS, shown here against a bed of the green mulberry leaves on which the silkworm thrives, exhibit variations produced by selective breeding. Today there are more than 1,000 varieties of silk moth, all descended from a common ancestor. The two white cocoons in the center are hardy strains used to improve weaker varieties. Others are valued for color or for the strength, length, fine quality or quantity of their thread.

MAN'S INFLUENCE ON EVOLUTION

In domesticated animals Darwin first saw selection at work

ON October 2, 1836, Darwin concluded his epic voyage and for the next two years lived mostly in London. As he went over his notes he became increasingly "haunted"—the word is his—by the conviction that the multifarious forms of life on earth had not been created separately but must have diverged from a smaller number of ancestral lines. It was plain to him that domestic animals had been profoundly altered, and were still being altered, by selective breeding. He decided, therefore, that "by collecting all facts . . . on the variation of animals and plants under domestication and [in] nature, some light might be thrown on the whole subject."

With his marvelous diligence, Darwin set out to trace widely differing breeds back to their wild origins. He studied sheep, cattle, pigs, dogs, cats, poultry, rabbits, pigeons, peacocks, canaries, goldfish, bees and silk moths, as well as cabbages, peas, beans, potatoes, fruit trees, nut trees, roses, dahlias and pansies. He interviewed breeders and gardeners, and devoured "heaps of agricultural and horticultural books." In later years he exclaimed, "When I see the list of books which I read and abstracted, I am surprised at my industry."

Darwin devoted special attention to pigeons, becoming a breeder himself and an ardent member of two London pigeon clubs. Pigeon raising, he once wrote to his son William, "is a majestic and noble pursuit that beats moths and butterflies, whatever you say to the contrary." Delving into the past, he discovered records of domesticated pigeons dating as far back as the Fifth Dynasty of Egypt, around 2500 B.C. He noted that the Romans paid "immense prices" for pigeons and that the 16th Century Mogul Emperor, Akbar, carried 20,000 of them in his entourage.

"The diversity of the breeds is something astonishing," Darwin declared. Yet in the end he concluded—and his opinion stands—that all the varieties of pigeons produced by selective breeding stem from a common ancestor. This was the wild rock pigeon, *Columba livia,* closely resembled today by its familiar descendant, the striped-winged, gray-blue street pigeon which roosts on the cliffs and ledges of the cities of the world. Darwin's studies of human selection led him ultimately to his vision of the slower, deeper processes of natural selection by which new species are continually created and transformed.

FANCY PIGEONS flutter above a lowly street pigeon, urban facsimile of the ancestral wild rock pigeon, now rare, which Darwin identified as the progenitor of all modern breeds. The fliers here, show birds bred by man for exhibition purposes, include *(at top, left to right)* a Fantail, a Baldhead Tumbler, a Nun, and *(below, clockwise from lower left)* a Show Tippler, an Oriental Frill, a Barb, a red Pygmy Pouter and a Long-faced Tumbler.

THE PROFUSION
OF PIGEONS

THE ENGLISH POUTER, which can inflate its crop, amused Darwin, who wrote, "The males glory in exercising this power." He added that fanciers blow air into their beaks to make them strut "puffed up with wind and pride."

THE FANTAIL was known in 16th Century India. As against the 12 tail feathers of most other pigeons, the Fantail boasts up to 48, which it can elevate in sunrise splendor. In prize specimens the head and tail feathers touch.

THE NUN, long prized for the beauty of its coloring, derives its name from the black veil it wears across its face. Darwin bred Nuns himself and imported specimens from India for comparison. He described them as "elegant" birds.

THE JACOBIN *(below)* wears a monastic hood of inverse plumage about its head. Admired and inbred for centuries, it has lost all ability to fly.

THE PARLOR TUMBLER is an earth-bound member of a breed well known in Darwin's day. Unlike its high-flying relatives, which combine aeronautical skill with acrobatics, it can barely flutter from the ground. In its struggle to fly, it somersaults as shown in this multiple exposure.

247

THE RAMBOUILLET was first bred by Louis XVI of France. Introduced to America in 1840, it is now the third most popular U.S. breed, esteemed for its large size and the fine-quality wool it provides for fragile clothing fabrics.

THE BORDER LEICESTER was developed from sheep common in the English Midlands in Darwin's day which had been the subject of early breeding experiments. A long-wool breed, its fleece falls in curly six-inch locks.

THE FAT-RUMPED SHEEP packs 25-40 pounds in its buttocks. Bred since ancient times, fat-rumps were known to Herodotus, who noted that Arabs valued their fat for lamp oil and their tails as delicacies when properly fried.

THE ASIATIC MOUFFLON IS BELIEVED TO BE THE

FIRST ENTICED

Of man's barnyard animals sheep and goats were probably the first enticed into the fold. It was in Neolithic times, perhaps 7,000 years ago, that certain wild sheep abandoned their Near Eastern ranges for the green pastures sown by man. Although Darwin was unable to untangle their genealogy, zoologists today are fairly certain that the Anatolian (or Asiatic) Moufflon (above), which still runs wild in the

THE LOP-EARED SHEEP of North Africa has a two-textured coat—half wool, half hair—long legs, a very long tail and no horns. An all-purpose animal, it supplies milk and coarse wool and, posthumously, meat and leather.

CHIEF PROGENITOR OF ALL DOMESTICATED SHEEP

INTO THE FOLD

hills of Iraq, Iran and Turkey, is the primary ancestral prototype. Hairy rather than woolly, it was probably domesticated originally for its meat and hide and only later bred for the soft winter underfur that in time evolved into wool. Of more than 200 breeds of sheep known today, most are classified by the type of wool they bear. But some are bred for the fantastic development of their tails *(below)*.

THE BLACKFACE HIGHLAND, a variety bred in Scotland, is prized for its mutton and long wool. Once called the "colley" (from the Anglo-Saxon *col*, black), it gave its name, a tradition says, to the collie dogs that herded it.

THE SOUTHDOWN SHEEP, classic source of English mutton, is also raised for its short, medium-quality wool. It is the most famous of several short-wooled breeds first produced on the South Downs in the 18th Century.

THE FAT-TAILED SHEEP of far eastern Asia, whose tail yields tallow, used to require a small cart to transport its tail around the barnyard. Today such excessively fat tails are rare; breeders prefer sheep that tote their own.

THE ZACKEL SHEEP, a type bred in southeastern Europe, yields a long, rough wool used for making rugs and peasant clothing. In wilder areas, the ram employs its extended spiral horns for spirited defense against predators.

249

ANCESTRAL TYPES ALIVE TODAY

Scientists have long pondered the question of how such formidable and often dangerous animals as wild cattle, wild horses and wild swine came to surrender their freedom and submit to the will of man. One plausible guess has it that young calves, colts and piglets were caught and cared for in captivity, and the sequence of their domestication is suggested by archaeological evidence. The first of the larger animals to follow sheep and goats into the barnyard were cattle or pigs. Last came the horses.

During countless millenniums large, long-horned wild cattle known as aurochs ranged the grasslands from Europe through the Near East. Their appearance is well known from skeletons and cave paintings of Paleolithic man. Darwin noted that although some were domesticated by the Neolithic Swiss Lake Dwellers about 2500 B.C., cattle still ran wild in Europe in Caesar's time. He also remarked that some direct descendants, smaller but little changed, had been preserved at Chillingham Park, Northumberland, at least since the 13th Century. More than two dozen of them still graze there.

The progenitors of the modern pig also ranged in a wide belt, stretching all the way from western Europe through the Far East. Two ancestral types survive today: the Eurasian common wild boar, *Sus scrofa (opposite page),* which still flourishes in parts of Europe and the Near East, and the common wild pig of eastern Asia, *Sus vittatus.* The horse, last of man's major animals to be domesticated, was probably tamed by nomads who roamed Central Asia about 4,000 years ago. Its original characteristics can be discerned through cave paintings, skeletons and early records of a wild horse of the Middle Ages known as the tarpan, recently re-created in a modern-day facsimile *(left, above)* by zoologists turning back the evolutionary clock.

EARLY HORSES *(above)*, facsimiles of the tarpans that ran wild in medieval Europe, have been "reconstructed" by crossing Icelandic ponies with Przewalski horses *(below)*, progeny of wild herds discovered in Asia in 1882.

ANCIENT BULL, modern link with the aurochs—wild cattle that ranged from Europe through the Near East in prehistoric times—survives today in an inbred herd that has been kept in Chillingham Park, England, since 1220 A.D.

ANCESTRAL BOAR, a forefather of the domesticated pig, still exists in parts of Europe and the Near East, though it is now extinct in Britain, where boar hunts, with spear and dogs, were popular in the Middle Ages. Known scientifically as *Sus scrofa,* the Eurasian wild boar stands three feet high and is armed with four tusks and 44 teeth, which can inflict fearsome wounds. It lives mostly on roots, raked from beneath the soil with its sensitive snout.

ANCESTOR
CORN

FAMILY TREE OF MODERN CORN

Speaking of corn, Darwin declared, "Botanists are nearly unanimous that all the cultivated kinds belong to the same species. It is undoubtedly of American origin, and was grown by the aborigines throughout the continent. . . . Its cultivation must have been extremely ancient . . . for I found on the coast of Peru heads of maize embedded . . . in a beach which had been upraised at least 85 feet above the sea. . . . The aboriginal form has not as yet been discovered." To this day the wild ancestor of corn has not been found in nature. Corn's history, however, has been traced back to 3600 B.C., when it was a basic food for Indians of North America. One of a very few products domesticated in the New World (others: the potato, tomato, tobacco, turkey, guinea pig, llama), corn is today the biggest U.S. crop, with an annual harvest of almost four billion bushels.

Corn is a kind of grass, a fact evident to anyone who has ever seen its shoots emerging; and there are grass plants thriving in the wild which are close relatives. From these and specimens found in ancient Indian caves, botanists envisage the ancestral corn as a grassy mite like the tiny ear at far left, an experimentally bred reconstruction. It was a pop corn with kernels that would explode when heated, and a pod corn whose kernels were attached to the cob by fragile stems that broke on maturity, ensuring seed dispersal. (Modern corn, with its tightly bound kernels and green husk, requires man's aid in reproduction.)

In this photograph are traced three developments in the evolution of corn, beginning with the primordial ear. The small cob just beside it was cultivated in Peru in 300 B.C. From here the three lines diverge. The lower branch, curving down to the left, shows some of the colorful corns that have been developed through the ages in Peru. The upper arm depicts the strains leading up to the giant Mexican Jala, largest corn in the world. The central, diagonal line follows the evolution of North American corn, which culminates finally in Corn Belt Dent *(lower right),* the pride and staple of the U.S. farm economy today.

IN THE KALAHARI DESERT, African Bushmen subsist by predomestication foraging. Here an old woman digs for roots with a pointed stick.

ON THE PLAINS OF KENYA, tribesmen laboriously water their cattle. Since no wild relatives of cattle live in Africa and no fossil remains have been found from earlier times, it is likely that cattle were introduced in early Neolithic migrations from centers of domestication in the Near East.

PRIMITIVE HUSBANDRY OF TODAY

"Savages are fond of taming animals," Darwin noted, "and if any of these produced young, and were at the same time useful, they would be at once domesticated." Darwin saw many primitive people with domesticated varieties of dogs, but he came to admit that "we shall probably never be able to ascertain their origin with certainty." The evidence of archaeology suggests that man domesticated the dog because it helped him hunt, in good times ate his refuse and in bad times served as his food.

Darwin was more concerned, however, with how man himself began to influence the evolution of domesticated animals. To critics who doubted that prehistoric man was intelligent enough to practice selective breeding, Darwin adduced the principle of "unconscious selection," which he saw as the result of man "naturally preserving the most valued and destroying the less valued individuals." The animals thus cared for would flourish and their offspring would become the subjects of further selection. Darwin found the same principle at work with plants. "It has consisted in always cultivating the best-known variety, sowing its seeds, and when a slightly better variety chanced to appear, selecting it."

Today, when Darwin's premises are accepted by scientists, primitive peoples, as shown here, offer continuing evidence of the early stages in the course of domestication.

IN THE SOLOMON ISLANDS, a native trader offers poultry and fruit domesticated in Southeast Asia, then dispersed through the Pacific.

IN THE AUSTRALIAN WASTES an aborigine and his yellow dingo dog squat together by the ashes of their campfire. One of the world's most primitive peoples, the aborigines are nomadic hunters, whose only domesticated animal is the dog. The tie is an easy one, for the dingo alternately joins man in his hunts and returns to the wild when times are hard. It was probably in this way that the dog first entered man's service perhaps 20,000 years ago.

A REINDEER ROUNDUP is held at least once a year by the Laplanders of northern Finland. The reindeer are a case of half domestication by a half-primitive people who thrive on the threshold of civilization but have not yet completely crossed it. The Lapps herd reindeer, milk them, train them as draft animals and as mounts, and use corrals for seasonal roundups like modern cattlemen. But reindeer migrate twice yearly with the seasons in

search of the lichens and grass on which they graze. And many Lapps, adapting themselves to the reindeer's habits, still migrate with them, thus clinging to a nomadic way of life. In this picture the reindeer are being rounded up in a corral at the village of Paistunturit. After running in circles for a few hours they will tire sufficiently so that their owners, who mark individual animals by notching their ears, can separate their own and select some for slaughter.

ON NUNIVAK ISLAND in the Bering Sea, musk oxen live as wards of the U.S. Though their favorite diet is willow leaves, they can subsist on shrubs and lichens. Unlike cattle, they can paw beneath the snows for food.

OUR NEW FRIEND: THE MUSK OX

Since Darwin's day naturalists have wondered why man did not stop after domesticating his pets, the cat and dog, and his five barnyard animals, the sheep, goat, cow, pig and horse. Serving man in special ways, there are the elephant and water buffalo of India, the reindeer of Lapland *(pages 260-261),* the camel of Africa and the llama of South America. But the only animals that have been selectively bred since the dawn of civilization, and exploited in both life and death for commercial gain, are the big five of the barnyard. Now, however, a new candidate has appeared in the musk ox *(right).* Its name is misleading, for it has no musk glands and is not an ox but a member of the sheep-goat family. Once far-ranging in North America, it has been driven deep within the arctic tundra by man's depredations. The herds, numbering only a few thousand, are protected by law. In 1954 the American anthropologist John J. Teal Jr. won permission from the Canadian government to capture musk-ox calves to start an experimental herd in Vermont *(below).* In 1958 two calves were born—an indication of the musk ox's domestication.

IN VERMONT *(left)* musk oxen transported from their arctic habitat have responded well in a farm environment. Docile and playful, they respond to human affection. On hot days they cool off by frequent dips in the pond.

A YOUNG MALE, captured five years ago as a calf in the Canadian tundra, reclines in happy domestication amid the lush pastures of its new home in Vermont. The musk ox's assets as a domestic animal are threefold: its long wool, which it sheds and grows anew each year and which has the fine quality of cashmere; its meat, which tastes like a blend of beef and mutton; and its extreme hardihood. A full-grown bull may weigh up to 1,400 pounds.

ORIGINS OF THE FARM

Archaeology still pursues Darwin's goal of tracing man's domestic breeds back to

A FEW months after the publication of his masterpiece, *The Origin of Species,* Darwin determined to expand its opening chapter, in which he discussed the amazing diversity of characteristics produced by man in his plants and animals through a few generations of selective breeding. Convinced that his whole theory of *natural* selection rested on detailed proof of the power of *human* selection to modify and improve domestic products, Darwin started gathering material and writing the second of his great works, *The Variation of Animals and Plants Under Domestication.*

As he recounts it: "On January 7th, 1860, I began arranging my notes for my work . . . but it was not published until the beginning of 1868; the delay having been caused partly by frequent illness, one of which lasted seven months, and partly by having been tempted to publish on other subjects which at the time interested me more."

In the compass of two massive volumes, totaling nearly 1,000 pages, Darwin set down everything he could assemble through research, experiment and personal observation on the origins, past history and current condition of animals, birds, grains, cereals, flowers, plants and trees domesticated by man, along with his own analysis of the causes and laws of variation, inheritance, crossbreeding, inbreeding, sterility, hybridism and reproduction. This monumental work was the most comprehensive study of domestication ever made, and nothing quite like it has been attempted by any scientist since.

In his introductory paragraphs Darwin states the essential thesis of his book: "Although man does not cause variability and cannot even prevent it, he can select, preserve, and accumulate the variations given to him by the hand of nature almost in any way which he chooses; and thus he can produce a great result. . . .

SORTING OUT CLUES in Iran, Dr. Charles Reed, a zoologist, separates 8,000-year-old bones into wild and domesticated categories during a 1960 expedition sponsored by the University of Chicago to study the beginnings of domestication.

Man may select and preserve each successive variation, with the distinct intention of improving and altering a breed, in accordance with a preconceived idea; and by thus adding up variations, often so slight as to be imperceptible to an uneducated eye, he has effected wonderful changes and improvements.

"It can, also, be clearly shown," continued Darwin, "that man, without any intention or thought of improving the breed, by preserving in each successive generation the individuals which he prizes most, and by destroying the worthless individuals, slowly, though surely, induces great changes."

Darwin was often bemused by the stubborn conviction of even sophisticated breeders—despite the manifest evidence of their own power to revise and alter the plant and animal species with which they dealt—that separate breeds were products of separate creation, and could not be related to a common ancestral tree. "Ask, as I have asked, a celebrated raiser of Hereford cattle, whether his cattle might not have descended from Long-horns, or both from a common parent-stock, and he will laugh you to scorn," he wrote. "I have never met a pigeon, or poultry, or duck, or rabbit fancier, who was not fully convinced that each main breed was descended from a distinct species."

With characteristic humility, Darwin confessed that when he became a pigeon fancier himself he found the fantastic variety of domesticated breeds almost impossible to reconcile with his belief in their divergence from a common ancestor. Yet he clung to his conviction that breeds must not be confused with species.

Darwin also met strong opposition among his fellow naturalists, who, "knowing far less of the laws of inheritance than does the breeder, and knowing no more than he does of the intermediate links in the long lines of descent, yet admit that many of our domestic races are descended from the same parents." But paradoxically these same naturalists, while accepting the concept of human selection, declined to extend the same clear logic to the idea of natural selection. In his investigations Darwin was, however, handicapped by obstacles far greater than mere skepticism. One of the most important was the fragmentary state of knowledge in an area of science which, in its later development, was to provide crucial evidence in support of his theories. This science was archaeology, which, incipient in Darwin's lifetime, gained momentum toward the end of the 19th Century, and in the 20th began to disclose the circumstances of man's earliest enterprises in agriculture and animal husbandry. Ironically, it was the intellectual ferment created by Darwin's work that enkindled scientific interest in the silent relics of man's prehistory on the planet. For Darwin had lifted the curtain on vistas undreamed of by earlier generations.

Darwin had, in turn, derived his perspective of the enormous span of animal life on earth from the work of his friend and sponsor, the eminent geologist Sir Charles Lyell. Outside the *avant-garde* of scientists like Lyell and Darwin, the prevailing estimate of the age of the universe was about 6,000 years—a figure based on the extrapolations of the 17th Century theologians Archbishop James Ussher of Armagh, Ireland, and Dr. John Lightfoot of Cambridge University. The latter proclaimed that his painstaking analysis of the Scriptures revealed the world had been created in the year 4004 B.C., on Sunday morning, October 23, at 9 a.m. In the attempt to reconcile the presumptive youth of the earth with recurring fossil finds of extinct monsters, a school of geology known as "catastrophism" developed in the late 18th and early 19th Centuries. It held that the earth was periodically convulsed by violent paroxysms—stupendous earthquakes, volcanic upheavals and floods—which altered the face of the land and extinguished whole populations. The last of these catastrophes was the Great Flood of Genesis. But Lyell, among others, deduced that mountains, valleys and all other features of the planet were formed slowly over immense periods of time by opposing forces—by internal pressures deep within the earth's mobile crust and by the external sculpture of rain, ice and running streams. It was Lyell's huge expansion of the geological time scale that supplied Darwin with the span of biological time he saw would be required for species to evolve.

As estimates of the earth's age lengthened, so, too, archaeologists (or antiquarians, as they were first called) began to appreciate the

ANIMAL

the wild ancestors of prehistoric times

age of man and study more closely his distant past. Egyptologists were beginning to decipher the hieroglyphic inscriptions on royal tombs beside the Nile. In Europe anthropologists uncovered the first of the kitchen middens of Denmark just a year after the return of the *Beagle;* 16 years later they found the relics of the Lake Dwellers of Switzerland. And in England diggers were beginning to turn up the bones of extinct animals in conjunction with those of man, and the flint hand axes and spear points with which he slew them.

In the Near East, more recently, archaeologists have excavated the sites of the early civilizations that flowered and fell on the Mesopotamian plain on the banks of the Tigris and Euphrates Rivers— Sumer, Akkad, Ur, Babylon, Nineveh and Ashur. But their purpose was the illumination of Biblical or conventional ancient history— not what occurred before. And conversely, paleontologists exploring Near Eastern caves for the remains of prehistoric man concerned themselves chiefly with the very beginnings of man at the dawn of Paleolithic times. Hence the period which interested Darwin—the transitional Neolithic period, when man taught himself agriculture and domestication—was neglected by prehistorians because it was too young and by historians because it was prehistoric.

It was not until the 1930s that the famed British anthropologist V. Gordon Childe emphasized that man's abandonment of a hunting way of life for life as a farmer and herder represented one of the most fateful moments in the entire span of human existence on earth. He termed this momentous event the Neolithic Revolution. For it was then that man ceased to be completely subject to circumstance and won control of his own environment.

MODERN archaeologists have endeavored to discern the circumstances that enkindled the Neolithic Revolution and resolve some of the questions that troubled Darwin a century ago. Prominent in the field have been scholars of the Oriental Institute at the University of Chicago, who in the dozen years following World War II have made several expeditions to the hills of Mesopotamia and western Iran in quest of the story of man's greatest conquest. They encountered many difficulties. One derives from the fact that during thousands of years of human settlement the same sites were in continuous occupancy—villages rose on the ruins of former villages, towns on former towns, cities on former cities. To get down to prehistoric levels, incomputable tons of useless accumulations had to be removed. As a consequence, Archaeologist Robert J. Braidwood of the Oriental Institute decided to ignore the great mounds and seek out small and inconspicuous sites which had *not* been occupied during the millenniums following their first prehistoric establishment.

In 1948 Dr. Braidwood found at Jarmo, in northeastern Iraq, remnants of the earliest purely farming village then known to archaeology. Here, sometime between 7000 and 4500 B.C., a community of perhaps 150 people had made their home, cultivating wheat and barley and attended by the goat and dog as their domestic animals. In the years that followed, Dr. Braidwood led other expeditions to other sites, assisted by a versatile staff of experts, among them Zoologist Charles A. Reed *(opposite page),* who was specifically searching for evidence of the origins of domestication. The task was not easy. At the earliest levels of the diggings it was virtually impossible to state with certainty whether skeletal remains were those of domesticated animals or of wild members of similar breeds that were killed or died in proximity to man.

But there is one conclusion on which the scientists of the Oriental Institute reached general agreement: that cultivation of plants and domestication of animals (save perhaps for the ·dog) began in the Near East, somewhere along the hilly flanks of the semicircular region known as the Fertile Crescent, extending from southwestern Iran to the Jordan. Here were the prizes for man's taking. Here wild wheat and wild barley grew in rich soil; and wild sheep, wild goats, wild cattle and wild swine ranged freely over an open, parklike land. Nowhere else in the world were all these elements found together in a single natural environment. It is not surprising, therefore, that the first great civilizations of history later arose in this region.

Contemporary archaeology has thus confirmed Darwin's theory of the evolution of domestic animals from wild species and their gradual improvement by human selection. Someday his questions concerning their initial origins may be fully answered.

FARM GOAT'S FOREBEAR, a specimen of an animal called *Capra hircus aegagrus* which roams the Zagros Mountains of Iran, is carried to camp by a Kurdish tribesman so its skeleton can be studied by the Chicago scientists.

HIDDEN
REALM
OF
REPRODUCTION

M ORE than any other liv-
ing creature on earth,
the small fruit fly shown here
reveling in the red juice of a
ripe raspberry is the mainstay
of research into the mysteries
of heredity. To the housewife it
is a wraith poised annoyingly
above the fruit bowl or the gar-
bage can. But for half a century biologists have maintained
it in countless numbers. Endlessly multiplying, maturing
and mutating, the fruit fly *Dro-
sophila melanogaster* is a model subject for laboratory study
in the growing field of genetics.

VARICOLORED DELPHINIUMS stand as vivid proof of Mendel's concept that hereditary traits continue unaltered through generation after generation, even though they may seem to disappear completely or assert themselves only partially in intermediate offspring. The ancestors of these plants were pure white and pure purple. The combinations of their genes produced many intermediate shades, but unalloyed purple and white endured to reappear again.

HIDDEN REALM OF REPRODUCTION

The laws of genetics now explain the mechanisms of evolution

IN the years following publication of *The Origin of Species*, Darwin fell under heavy attack not only from organized religion, as he had anticipated, but also from fellow scientists. They felt he had not adequately explained the mechanics of inheritance or the way in which new physical characteristics suddenly arise within a species. His monumental work had convinced them of the fact of evolution. But he had failed to describe in precise biological terms how natural selection could permanently alter species. Darwin himself confessed that "Not in one case out of a hundred can we pretend to assign any reason why this or that part has varied."

In Darwin's day the modern science of genetics was yet unborn. The prevailing theory of heredity held simply that offspring represented an approximate blend of their parents. Given this vague concept of "blending" through the admixture of blood, Darwin could only hypothesize, remarking, "Everyone would wish to explain to himself how it is possible for a character possessed by some remote ancestor suddenly to reappear in the offspring."

It is a double irony of history that at the very time Darwin most desperately needed them the laws of inheritance were being revealed with incontrovertible accuracy in a classic series of experiments by the other great biologist of the 19th Century. In the solitude of a monastery garden the Austrian monk Gregor Mendel spent the years between 1854 and 1866 crossbreeding flowering peas. He noted that the physical traits of each parent, though they might not be apparent in the progeny, nevertheless persist unseen and can reappear predictably from generation to generation. He published his findings in 1866, but they stirred no significant interest and lay ignored until 1900—16 years after his death and 18 years after Darwin's.

Once discovered, Mendel's laws became the pillars of modern genetic research into the mysteries of life. It is known today that the hidden hereditary mechanism for passing traits through successive generations lies in invisible factors called genes, contained in threadlike bodies called chromosomes within the nuclei of cells. It is the genes that shape each living creature into an elephant, a chipmunk or a man—and if a man, predestine him to have blue eyes or a size 10 foot. Since man has 46 chromosomes in each cell (a fruit fly has eight, an onion 16, a crayfish 200), and since each chromosome has perhaps 1,000 genes which are shuffled in the process of sexual reproduction, the number of possible genetic combinations is incomputable. A further factor known as mutation also comes into play, mysteriously altering an individual gene to introduce totally new characteristics, such as the varicolored eyes of the flies shown opposite.

DISSIMILAR FRUIT FLIES, shown here magnified 80 times, include one normal, red-eyed insect and two mutant forms, one with sepia and the other with white eyes. Since the fruit fly can reproduce every 17 days, the effects of crossbreeding experiments can be traced through many generations in a relatively short time. The chromosomes present in the fruit fly's salivary gland are the largest of any organism and therefore can be easily prepared for study.

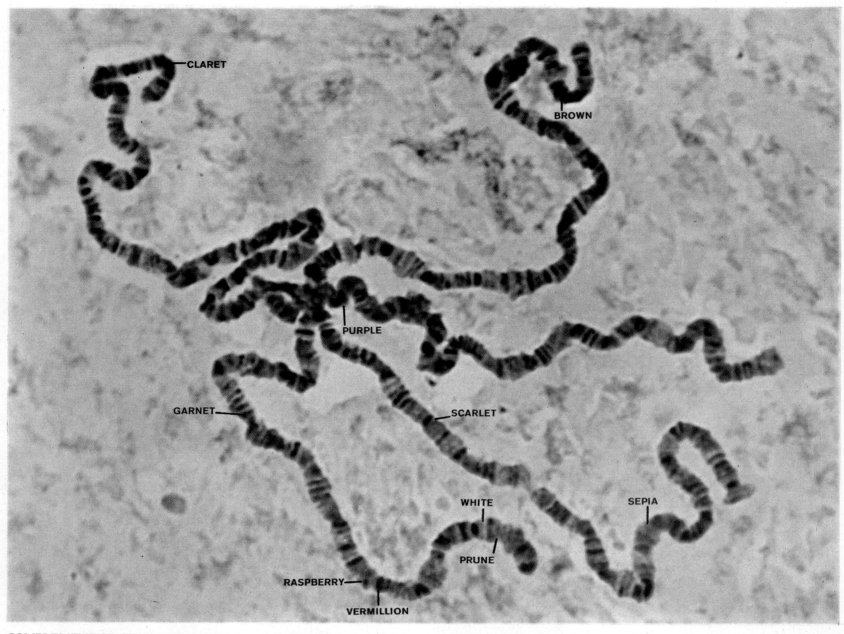

COMPLEMENT OF CHROMOSOMES from a fruit fly cell consists of sets contributed by each parent intertwined in strands of varying length, gathered at their centers. Each band on the chromosome strings is associated with some trait. Those marked are related to the color of the eyes. Scientists have deduced that whenever the specified color variations—or mutations—occur a change has occurred in the corresponding banded spot in the chromosome.

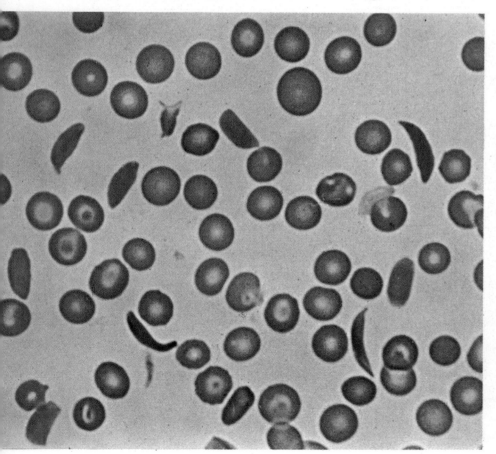

SICKLE CELL BLOOD is caused in humans by a mutated gene. One gene inherited from one parent causes some cells to deflate into a sickle shape. Two genes, one from each parent, are usually fatal as all cells may deflate.

THE SOURCE
OF HEREDITY

Once Mendel's breakthrough was rediscovered by biologists, the science of genetics flourished. A Dane named W. L. Johannsen did meticulous work on the interaction of environment and the hereditary factors, for which he coined the name that still endures. "Many properties of the organism," he wrote, "are determined by special, separable, and therefore independent 'conditions,' 'bases,' or 'materials'—in short what we shall call genes."

The gene still remains a hypothetical, impalpable unit, purely a genetic concept. But the U.S. biologist W. S. Sutton and the German cytologist Theodor Boveri deduced that the vehicles for the mysterious gene are the chromosomes lying in the nuclei of all cells. Research with fruit flies proved that on the chromosomes' sinuous members, certain widely separated bands mark spots all of which have a part in controlling a specific trait, such as the color of the eyes. A single band may control many or only one trait. How this is effected remains obscure. But biologists know that it is accomplished by the complex chemical structure within the chromosome.

Genes are transmitted to offspring in the chromosomes of the sperm and eggs. As cells created by the meeting of sperm and egg duplicate themselves and divide in the growth process, the gene-bearing chromosomes within them also duplicate and divide. Thus every cell in the offspring is imbued with a combination of potential traits. But if an accidental alteration occurs in the chromosomes of either egg or sperm, an entirely new trait may be born—as in the case of the fruit fly eye colors above. Thus are born the strange mutants within species.

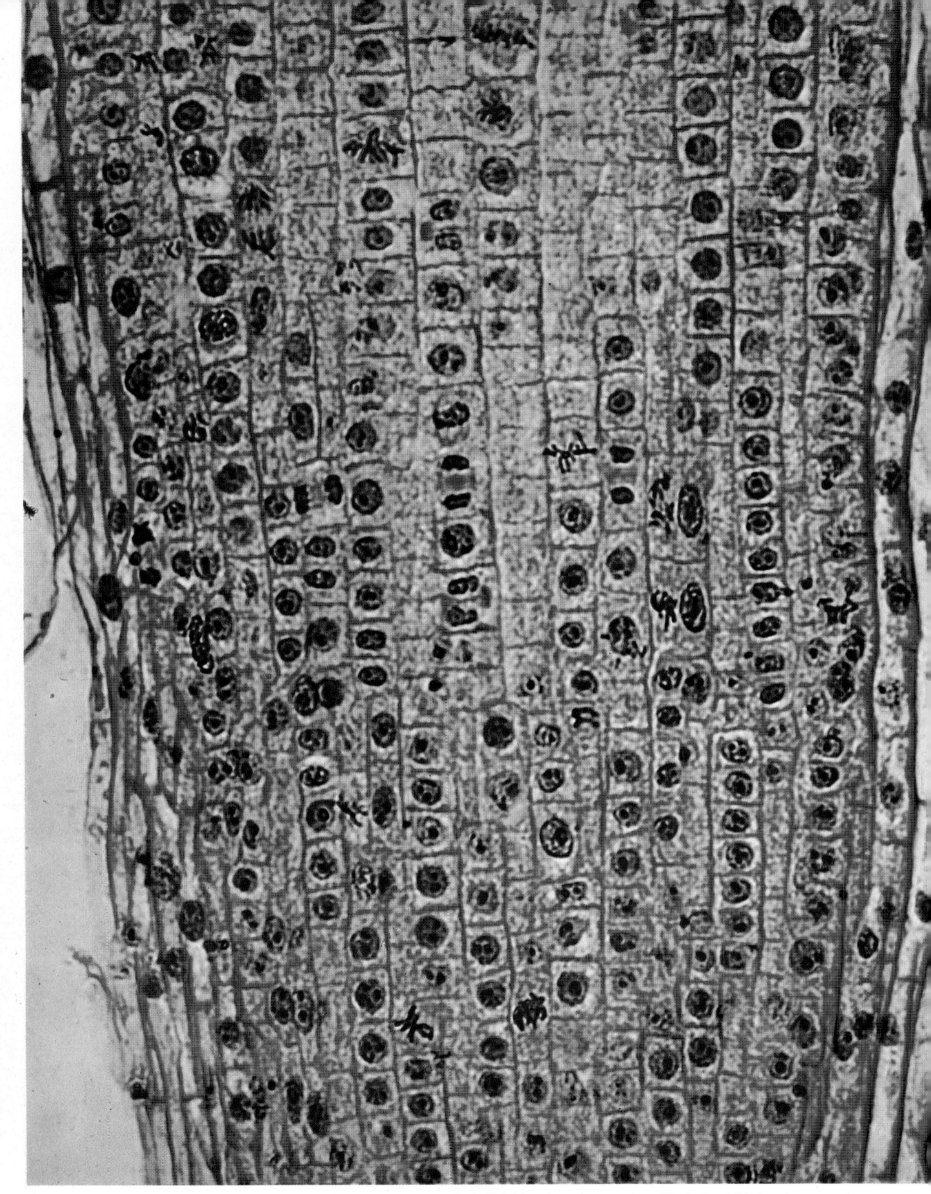

STAGES OF CELL LIFE appear in a microscopic slice of an onion root tip magnified 700 times. The round objects in the various rectangular cell compartments contain chromosomes at rest. When the chromosomes are ready for cell division they take on a threadlike look, visible in other compartments. Elsewhere the chromosomes have divided as two new cells form. Cells kept at a temperature of 70 degrees divide about once every three hours.

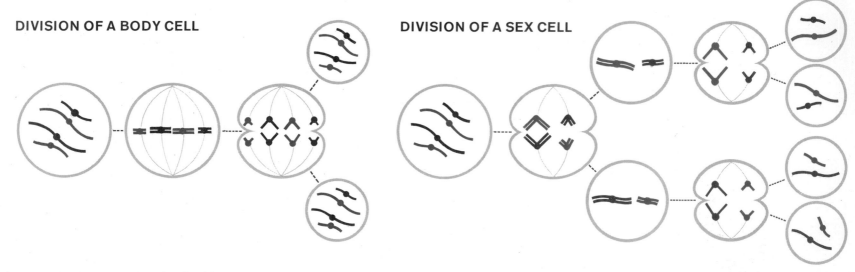

DIVISION OF A BODY CELL

DIVISION OF A SEX CELL

DIVISION OF CHROMOSOMES takes place in two ways. At left, two pairs of chromosomes in a body cell (red from one parent, black from the other) double and divide to duplicate themselves. At right, chromosomes in a sex cell double and divide twice to produce four sperm or egg cells. The single set of chromosomes in each cell, descended from the parental pairs and distributed at random, are now ready to be joined in mating by another set.

THE AGENTS OF HERITAGE

In his long years of puttering with the peas of his monastery garden, Gregor Mendel discovered two lasting principles. First, the characteristics of parents—such as the brown eyes of a man and the blue eyes of his wife—never blend in offspring but are passed on as distinct factors now called genes. Second, the characteristics of each parent can appear in their offspring in a variety of combinations.

By the crossing and recrossing of generations of pure lines of his flowering peas, Mendel discovered that the parental characteristics would reappear time and again in predictable statistical ratios. When a smooth pea was bred with a wrinkled pea only smooth peas would result in the first generation. But if two members of that generation were bred again, 25 per cent of the succeeding generation would bear the wrinkled surfaces. Mendel concluded that there were pairs of factors—one from each parent—which sometimes showed an unequal ability to assert themselves. He labeled those characteristics which appeared in the first generation "dominant." Those which were not apparent then but reappeared in successive generations—like the wrinkled surface of the peas—he called "recessive." The reappearance of recessive characteristics, he decided, came about when offspring inherited them from both parents.

Modern geneticists have since learned that the physical basis of Mendel's laws lies in the process whereby chromosomes divide *(above)*. As shown on these pages, the laws apply as predictably for generations of fruit flies as they did for the flowering peas in Mendel's garden.

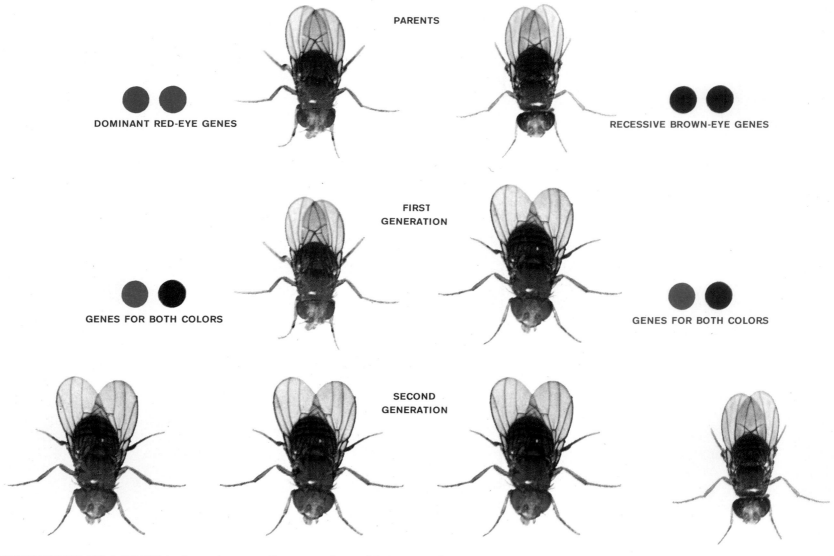

PARENTS

DOMINANT RED-EYE GENES

RECESSIVE BROWN-EYE GENES

FIRST GENERATION

GENES FOR BOTH COLORS

GENES FOR BOTH COLORS

SECOND GENERATION

RECURRENCE OF A TRAIT is shown in succeeding generations of fruit flies. Brown eyes are a recessive characteristic of fruit flies and apparently vanish in the first generation *(middle row)* as the dominant red-eye genes triumph over brown. But the brown-eye genes remain dormant within the chromosomes and reappear in the second generation *(bottom)*, producing an average of one brown-eyed fly in every four grandchildren of the original pair.

268

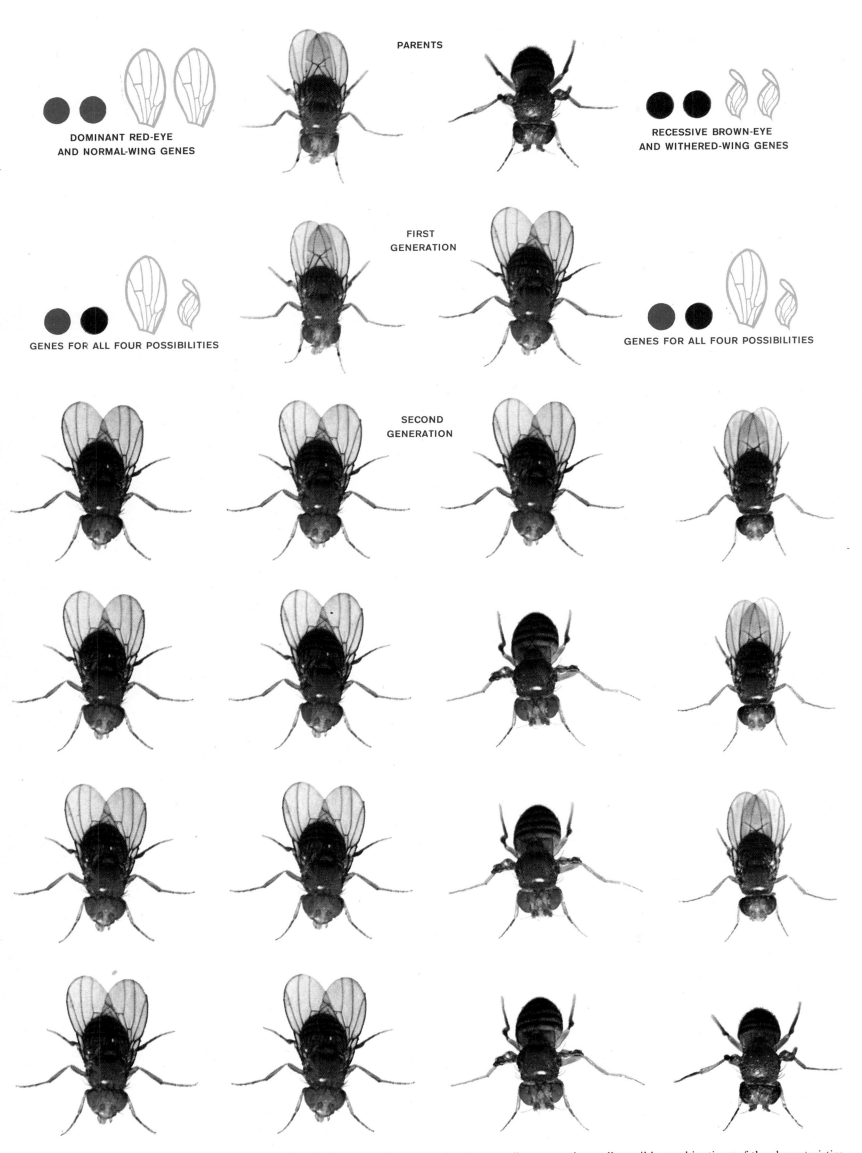

PARENTS

DOMINANT RED-EYE
AND NORMAL-WING GENES

RECESSIVE BROWN-EYE
AND WITHERED-WING GENES

FIRST
GENERATION

GENES FOR ALL FOUR POSSIBILITIES

GENES FOR ALL FOUR POSSIBILITIES

SECOND
GENERATION

VARIETY OF TRAITS is displayed in generations of fruit flies. One of the original pair *(top)* has normal red eyes and long wings, the other recessive withered wings and brown eyes. Their children bear red eyes and long wings.

But in succeeding generations, all possible combinations of the characteristics appear—red eyes and normal wings, red eyes and no wings, brown eyes and long wings, and even a doubly recessive unwinged brown-eye *(lower right)*.

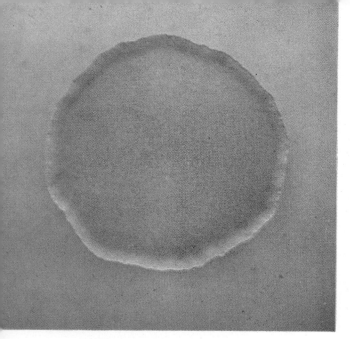

HOMOGENEOUS BACTERIA, a colony of *Escherichia coli* (intestinal bacteria), displayed no mutants after one day in a laboratory culture.

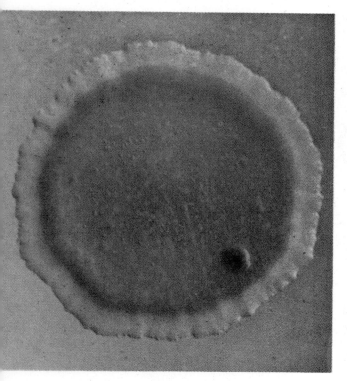

SUGAR-EATING MUTANT and its progeny *(red spot)* appeared after 48 hours. Normal bacteria could not use the sugar in the diet provided.

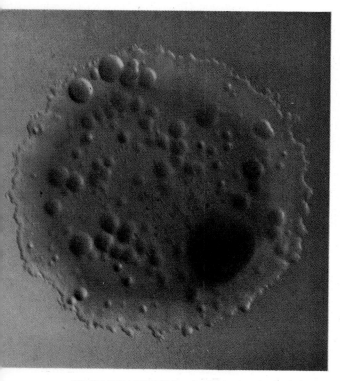

VAST CHANGES by the fifth day included new mutants *(puffy circles)* able to live on decreasing food supply, and new sugar eaters *(tiny specks)*.

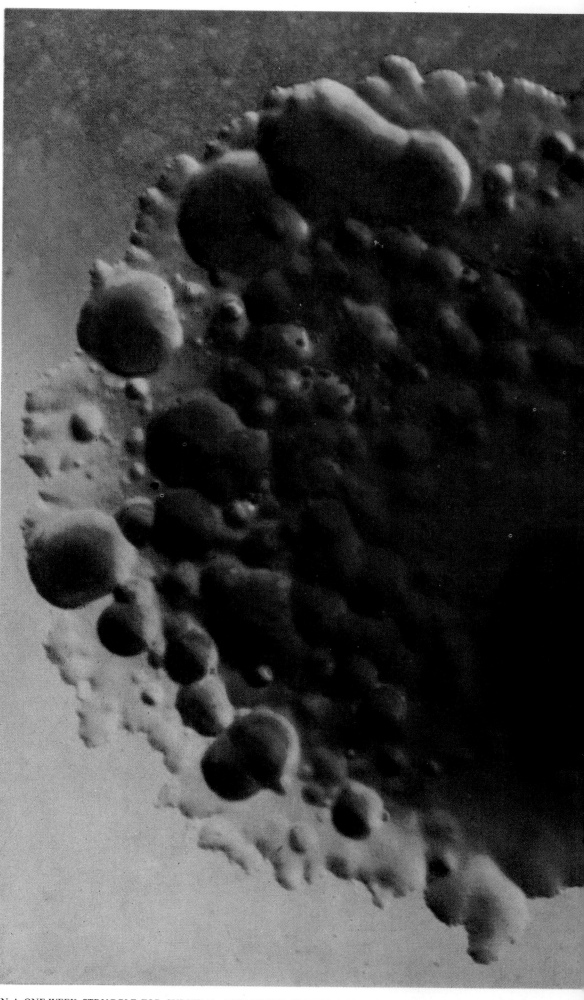

IN A ONE-WEEK STRUGGLE FOR SURVIVAL, MUTATIONS CREATE A STRIKING ARRAY OF SHAPES, COLORS

SURVIVAL THROUGH MUTATION

Evolutionary progress depends on mutations —the sudden, mysterious variations within the chromosomes of an organism, which can result in new characteristics. This process occurs constantly in all living beings, but those changes which are disadvantageous to the organism—or which make no difference in its struggle for survival—will be kept from being widely distributed by the workings of natural selection. Similarly, it is natural

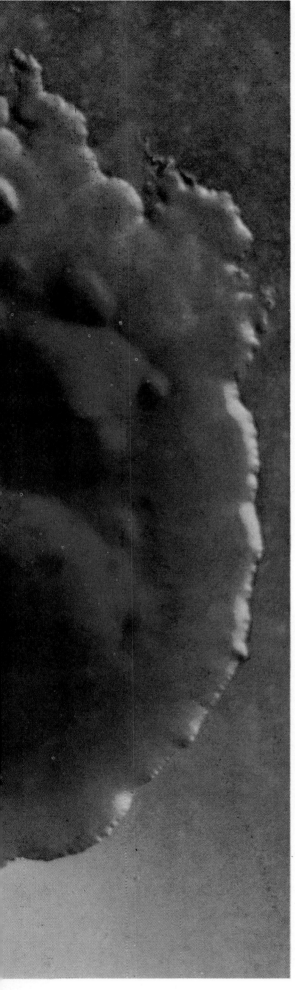

AND SIZES IN A LABORATORY BACTERIA COLONY

FAVORABLE MUTATIONS occur in *Staphylococcus aureus* bacteria subjected to penicillin. The small colonies at the top have been retarded by the drug. Those at the bottom, where the concentration is heaviest, are wiped out. But mutant bacteria have formed large colonies able to resist.

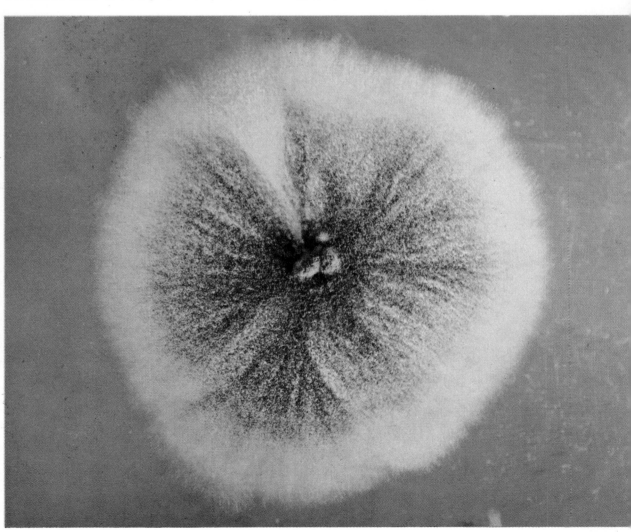

UNFAVORABLE MUTATION occurs in fungus *Aspergillus terreus,* which radiates branches that grow green spores which will start new colonies. A mutation in one branch *(white "V" at top)* prevented spore formation. Unable to reproduce, it will die out when the growth of this colony stops.

selection which perpetuates the mutational change that aids in the struggle for survival. Eventually this process may lead to the creation of new species in the succession of generations.

Shown here are mutations appearing during the growth of a fungus and in minute bacteria—excellent creatures for laboratory observation since, dividing by mitosis, they produce a new generation every 20 minutes.

IN ISOLATION, THE ORIGIN OF SPECIES

By the time the *Beagle* voyage had ended, Darwin was convinced that the physical separation of plants and animals played a crucial role in the creation of new species. "It would have been a strange fact," he wrote to a friend in later years, "if I had overlooked the importance of isolation, seeing that it was such cases as that of the Galápagos Archipelago, which chiefly led me to study the origin of species." Nevertheless, he believed in addition that "many perfectly defined species have been formed on strictly continuous areas"—a conclusion alternately endorsed and disputed by naturalists in the years after the publication of *The Origin of Species.*

Only recently, with the growth of the new science of genetics, has the problem begun to be resolved. The evidence indicates that it is indeed largely in geographic isolation—on the far removed islands of the oceans, on the opposing sides of deserts, in enclosed valleys—that new species arise out of the genetic structure of parent stocks. If natural cataclysm, or even so small an event as a stream changing course to cut a new division across a meadow, should separate any members of a single species from their cohorts, changes in their

characteristics begin to appear as time passes—as with the iridescent, swallow-tailed butterflies shown above. Sometime in the remote past—probably in the Pleistocene, when New Guinea is thought to have broken off from the Australian land mass—these insects were isolated from one another. Each group thereafter developed in its own way, producing the changes which now mark them apart.

Isolation encourages major changes in traits for a simple reason: the number of genes in any group of organisms is vast but not infinite—*i.e.,* the "gene pool" is limited. Consequently there are only so many possible combinations of characteristics. The interchange of genes within an isolated group will eventually result in a relatively uniform combination among all the individuals of the group. But given the long march of generations through time, the differing play of the forces of natural selection to which the separated populations will be subjected, and the possibility of sudden, beneficial mutation *(preceding page)* unshared by the group's cousins isolated elsewhere, an entirely new species will inevitably arise to take its own ecological niche in the vast and complex structure of nature.

SOUTH PACIFIC BUTTERFLIES, shown here against a map of New Guinea and nearby islands where a population of each is found, demonstrate the effects of evolution when groups of one species are isolated from each other. These insects have developed markedly differing arrangements of wing spots, as well as variations in coloring, both caused by the separate evolution of each group. Their progenitor may have originated in Australia.

AMERICAN BUTTERFLIES, intermingling on the same land mass, display individual variation in one population. Although their habitat ranges from Pennsylvania to Nicaragua, these insects are not separated by geographical barriers and therefore their genes are circulated through the population. Consequently all share much the same appearance, with normal variations in coloring, shape and size which would supply the basis for separate evolution.

273

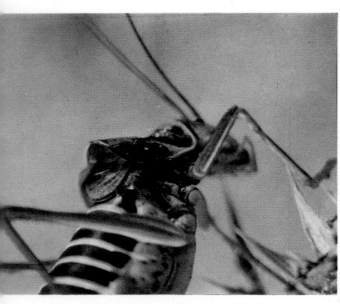

A MALE GRASSHOPPER rubs the saw-toothed surface of one wing against the other to produce the high-pitched tone typical of its species.

THE WAYS
OF KEEPING
IDENTITY

Having discovered how new species originate, naturalists are now investigating the question of how they maintain their identity. In widely dissimilar species the answer is obvious: the giraffe does not mate with the antelope. But even if different species did interbreed, the offspring would be sterile —as is the mule, produced by man with the mating of horse and jackass.

To avoid such mistakes in nature, species are able to recognize their own kind, even when living with other closely related species. Some creatures, like the grouse *(opposite page, top),* perceive their mates by the display of their plumage. Others know them by their songs. But most creatures—like the frogs shown on pages 276-277—employ a combination of recognition methods, the better to ensure the identity of their species.

A PAIR OF KATYDIDS of an identical species meet on a leaf as a result of the male's distinctive mating call, made by rubbing his wings together.

TWO SPECIES OF CICADAS known as 17-year locusts intermingle as their mating season—the last six weeks of their lives—begins. Soon they will separate, calling out to one another with their distinctive cries: a chirping in chorus by the larger species and in relays by the smaller one.

A MALE GROUSE courts a mate with a rhythmic drumming of its pendulous wings, a gesture that displays the pattern of his plumage and enables the female to recognize him as a member of her own species. The complexity of the patterns of male grouse seems to have evolved according to the number of species sharing the same habitat. This specimen, which is less elaborately marked than others, has less competition in the areas that it inhabits.

A SHIELD DARTER, identifiable by its crestlike markings, favors for its breeding grounds rapidly running water over a gravel bottom. Its near relative, the Johnny darter, shares its habitat but breeds under rocks in the quiet water closer in toward the shore. Furthermore, to avoid interbreeding, the shield darter begins its mating season in the spring when the water runs high and cold, while the Johnny darter waits for the warm beginnings of summer.

275

PINEWOODS TREE FROG
BARKING TREE FROG
GREEN TREE FROG
SQUIRREL TREE FROG

HARKER

HOW FROGS FIND
THEIR OWN KIND

The soprano peeps and basso croaks of frogs chorusing from swamps and thickets in the summer twilight are merely pleasant sounds to the human ear, but they are of vital importance to the frogs themselves. Amid related amphibians, the various couples must sort themselves out by species.

Among frogs this process is the responsibility of the female: it is she who must somehow find her way through the grass and water to

MIDGET GRASS FROG   LEOPARD FROG   GOPHER FROG

a partner of her own species. This is accomplished partly by ear and partly through rendezvous points. As shown in the painting above, the males of each species select a distinctive calling site, their specialized vocal sacs inflating hugely as they render their mating croaks.

The five frogs at left, clinging to the grasses at the pond's edge, are all different species of the genus Hyla (tree frogs), which come down to lower levels for breeding. Even among the tree frogs each group

has its own trysting place. The female green tree frog knows her mate's niche is usually beneath some overhanging cover. And only the squirrel tree frog habitually shinnies up a stick.

The more aquatic frogs at right, closely related members of the genus Rana, have equally specific trysting sites. The brightly mottled leopard frog stays in the shallow water near the pond's bank, while the gopher frog floats in deeper water to await his lady love.

SECRET PROCESSES OF

Mysteries of reproduction that troubled Darwin all his life are being resolved

"THE laws governing inheritance are for the most part unknown," Darwin acknowledged in the opening pages of *The Origin of Species*. "No one can say why the same peculiarity in different individuals of the same species, or in different species, is sometimes inherited and sometimes not so; why the child often reverts in certain characters to its grandfather or grandmother or more remote ancestor; why a peculiarity is often transmitted from one sex to both sexes, or to one sex alone."

He had ransacked libraries and tapped the brains of his friends and colleagues in quest of the solution to some of the riddles that haunted him to the end of his days. As years passed, intellectual battles raged over specific details of his theory of evolution. Certain acidulous critics contended that natural selection was less the mainspring of evolution than simply an agency to wipe out its failures. Suppose an individual emerges with superior or beneficial characteristics, they asked, what would happen then? According to Darwin's theory, his offspring would prosper and transmit their favorable traits to the future progeny of their line. Not so, his adversaries retorted. For if inheritance is a process of blending, the emergent characteristic would be swamped by crossing with the mass of his less favored kin, and soon it would vanish like a drop of water in the sea.

As an honest man who refused to defend a position because of personal pride, Darwin recognized the validity of this argument. But his attempts to cope with it hypothetically were fatally crippled by his, and the world's, unfortunate ignorance of the work of Mendel. There was no way that Darwin could know of Mendel's crucially important discovery that inheritance is not a matter of accidental blending—like the mixing of two liquids in a jug—but that the individual characteristics are transmitted in separate, discrete, immutable units which are not altered in transmission, and that their transmission and combination follow predicta-

PIONEER GENETICISTS Julius Marmur *(foreground)* and Paul Doty of Harvard University work with DNA, the basic material of genetics. By uniting DNA strands from related bacteria, they have succeeded in combining characteristics of each.

ble mathematical laws. Neither Darwin nor Mendel had ever heard the words "chromosome" or "gene," or witnessed the division of a cell. Indeed, Mendel was entirely ignorant of the microscopic processes of mitosis *(pages 268-269)* underlying the beautiful order of hereditary succession which he so accurately observed and recorded. Unlike Darwin, whose achievements were greatly honored in his lifetime, Mendel died in obscurity without ever knowing that a generation hence his findings would be acclaimed by the world as an epic advance in the history of man's continuing endeavors to comprehend the mystery of life.

To appreciate the magnitude of Darwin's and Mendel's discoveries, it is necessary to understand that at the time of their work the realm of thought now known as genetics comprised a hodgepodge of conjecture, folklore and superstition, overlaid by the shoptalk of professional animal breeders. The fact that crops and herds could be improved by human selection had been known for many centuries. The fact that mules were sterile hybrids had been known since the

age of Homer. The fact that children sometimes resembled one parent, sometimes another, and sometimes reverted a generation to their grandparents, had been noted by the Roman philosopher-poet Lucretius, among countless others. But throughout the Middle Ages and even later, the whole subject of heredity was dominated by imaginative tales of monsters and monstrous births, alleged offspring of intercourse between man and beast, and such supposed products of animal miscegenation as the cameleopard—actually the giraffe. It was generally believed that worms, flies and all types of vermin generated spontaneously in filth.

It was not until the 17th Century that some knowledge of the reproductive process began to cohere. In 1672 a young Dutch surgeon named Regnier de Graaf discovered egg cells in the ovaries of rabbits, ewes and women, and was accordingly able to announce that mammals—like birds, fish and reptiles—also produced eggs. But theorizing further, he then concluded that the ovum contained the fully formed embryo and that the only function of the male semen was somehow to trigger it into growth. Three years later another Dutchman, the famous lens-maker and microscopist Anton van Leeuwenhoek, looked for the first time upon living spermatozoa—animalcules, he called them. In opposition to De Graaf, Leeuwenhoek decided that the male sperm was a prototype of the adult human and that the only function of the female was to house and nourish it while it was growing.

The battle that ensued between De Graaf's ovists and Leeuwenhoek's animalculists was still raging in Darwin's day. It was not until 1854 that a male sperm was first seen penetrating the ovum of a frog and the reciprocity of the male and female sex cells became clear. It was not until 1875 that the process of cellular division through the reproduction of the chromosomes was observed and analyzed *(pages 268-269)*. And it was not until 1882, the same year as Darwin's death, that this process received its scientific name, *mitosis*. Under the circumstances, without benefit of the subsequent great discoveries of cytology—the study of microscopic cellular life—it is extraordinary that Darwin could exclaim in 1868, "The whole subject of inheritance is wonderful. . . . What can be more wonderful than that some trifling peculiarity, not primordially attached to the species, should be transmitted through the male or female sexual cells, which are so minute as not to be visible to the naked eye, and afterwards through the incessant changes of a long course of development, undergone either in the womb or in the egg, and ultimately appear in the offspring when mature, or even when quite old!"

In order to explain these wonders and reply to his critics, Darwin developed a theory of inheritance called *pangenesis* "which implies that every separate part of the whole organization reproduces itself." He postulated that each cell produces minute seeds or particles, which he termed "gemmules," and that these are drawn from various parts of the body into the sexual cells where they combine to form

HEREDITY

by brilliant discoveries of geneticists

another potential individual. New gemmules are constantly engendered, reflecting any changes or modifications that may take place through environmental adaptation. "Free" gemmules may be transmitted during reproduction in a dormant state, and these may reproduce themselves in the future to express the characteristics of distant forebears. Today Darwin's theory of pangenesis is chiefly of interest to historians of science. But it clearly reveals his intuitive sense that the secret of heredity could best be explained not by the "blending" of inchoate streams of life stuff, but by some kind of particulate or corpuscular mechanism analagous to the atomic structure of matter. The accuracy of his intuition was confirmed in 1909 when the Danish botanist Wilhelm Johannsen deduced that the vague hereditary "factor" postulated by Mendel must be a physical entity within the reproductive organism and gave it the name "gene."

The science of genetics is the creation of many dedicated biologists. Its two most eminent godfathers—Darwin and Mendel—approached the field from quite antipodal points of view. On the one hand, Darwin was interested in change and variation. On the other hand, Mendel (who was quite familiar with Darwin's work and works) was interested in genetic stability and the persistence of biological form. This combination of the visionary theorist, watching the whole pageant of life march down the enormous corridors of prehistoric time, and the patient experimentalist, noting small changes in one small organism in a small walled garden, laid the foundations of modern genetics, youngest of the natural sciences.

ITS birthdate is usually fixed at 1900, when three biologists in different countries, working independently, rediscovered the lost paper and the lost principles of Gregor Mendel. Thereafter events moved swiftly. Better microscopes and better observations enabled cytologists to penetrate far more deeply into the mysterious chambers of the cell and the interwoven enigmas of heredity and life. The Dutch botanist Hugo de Vries, through studies of the evening primrose, introduced the term *mutation* to define drastic changes in living organisms, and thus reconciled Mendelian laws with Darwin's theory of evolutionary change through variation. The proof of mutation was provided by the Nobel Laureate Thomas Hunt Morgan in his experiments with the fruit fly at Columbia University between 1910 and 1920. And even more significantly Morgan was able to correlate mutations—*i.e.,* outward changes, such as eye color and wing shape—with visible alterations in specific areas of specific chromosomes. In 1926 another Nobel Laureate, Hermann H. Muller, now of Indiana University, discovered that mutations could be artificially induced by X rays, as well as by certain other types of radiation and chemical agents.

And so in time geneticists have found themselves able to draw detailed chromosome "maps," fixing the precise locations of control for particular hereditary characteristics. And gradually the fact was recognized that the entire potential of every living thing on earth—plant, animal, human—resides in its unique and individual chromosomes and their constituent genes.

Modern geneticists are confident that the chemical basis of the gene is a giant, complex, long-chain molecule of deoxyribonucleic acid, familiarly known as DNA. Each chromosome contains 10,000 to 100,000 of these DNA molecules. One theory holds that the gene, which until now has never been physically described, may be equal to a single DNA molecule; others have suggested that the giant molecule, with its thousands of components—sugar, phosphates and special nitrogenous compounds, all bound together in the complex spiral structure shown in the model at right—may possibly represent an entire manifold of genes.

It is believed today that DNA is the fateful substance that determines heredity and directs the development of life. Within its interlocking spirals, geneticists suspect, the patterns or blueprints for each living organism lie encoded—as complex as the circuits of a computing machine, and as definitive in shaping the design, behavior and individuality of the organism that emerges finally from its arcane core. From the medical standpoint it may be that DNA will reveal the secrets of normal cellular growth as well as those abnormal processes that cause cancer. From a deeper philosophical perspective one may conjecture that on some far distant day this master molecule will help man unravel the knot of human fate.

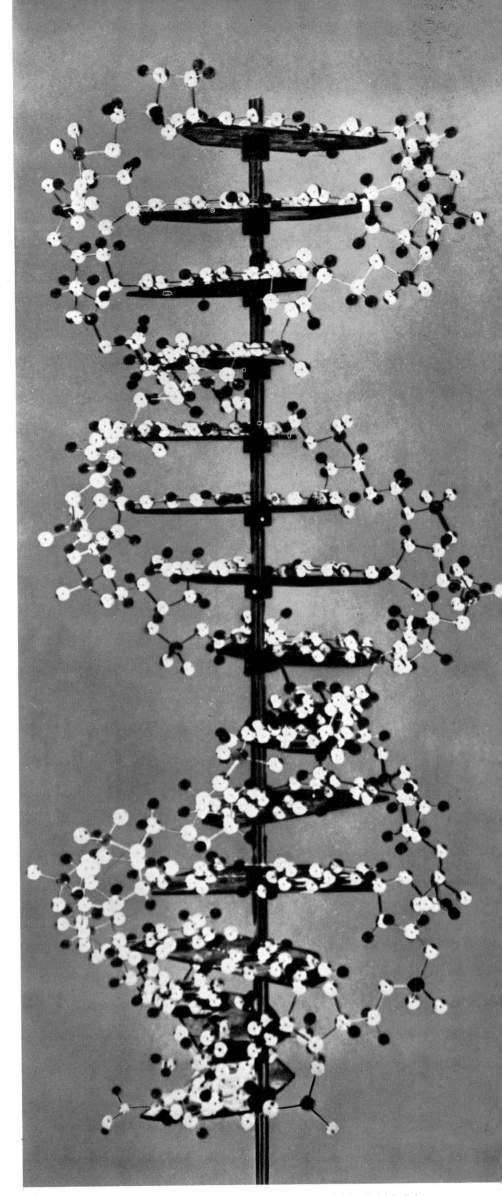

MODEL OF DNA shows its molecular structure as conceived by British Scientists James D. Watson and Francis H. C. Crick. Sugar and phosphate ingredients spiral around nitrogenous bases, arranged like a circular staircase.

EPILOGUE

IN the long chain of evolution there are many missing links—transitional organisms marking the passage of one type of creature to its modified descendants. From time to time these missing links are found. In 1958 the small mollusk, Neopilina *(shown in both bottom and top view at right and lower center),* was hauled up from the Pacific floor off Peru. Strange survivor of an order believed extinct 300 million years ago, Neopilina may be a link in the evolution of segmented worms to snails.

EVOLUTION AS

WHEN Darwin published *The Origin of Species* in 1859, his great work touched off an explosion that derived much of its force and fury from the human reluctance to admit common lineage with lower orders of the animal kingdom. Yet curiously man is mentioned only once in *The Origin,* and then at the very end.

"In the future," Darwin remarked in the final chapter, almost as an afterthought, "I see open fields for far more important researches. . . . Much light will be thrown on the origin of man and his history."

While the public proceeded to draw its own outraged inferences, Darwin decided to face the issue of human ancestry. In *The Descent of Man,* published in 1871, he wrote, "We are naturally led to inquire, where was the birthplace of man? . . . In each great region of the world, the living mammals are closely related to the extinct species of the same region. It is therefore probable that Africa was formerly inhabited by extinct apes, closely allied to the gorilla and chimpanzee; and as these two species are now man's nearest allies, it is somewhat more probable that our early progenitors lived on the African continent than elsewhere."

Here again Darwin showed the uncanny insight that repeatedly enabled him to forecast discoveries that in time would sustain his theories. For accumulating evidence of recent years points increasingly to Africa as the continent on which the earliest members of *Homo sapiens'* genus emerged. During the period of Darwin's major endeavors, the science of paleontology was barely fifty years old—dating only from 1801, when Baron Georges Cuvier proclaimed his discovery of 23 species of animals no longer alive on earth. It was only in Darwin's latter years that the rich store of fossil evidence began to issue from the silent earth to confirm his vision of a grand procession of living creatures extending from the unimaginable past down to present times, and to attest that man, like other animals, had evolved from earlier forms. Darwin never contended, as his adversaries charged, that man had descended from apes. He believed that modern man and modern apes had diverged at some remote point in prehistory from a common ancestral line. And that remains the position of scientists today.

SINCE evolution is a continuum—an endless chain of life—it involves many links joining epoch to epoch and form to form, from the time the first animal organism appeared in the waters of earth. Some of these crucial links are still missing. Although many have been found in recent years, for every link uncovered by the scientist's spade, new empty spaces are revealed above and below in the evolutionary chain. And even though the gaps grow smaller with each discovery, it is likely that some will never be filled, that missing links will always evade and challenge man's imagination. For the history of evolution is a history of vast extinctions as well as of progress and change. Today we know that virtually all of the vertebrate families now alive on earth are descended from only eight of

the countless multitudes that flourished in the Mesozoic era 75 million years ago and then vanished from the earth forever.

In view of the scanty fossil evidence which was available to Darwin, it is astonishing that he was able to discern the progression of life from invertebrate to fish, from fish to amphibian, from amphibian to reptile, and from reptile to mammal and bird. None of the striking transitional forms shown on the following pages, which now so perfectly document his thesis, had been discovered at the time of his labors on *The Origin of Species.* Only one of them, Archaeopteryx, the reptile-bird, turned up during his lifetime—in 1871, 12 years after publication of his masterpiece. Pithecanthropus, the earliest undoubted man, was not found until 1891, nine years after Darwin's death. Nor was Darwin ever granted the opportunity to study the now famous series of fossils that trace the evolution of the horse, step by step, from its tiny ancestor which ranged the Eocene plains 60 million years ago down to the present time.

Denied full knowledge of the record concealed in the rocks, and denied all knowledge of Mendelian law and the discoveries of modern genetics described in the preceding chapter, Darwin had to turn to other branches of science in his inductive search for data. He noted the findings of comparative anatomy, which revealed that the forelimbs of all the vertebrates—whether amphibians, reptiles, birds or mammals, and whether used for swimming, flying or walking—are built on an identical structural plan, consisting of one bone in the upper arm, two bones in the forearm, several in the wrist and five in the hand with finger joints attached. Marveling at this correspondence of anatomical form in such varied classes, Darwin exclaimed: "What can be more curious than that the hand of a man formed for grasping, that of a mole for digging, the leg of a horse, the paddle of the porpoise, and the wings of a bat, should all be constructed on the same pattern, and should include similar bones, in the same relative positions?"

Answering his own question, Darwin continued: "The similar framework of bones in the hand of a man, wing of a bat, fin of the porpoise, and leg of the horse—the same number of vertebrae forming the neck of a giraffe and of the elephant—and innumerable other such facts, at once explain themselves on the theory of descent with slow and slight successive modifications."

Darwin also cited discoveries in the field of embryology which revealed amazing similarities in the embryos of such disparate classes as fish, birds and man. The embryos of all three, for example, have gill slits and tails—vestiges of their ancestors which came from the sea. For every higher animal on earth retraces briefly in its fetal development the entire history of its race. Long before birth the human embryo closes its gills and curls its tail into a coccyx. Yet each man carries in adult life certain useless vestiges of his past: patches of mammalian hair, wisdom teeth, an appendix and rudimentary muscles with which his animal forebears twitched their ears. To Darwin these

DISCOVERERS OF FOSSIL MAN, British Anthropologist L.S.B. Leakey and his wife Mary examine a human jaw believed to be 600,000 years old. It was found in the Olduvai Gorge of East Africa, where the Leakeys have worked for the last 26 years.

IT STANDS NOW

curious facts pointed to an inescapable conclusion: that man and all other vertebrate animals are descended from a common progenitor.

Since his death new scientific disciplines of which he knew nothing have repeatedly confirmed Darwin's views. Recent findings in the fields of biochemistry, serology, physics and comparative behavior have all pointed to community of descent. Darwin had noted that man contracted certain diseases from animals—*e.g.,* rabies, cholera—and sometimes conveyed his ills to them. He did not know, however, that apes—especially chimpanzees—are subject to syphilis, nor that their arteries contain the same ABO blood-group system as man's. Nor did he live to learn of the enormous contributions to research made by the discovery of radioactivity, which now enables geologists and paleontologists to compute accurately the age of rock strata and hence of whatever fossils lie embedded within them. The so-called "radioactive time clock," based on analysis of uranium-bearing deposits, has made possible statistical studies of evolution rates. In one study of this kind the evolution of the horse from ancestral Eohippus to modern Equus was determined precisely for a period of 60 million years—through its eight genera, 30 species and 15 million generations.

BECAUSE these developments came too late to document Darwin's inspired conjectures, hostile specialists in many varied realms of science leaped to attack whatever breaches they could find in the structure of his theory. On the one hand there were the biologists, still defending the cause of special creation, who insisted that Darwin may have proved that the fittest survive but had not explained how they became the fittest in the first place. From an-

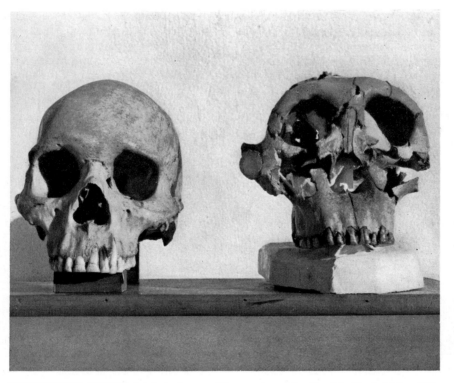

NEW FOSSIL SKULL *(right)* of a manlike creature who lived in East Africa 600,-000 years ago has a smaller brain case, lower forehead than the skull of a modern Australian aborigine at left. But he made tools, hence is classified as a human.

other quarter he was assailed by the formidable fellowship of paleontologists who asked a number of difficult questions. Why, they wondered, if evolution were a fact, did the rocks not contain more transitional species, or "missing links"? Given current estimates of the age of the earth, how could such great evolutionary changes have taken place as Darwin presupposed? Why did certain species appear suddenly and abruptly in certain formations rather than in a more gradual fashion? Why does life first emerge without antecedents in the lowest fossil-bearing strata—the Cambrian—and not in the pre-Cambrian?

Darwin's answer to these questions rested on the imperfection of the geological record—the fact that science had only recently begun to scratch the surface of the earth in quest of fossil remains, had not yet learned to interpret its discoveries and had little comprehension of the stupendous span of terrestrial time.

"For my part," Darwin wrote in *The Origin of Species,* "I look at the geological record as a history of the world imperfectly kept, and written in a changing dialect; of this history we possess the last volume alone, relating to two or three countries. Of each volume, only here and there a short chapter has been preserved; and of each page, only here and there a few lines."

In addition to those recognized scientists who expressed serious misgivings, Darwin also found himself bombarded by many scientific splinter groups and eccentrics: German teleologists who felt that nature must have a grand purpose or plan which Darwin had neglected to reveal; vitalists who held that each individual shaped his own evolution by living forces from within; Lamarckians who believed that changes produced by environment in one generation could be passed on to the next. To disprove the latter point a pro-Darwinian biologist cut off the tails of 12 mice who produced, in the ensuing year, 333 offspring, all with tails. He then cut off the tails of the next five generations. Each new generation was born with tails.

A gentle, self-effacing man, endowed with the humility that sometimes cloaks great genius, Darwin attempted conscientiously to answer all the objections to his theories. Whenever he read or heard of an antipathetic comment, he made a note of it. "For," he explained, "I had found by experience that such facts and thoughts were far more apt to escape from the memory than favorable ones." In *The Origin* he began the sixth chapter, entitled "Difficulties of the Theory," with a disclaimer which is surely unique in the literature of science: "Long before the reader has arrived at this part of my work, a crowd of difficulties will have occurred to him. Some of them are so serious that to this day I can hardly reflect on them without being in some degree staggered."

Although the informed scientific opposition to Darwin subsided, with what seems in retrospect remarkable swiftness, evolution remained a subject for witticism. In the House of Commons, Disraeli remarked, "Is man an ape or an angel? I, my Lord, am on the side of the angels." And *Punch* played many variations on the theme: *e.g.,* "I could a tale unfold." "Could you? Then lose not a moment, but go instantly to Mr. Darwin. He will be delighted to see you." Fundamentalist opposition also continued—as it does sporadically today. But within a decade after publication of *The Origin* few reputable scientists remained skeptical. Shortly before Darwin died, Cambridge awarded him an LL.D. degree. The speaker was Thomas Huxley who, after scolding the university for waiting until it was "safe and superfluous" to honor its great alumnus, declared that "from Aristotle's great summary of the biological knowledge of his time down to the present day there is nothing comparable to *The Origin of Species* as a connected survey of the phenomena of life permeated and vivified by a central idea."

IN the decades since Darwin's death the broad outlines of his theory have remained unshaken. "A new scientific truth does not triumph by convincing its opponents," the great German scientist Max Planck observed, "but because its opponents die, and a new generation grows up that is familiar with it."

Today some searching questions are still asked, some objections still adduced. What caused the mass extinctions at the end of the

Mesozoic era, when the huge dinosaurs that trod the trembling earth for 100 million years abruptly disappeared? What brought about the second great dying at the end of the Pleistocene, when the most splendid aggregation of mammals that ever lived vanished as swiftly as the dinosaurs before them? And why did some orders of life evolve with great speed, while others have stagnated, unchanged, for millenniums—like the small mollusk shown in the frontispiece of this chapter and the coelacanth, the extraordinary living fossil fish pictured on pages 286-287?

IN addition to such musings, several great mysteries of evolution persist. One involves the origins of man—the unique, tempestuous, rational, passionate, esthetic, irascible, proud, anxious, toolmaking, troublemaking animal that has dominated the planet for the last half million years. To the anthropologist the evolutionary line of descent leading from man's dark and scattered beginnings down to *Homo sapiens* of today seems physically continuous, though held together here only by a segment of skull, there by a crumbling jawbone. Yet the point of man's emergence as a human being, the threshold he crossed to enter the realm of self-awareness, the moment of his attainment of personality and spirit—these remain still shrouded in the shadows of the prehistoric past.

From time to time new fragments turn up to augment the bony links. The most recent and one of the most important was unearthed in July 1959 by the British anthropologist Dr. L. S. B. Leakey, who discovered in the Olduvai Gorge in Tanganyika the skull of a primitive hominoid creature that seemed to confirm Darwin's surmise that Africa would prove to be the birthplace of man. In some aspects Dr. Leakey's discovery suggested a distant kinship with a subhuman species of ape man called Australopithecus, whose likeness is shown on the opposite page. But there is a crucial difference, a difference which anthropologists believe may define the frontier of humanity.

It was in 1924 that the rather abundant remains of Australopithecus were first exhumed in South Africa. Combining human and apelike characteristics to a curious degree, Australopithecus strikingly fulfilled the specifications for a missing link. His facial contours were simian, but he could walk erect in almost manlike fashion. Precisely where Australopithecus stands on the evolutionary tree has not yet been determined. Although he lived half a million years ago—at the same time as Pithecanthropus, Heidelberg Man, Swanscombe Man and other definitely human subspecies—it is believed that he evolved much earlier, wandered down a bypath off the main evolutionary corridor and then died out.

Dr. Leakey's find, to which he has given the scientific name Zinjanthropus and the informal nickname "Nutcracker Man" because of his massive molar teeth, differs from Australopithecus in a number of anatomical respects—a pronounced nose, a larger brain. But far more significant is the fact that his remains were found in conjunction with typical Old Stone Age tools—parts of a hammer stone and waste flakes from the manufacture of a chopper—and the bones of animals he had killed and eaten. There are in nature certain animals which use natural objects as tools—*e.g.*, one of Darwin's Galápagos finches *(pages 32-33)*, which uses a cactus spine to dislodge insects from deep crevices. But only man selects objects for a purpose and then trims and alters them to a set pattern. It is for this reason that anthropologists are generally agreed that the criterion which distinguishes man from other orders of life is his ability to fashion tools. Australopithecus may have been a regular user of such implements as antelope bones and jagged stones in the pursuit of his hunting activities. But Zinjanthropus, by improving on nature, crossed the threshold of mankind.

FOR many reasons anthropologists reject the challenge to pinpoint the birthplace of man or the date of his advent. Current evidence indicates that Zinjanthropus is more than 600,000 years old and flourished at a time when the first great glacial advance of the Pleistocene was refrigerating the Northern Hemisphere. He may thus be 100,000 years older than Pithecanthropus and, as Dr. Carleton Coon of the University of Pennsylvania has observed: "Evolution was working overtime in the primate family. . . . Somewhere between one million and 700,000 years ago this line of evolution had produced a number of erect, two-legged genera and species, including ape men, half-brained men, men with beetling brows and muzzles, and men with brains, heads and faces like those of people living today."

To evolutionary theorists the delineation of the physical history of man is no longer one of the great unsolved tasks of science. A far deeper mystery is the advent of life itself, the initial rung on the evolutionary ladder. Paleontologists still wonder why fossil evidence of life on earth appears abruptly in rocks of the Cambrian period, 500 million years ago. Why are there so few traces of life in the

pre-Cambrian, which lasted 1.5 billion years, three quarters of the total age of the earth? Cambrian life was not merely incipient; it had already evolved into most of the primary classifications known today.

A possible answer to this enigma has been suggested by Dr. G. Evelyn Hutchinson of Yale University and Dr. Harold K. Brooks of the University of Florida. They suspect that no earlier fossils will be found because there are none. Only creatures with bones or shells leave imprints in the sediments of time. Pre-Cambrian creatures were soft-bodied. They required no armor because the world was peaceful, non-predatory, vegetarian. Then, for some unknown cause, the first aggression was committed, and the small animals of the primeval waters learned to hunt and eat each other. Through natural selection, certain lines developed defensive armor-shells, exoskeletons, claws—and the fossil record of the earth began.

Granted the existence of soft-bodied animals in the primordial seas, the question then arises: how did they originate? Here the evolutionist must shift his perspective from the realm of paleontology to that of biochemistry. For among the great dualisms of philosophy, defining the frontiers between the lower animal orders and man, and between mind and matter, it is the thin borderline between the living and the nonliving that is engaging some of the most concentrated scientific study today. What is life? The question has long been the province of metaphysicians. But now in many laboratories research chemists are attempting to analyze and synthesize the complex proteins, enzymes, and nucleic acids such as DNA *(pages 278-279)* that constitute the building blocks of all living things. Efforts have been made to duplicate in the laboratory the chemical composition of the sea and atmosphere at the dawn of earth's history and to re-enact the event—a lightning flash, perhaps—that suddenly transmuted dormant molecules of inorganic matter into substances endowed with the capacity to reproduce themselves. When science has accomplished this—and many biochemists believe that success lies not too far in the future—the first great link between the processes of inorganic evolution and organic evolution will have been forged.

At the other end of the chain there loom the clouded perspectives of the future. What course will human evolution pursue henceforth? Biologists are agreed that man's physical evolution has ceased, by virtue of the fact that he now controls his own environment. No longer subject to irresistible imperatives of nature, he has no large adversaries but himself. During his relatively brief reign on earth—barely one per cent of the hegemony of the dinosaurs—man has effectively extinguished innumerable species of higher plants and animals, save those he tolerates or chooses to cultivate or conserve. In the near future, through his mastery of the forces that engender stars, he may subject all life, including his own, to crises greater than those dreamed of by the catastrophists of Darwin's day. For modern experimental genetics has shown that the orderly laws of inheritance which constitute man's clear corridor through time may be utterly shattered by the penetrating power of radiation. Unless man chooses self-destruction his evolutionary path lies in the realm of his most unique and precious endowment—his mind.

IN the light of all remaining riddles and missing links, the mighty architecture of Darwin's creative reason stands today on foundations that have been reinforced with every advance of human knowledge. Can it be said, then, that evolution is no longer a theory, subject to revision or rejection, but a fact? Among scientists there are some who distrust the word "fact," recalling the fate that has befallen so many "facts of science" and "laws of nature" in the long and variable history of man's effort to understand his environment. Dr. Hutchinson, for example, prefers to describe evolution as a "verified theory"—an interpretation of the natural world so logical, so convincingly corroborated that it compels acceptance as the only plausible explanation of the grand panorama of life on earth.

The implications of evolution have extended far beyond the biological realm; they have invaded every domain of human inquiry. For into the snug, complacent parlors of 19th Century thought, Darwin projected a tremendous, shattering idea—that nothing is permanent, that change rather than immutability is the rule of the universe and the law of life. Because of his disturbing insight, Darwin was often assailed unjustly as a cold and heartless materialist. Yet nothing could have been further from the truth. Throughout his life he was motivated by warmth and compassion and a sense of kinship with all living things.

In one of his early notebooks, he wrote, "If we choose to let conjecture run wild, then animals, our fellow brethren in pain, disease, suffering and famine—our slaves in the most laborious works, our companions in our amusements—they may partake of our origin in one common ancestor—we may be all melted together."

AN AFRICAN "APE MAN" is shown attacking a gang of baboons, using an antelope bone as a bludgeon. When his remains were discovered in 1924, Australopithecus was first acclaimed as a missing link in the Darwinian view of man's descent. Today evolutionists regard him as an isolated survivor of the common line from which both modern man and modern apes evolved. His brain is little larger than a gorilla's. But his teeth and limbs are almost human.

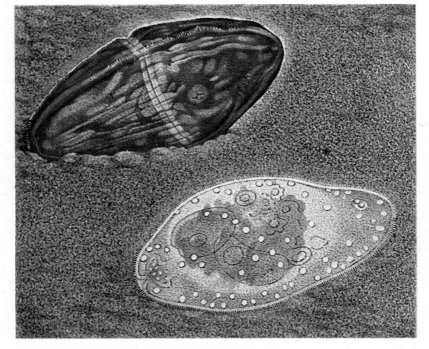

THE OLDEST CRAWLING CREATURES of the sea, save for one-celled protozoans, are flatworms Xenoturbella *(top)* and Nemertoderma. The former is about an inch long. Nemertoderma *(enlarged here)* is barely visible.

THE OLDEST FISH known on earth today is the coelacanth, which has existed virtually unchanged for 300 million years. Close kin of an extinct suborder of fish that ventured onto land and there engendered the amphibians

LIVING LINKS IN

Up from the depths of the sea there occasionally emerges an unsuspected form that somehow has survived unchanged from distant epochs of the past. Such anachronisms are known as "living fossils," a paradoxical but useful term which Darwin coined. Three striking specimens are shown on these pages. Each has lain dormant in its biological backwater for untold millions of years. Each is remarkable as an extant—not a missing—link between vanished forms of life and those we know today.

The two tiny organisms at left date from the very dawn of life. Dwelling in bottom mud at depths of a few hundred feet, they represent two of the most primitive crawling animals in the world. Although they were first discovered in 1926 and 1930, it is only recently that scientists have come to realize their importance in a crucial chapter of evolution that occurred in primordial seas nearly two billion years ago, when single-celled animals somehow evolved into multicellular creatures. Xenoturbella and Nemertoderma represent a transitional or intermediate stage in this momentous advance.

The equally minute crustacean at right first came to scientific light in Long Island Sound in 1954. Known as Hutchinsoniella, it has

from which terrestrial vertebrates arose, the coelacanth lives in the vast
depths of the ocean, almost secure from man's observations. The first specimen caught weighed 127 pounds and measured five feet from teeth to tail.

THE AGELESS SEA

great significance as a link in the evolution of its modern cousins
which now please man's palate in crab-meat salad, a shrimp cocktail
or a bowl of lobster bisque. A primitive and generalized form,
Hutchinsoniella has features in common with both existing crustacea and the long-extinct trilobites that dominated the seas of earth
in Cambrian times a half billion years ago.

By far the most famous of living fossils is the coelacanth *(above)*,
a big fish which turned up dramatically in the nets of a South African trawler in 1938 and fought aggressively for life, flopping violently about the deck, snapping viciously at anyone within range, until
it expired more than three hours later. This catch astonished marine
biologists, for although coelacanths were well known through fossil
remains as members of the crossopterygian order of fishes, they were
believed to have been extinct for 70 million years.

South Africa's leading ichthyologist, Dr. J. L. B. Smith, offered re-
wards for specimens, and in 1952 another coelacanth was caught.
Since then several more have been hauled up. Other crossopteryg-
ians crawled out onto dry land and became amphibians some 300
million years ago. But the coelacanths chose to stay in quiet waters.

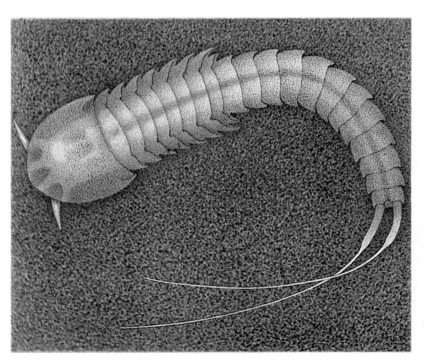

THE OLDEST CRUSTACEAN known today is Hutchinsoniella, a resident
of American East Coast waters. Only one tenth of an inch long, it links modern crustacea such as shrimps, lobsters, crabs with their extinct ancestors.

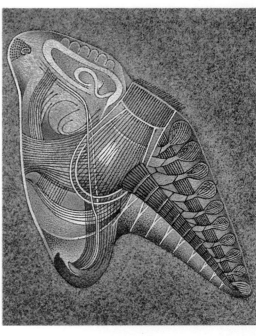

THE FIRST MAMMAL may have looked like Morganucodon. Dating back about 160 million years, Morganucodon, an unprepossessing beast about four inches in length, resembled the modern shrew and lived in South Wales. Though a furry animal, it had some reptile characteristics.

THE FIRST VERTEBRATE perhaps resembled this fossil sea creature, Ainiktozoon. It had no head but had the beginnings of a segmented spine.

LONG-DEAD PIONEERS

In the continuous mainstream of evolution, certain creatures mark great turning points. On these pages are shown some of the animals, now extinct and reconstructed from fossil remains, which stand out as pioneers —the air-breathing fish that became an amphibian, the stranded amphibian that became a reptile, the energetic reptile that became a mammal. One of the first fossil finds to document Darwinian theory was Archaeopteryx *(opposite page)*. Darwin's critics had stressed the mystery of birds—a class so unique as to suggest that their existence could be explained only by special creation. A few years after publication of *The Origin*, fossil prints in a Bavarian slate bed revealed the remains of a feathered reptile. Later finds have attested to the descent of all modern fowl from Archaeopteryx, the reptile-bird.

THE FIRST REPTILE, Seymouria, may be regarded also as a highly developed amphibian. The emancipation of life from water came when some amphibious lines hatched hard-shelled eggs on land. Seymouria (named because it was found near Seymour, Texas), or its kin, gained this skill.

THE FIRST AMPHIBIAN, Ichthyostega, was a slow-moving but probably predatory creature about four feet long, descended from the pioneering line of fish which had wriggled out of the water onto land and there developed legs. Flourishing in Greenland perhaps 300 million years ago, Ichthyostega is the oldest four-legged animal known to man. Its stubby legs are definitely terrestrial, but its fishy past is revealed in its body scales and the fin on its tail.

THE FIRST BIRD took to the air about 130 million years ago. Archaeopteryx was anatomically an agile, acrobatic, airborne lizard, fancied up in feathers. Its scaly head was equipped with teeth instead of a beak; its brain was reptilian; its lizardlike tail was longer than its body. But from its line came all the birds that cleave the skies today. In this painting one Archaeopteryx is about to devour a big dragonfly in the lee of an ancient cycad plant.

ACKNOWLEDGMENTS

LIFE is indebted to DR. S. DILLON RIPLEY, Director of the Peabody Museum of Natural History, Yale University, for his generous help and guidance in the preparation of *The Wonders of Life on Earth* and to the authorities and institutions listed on this page. However, LIFE assumes responsibility for the selection and arrangement of all the material in the book and the viewpoints expressed.

ALDRICH, JOHN W.—Chief, Section of Distribution of Birds and Mammals, U.S. Department of the Interior

ALEXANDER, DR. RICHARD D.—Department of Zoology, University of Michigan

AMADON, DR. DEAN—Chairman and Lamont Curator of Birds, The American Museum of Natural History

ARCHEY, DR. GILBERT—Director, Auckland Institute and Museum, Auckland, New Zealand

ATZ, JAMES—Associate Curator, New York Aquarium

BARRETO, DR. HENRIQUE LAMEYER DE MELO—Director, Zoological Gardens, Rio de Janeiro

BARRIA, GERARDO—Entomologist, Santiago, Chile

BARROS, ALFREDO REGO—Museo Nacional, Rio de Janeiro

BAYER, DR. FREDERICK M.—Associate Curator, Division of Marine Invertebrates, Smithsonian Institution

BOGERT, DR. CHARLES M.—Chairman, Department of Amphibians and Reptiles, The American Museum of Natural History

BOWMAN, DR. ROBERT I.—San Francisco State College

BROWN, DR. WILLIAM L., JR.—Associate Curator of Insects, Museum of Comparative Zoology, Harvard University

CALIFORNIA ACADEMY OF SCIENCES, San Francisco

CARVALHO, DR. JOSE CANDIDO DE MELO—Director, Museo Nacional, Rio de Janeiro

CARPENTER, DR. C. R.—Pennsylvania State University

CATALA, DR. RENE—Director, Nouméa Aquarium, New Caledonia

CHACE, DR. FENNER, JR.—Curator, Division of Marine Invertebrates, Smithsonian Institution

CHILEAN NAVY, THE

CONSERVATION FOUNDATION, THE, New York

COON, DR. CARLETON S.—Professor of Anthropology, University of Pennsylvania

CONWAY, WILLIAM G.—Curator of Birds, New York Zoological Society

DE BEER, SIR GAVIN—Director, British Museum, London

DUFF, DR. ROGER—Curator, Canterbury Museum, Christchurch, New Zealand

EGLER, DR. WALTER ALBERTO—Director, Goeldi Museum, Belem

EIBL-EIBESFELDT, DR. IRENAUS—Director, Max Planck Institute, Seewiesen, Germany

EISELEY, DR. LOREN—Provost of the University of Pennsylvania

ENRIQUES, DR. CAMILO PONCE—President of Ecuador, and his Ministers

ERIKSSON-TAPLINGER CO.—Publishers of *Tukani*, by Helmut Sick

FISHER, JAMES—Ornithologist, Ashton, Northampton, England

FLEAY, DAVID HOWELLS—Director, Research Reserve, Queensland, Australia

FOSBERG, DR. F. R.—Botanist, U.S. Geological Survey

FRANZEN, DR. AKE—Uppsala University, Sweden

GIBSON-HILL, C. A.—Raffles Museum, Singapore

GILLIARD, DR. E. THOMAS—Associate Curator, Department of Birds, The American Museum of Natural History

GILPIN, ORVILLE L.—Department of Geology, Chicago Natural History Museum

GRISWOLD, JOHN A.—Curator of Birds, Philadelphia Zoological Garden

GREGG, COLONEL CLIFFORD C.—Director, Chicago Natural History Museum

HALLSTROM, SIR EDWARD J.—Director, Taronga Park Zoo, Australia

HAMMEL, DR. H. T.—Assistant Professor of Physiology, University of Pennsylvania

HERSHKOVITZ, PHILIP—Curator of Mammals, Department of Zoology, Chicago Natural History Museum

HOLDGATE, DR. MARTIN W.—Zoologist, University of Durham, England

HORN, THOMAS C.—Manager, Tule Lake National Wildlife Refuge

HUMPHREY, DR. PHILIP S.—Assistant Professor of Zoology, Yale University

HUTCHINSON, DR. G. EVELYN—Sterling Professor of Zoology, Yale University

INTERNATIONAL COMMITTEE FOR BIRD PRESERVATION

INTERNATIONAL UNION FOR THE CONSERVATION OF NATURE AND NATURAL RESOURCES

JARVIK, DR. ERIK—Swedish Museum of Natural History, Stockholm

KAUFMANN, DR. B. P.—Acting Director, Department of Genetics, Carnegie Institution of Washington, Cold Spring Harbor, N.Y.

KERMACK, DR. K. A.—University College, London

KETTLEWELL, DR. H. B. D.—Oxford University, England

KING, DR. JAMES C.—Columbia University

KLOTS, DR. ALEXANDER B.—Research Associate, The American Museum of Natural History

KRAMER, the late DR. GUSTAV—Max Planck Institute, Wilhelmshaven, West Germany

LADD, DR. HARRY S.—U.S. Geological Survey, Washington, D.C.

LAMING, ANNETTE—University of Paris, France

LIMA, DR. ANGELO MOREIRA DA COSTA—Instituto Oswaldo Cruz, Rio de Janeiro

LINDEMAN, ROLAND—Catskill Game Farm, Catskill, N.Y.

LUTZ, DR. BERTA—Museo Nacional, Rio de Janeiro

MANGELSDORF, DR. PAUL C.—Professor of Botany, Harvard University

MENZIES, DR. ROBERT—Resident Associate in Geology, Columbia University's Lamont Geological Observatory

MILLOT, DR. J.—Director, Institute of Scientific Research, Madagascar

MOORE, DR. JOHN A.—Department of Zoology, Columbia University

MURPHY, ROBERT CUSHMAN—Research Associate in Oceanic Birds, The American Museum of Natural History

NEWELL, DR. NORMAN D.—Curator of Historical Geology and Fossil Invertebrates, The American Museum of Natural History

OAKLEY, DR. KENNETH—Geologist, British Museum, London

OSBORN, DR. FAIRFIELD—President, New York Zoological Society

PATTERSON, PROFESSOR BRYAN—Museum of Comparative Zoology, Harvard University

PENA, LUIS E.—Entomologist, Santiago, Chile

PETERSON, DR. ROGER TORY—Director, National Audubon Society

PETTER, JEAN-JACQUES—Zoologist, Paris Natural History Museum

PETTER-ROUSSEAUX, ARLETTE—Paris Natural History Museum

PHILLIPS, DR. RALPH W.—U.S. Department of Agriculture

PIRES, DR. FERNANDO DIAS DE AVILA—Museo Nacional, Rio de Janeiro

POHL, DR. LUCIAN—Conchologist

REED, DR. CHARLES A.—Iran Prehistoric Project, Oriental Institute, University of Chicago

RETTENMEYER, CARL—University of Kansas

RIBEIRO, PAULO DE MIRANDA—Museo Nacional, Rio de Janeiro

RIEDL, DR. RUPERT—Zoological Institute, Vienna

ROCKEFELLER FOUNDATION AGRICULTURAL PROGRAM

ROMER, DR. ALFRED S.—Director, Museum of Comparative Zoology, Harvard University

RYAN, DR. FRANCIS J.—Department of Zoology, Columbia University

SANDERS, DR. HAROLD—Woods Hole Oceanographic Institution, Woods Hole, Mass.

SAUER, DR. FRANZ—University of Hamburg, West Germany

SCHNEIRLA, DR. THEODORE C.—Curator, Department of Animal Behavior, The American Museum of Natural History

SCHULTZ, DR. LEONARD P.—Curator, Division of Fishes, Smithsonian Institution

SICK, DR. HELMUT—Museo Nacional, Rio de Janeiro

SQUIRES, DR. DONALD F.—Associate Curator, Fossil Invertebrates, The American Museum of Natural History

STEINBOCK, DR. OTTO—Zoological Institute, Innsbruck, Austria

STEPHENSON, DR. WILLIAM—University of Queensland, Australia

STIRTON, DR. RUBEN A.—Chairman, Department of Paleontology, University of California

SUTTER, DR. ERNST—Natural History Museum, Basel, Switzerland

TEAL, DR. JOHN J., JR.—Director, Institute of Northern Agricultural Research, Huntington Center, Vermont

TINDALE, NORMAN B.—Curator of the Adelaide Museum, Australia

TRACEY, DR. JOSHUA I., JR.—U.S. Geological Survey

TRAVASSOS, DR. LAURO—Instituto Oswaldo Cruz, Rio de Janeiro

TURNBULL, WILLIAM D.—Assistant Curator of Fossil Mammals, Chicago Natural History Museum

UNITED NATIONS EDUCATIONAL, SCIENTIFIC AND CULTURAL ORGANIZATION

VANZOLINI, DR. PAULO EMILIO—Zoologist, University of São Paulo

VAURIE, DR. CHARLES—Assistant Curator, Department of Birds, The American Museum of Natural History

WELLS, DR. JOHN W.—Professor of Geology, Cornell University

WILSON, DR. E. O.—Associate Professor of Zoology, Harvard University

WORZEL, DR. J. LAMAR—Professor of Geology, Columbia University's Lamont Geological Observatory

XAVIER, DR. ANTONIO AUGUSTO—Director, Instituto Oswaldo Cruz, Rio de Janeiro

ZANGERL, DR. RAINER—Curator of Fossil Reptiles, Chicago Natural History Museum

PICTURE CREDITS

This list shows the sources from which the illustrations were gathered. Credits are separated from left to right by commas, and from top to bottom by dashes.

Frontispiece   MARK KAUFFMAN

INDEX

*This symbol in front of a page number indicates that an illustration as well as mention of the subject is to be found on the page thus marked.

ALL TYPE MATTER PHOTOCOMPOSED ON PHOTON EQUIPMENT IN THE
EDITORIAL OFFICES OF TIME INCORPORATED, NEW YORK, NEW YORK

FOUR-COLOR ENGRAVINGS BY R. R. DONNELLEY & SONS COMPANY, CHICAGO, ILLINOIS
AND GRAPHIC COLOR PLATE, INC., STAMFORD, CONNECTICUT
OTHER ENGRAVINGS BY THE BINGHAM PHOTO ENGRAVING CO., INC., NEW YORK, NEW YORK
AND LIVERMORE AND KNIGHT CO., PROVIDENCE, RHODE ISLAND

PRINTED BY LIVERMORE AND KNIGHT CO., PROVIDENCE, RHODE ISLAND
BOUND BY AMERICAN BOOK-STRATFORD PRESS, INC., NEW YORK, NEW YORK
PAPER BY THE MEAD CORPORATION, DAYTON, OHIO